MULTIPHASE TRANSPORT
Fundamentals, Reactor Safety, Applications

Volume 3

*Multi-Phase flow and heat transfer
Symposium-Workshop, Miami Beach,
Fla., 1979.*

Edited by

T. Nejat Veziroğlu

Clean Energy Research Institute, University of Miami

● HEMISPHERE PUBLISHING CORPORATION

Washington   New York   London

DISTRIBUTION OUTSIDE THE UNITED STATES

McGRAW-HILL INTERNATIONAL BOOK COMPANY

Auckland   Bogotá   Guatemala   Hamburg   Johannesburg
Lisbon   London   Madrid   Mexico   Montreal
New Delhi   Panama   Paris   San Juan   São Paulo   Singapore
Sydney   Tokyo   Toronto

Proceedings of the Multi-Phase Flow and Heat Transfer Symposium-Workshop, held in Miami Beach, Florida, U.S.A., on 16–18 April 1979, and presented by the Clean Energy Research Institute, School of Engineering and Architecture, University of Miami, Coral Gables, Florida, U.S.A.; sponsored by the National Science Foundation, Washington, D.C., U.S.A., the Office of Naval Research, Washington, D.C., U.S.A., and the School of Continuing Studies, University of Miami, Coral Gables, Florida, U.S.A.; in cooperation with the International Association for Hydrogen Energy, Middle East Technical University, Ankara, Turkey, and the Department of Mechanical Engineering, University of Miami, Coral Gables, Florida, U.S.A.

EDITOR

T. Nejat Veziroğlu, Clean Energy Research Institute, University of Miami, Coral Gables, Florida, U.S.A.

EDITORIAL BOARD

Laxman G. Phadke, Northeastern University, Department of Physics, Tahlequah, Oklahoma, U.S.A.

Sadik Kakaç, Mechanical Engineering Department, Middle East Technical University, Ankara, Turkey

John W. Sheffield, Mechanical Engineering Department, University of Miami, Coral Gables, Florida, U.S.A.

MANUSCRIPT EDITOR

Helen M. Hooper, Clean Energy Research Institute, University of Miami, Coral Gables, Florida, U.S.A.

MULTIPHASE TRANSPORT: Fundamentals, Reactor Safety, Applications

1 2 3 4 5 6 7 8 9 0   B R B R   8 9 8 7 6 5 4 3 2 1 0

Library of Congress Cataloging in Publication Data

Multi-Phase Flow and Heat Transfer Symposium-Workshop,
    Miami Beach, Fla., 1979.
    Multi-phase transport.

    ''Proceedings of the Multi-Phase Flow and Heat Transfer Symposium-Workshop, held in Miami Beach, Florida, U. S. A., on 16–18 April 1979, and presented by the Clean Energy Research Institute, School of Engineering and Architecture, University of Miami, Coral Gables, Florida, U. S. A.; sponsored by the National Science Foundation . . . [et al.] .''
    Bibliography: v., p.
    Includes index.
    1. Multiphase flow—Congresses. 2. Heat—Transmission—Congresses. 3. Nuclear reactors—Safety measures—Congresses. I. Veziroğlu, T. Nejat. II. Miami, University of, Coral Gables, Fla. Clean Energy Research Institute. III. United States. National Science Foundation. IV. Title.
TA357.M83   1979   620.1'064   80-11157
ISBN 0-89116-159-7 (set)
ISBN 0-89116-205-4 (v. 3)

Contents

VOLUME 1

INTRODUCTION

MULTI–PHASE PHENOMENA

MULTI-PHASE FUNDAMENTALS

MATHEMATICAL MODELING

VOLUME 2

BOILING

CONDENSATION

HEAT TRANSFER

PRESSURE DROPS

VOLUME 3

INSTABILITIES

REACTOR SAFETY AND APPLICATIONS

VOLUME 4

PUMPING

GAS/PARTICLE SYSTEMS

FLUIDIZED BEDS

VOLUME 5

WORKSHOP REPORTS

Preface

The subject of multiphase flow and heat transfer is growing in importance as its applications increase, including applications in the energy field. Multiphase applications are now found in boiling water nuclear reactors, pressurized water nuclear reactors, conventional steam power plants, evaporators of refrigeration systems, and a wide variety of evaporative and condensive heat exchangers in chemical and petroleum industries. Over the last two decades, two-phase flow heat transfer and instability problems have been a challenge to many researchers. Such instabilities could induce a boiling crisis, disturb control systems, and/or cause mechanical damage. It is important to be able to predict the conditions under which a two-phase flow system will perform without instability and under optimum conditions. Therefore, the understanding of two-phase flow phenomena is very important to the design, control, and proper performance of such systems.

As a result of the growing energy crisis, many other multiphase flow and heat transfer problems have also become important. Some of them are the modeling of the loss of coolant accident in pressurized water and breeder reactors, scaling up of fluidized bed reactors for converting coal to synfuels, and designing heat exchangers for liquified natural and petroleum gases.

After the successful Two-Phase Flows and Heat Transfer Symposium of 1976, the MultiPhase Flow and Heat Transfer Symposium-Workshop provided the opportunity for the scientists and engineers in this field to present the latest research results, to exchange their ideas and experiences, to assess the state-of-the-art of multiphase flow and heat transfer studies, and to identify the areas of future research and application.

The papers recommended by the session chairpersons and co-chairpersons, the opening lecture and the banquet address, and the workshop reports have been divided by their subject matter into sixteen parts. The reader should be advised that it was difficult to specifically classify some papers when there was an overlap in the subject matter. In such cases, we tried to make the best possible choice.

Multiphase Transport should serve as a valuable reference covering the latest developments in the growing field of multiphase flow and heat transfer, including fundamentals, reactor safety, and applications.

T. Nejat Veziroğlu

Acknowledgments

The Symposium Committee gratefully acknowledges the financial support of the National Science Foundation and the Office of Naval Research, and the support and services provided by the School of Continuing Studies, University of Miami. We also thank the International Association for Hydrogen Energy, Middle East Technical University, Ankara, Turkey, and the Mechanical Engineering Department, University of Miami, for their generous cooperation.

We wish to extend our sincere appreciation to the Keynote Speaker, Win Aung, National Science Foundation, Washington, D.C.; to the Opening Lecturer, Arthur E. Bergles, Iowa State University at Ames; and to the Banquet Speaker, Chang-Lin Tien, University of California at Berkeley. We also thank M. Keith Ellingsworth of the Office of Naval Research and Morris S. Ojalvo of the National Science Foundation for their support of and interest in the symposium.

Special thanks are due to our authors, lecturers, and workshop moderators who provided the substance of the Symposium-Workshop as published in the present proceedings.

And last, but not least, our debt of gratitude is owed to the Session Chairpersons, Session Co-Chairpersons, and Workshop Moderators in organizing and executing the technical sessions and/or workshops. In acknowledgment we list these session and workshop officials on the following pages.

Symposium Committee

Symposium and Session Officials

SYMPOSIUM COMMITTEE

Chairperson: *T. Nejat Veziroğlu*, University of Miami, Coral Gables, FL, USA

Co-Chairpersons: *Sadik Kakaç*, Middle East Technical University, Ankara, Turkey, and *John W. Sheffield*, University of Miami

Members: *Arthur E. Bergles*, Iowa State University, Ames, IA, USA, *Dimitri Gidaspow*, Illinois Institute of Technology, Chicago, IL, USA, *Samuel S. Lee*, University of Miami, and *Robert Lyczkowski*, Lawrence Livermore Laboratory, Livermore, CA, USA

SESSION OFFICIALS

Session 1: Conference Opening

Chairperson: *J. Catz*, University of Miami

Co-Chairperson: *J. W. Sheffield*, University of Miami

Session 2A: Multi-phase Flow Fundamentals

Chairperson: *D. Gidaspow*, Illinois Institute of Technology

Co-Chairperson: *N. M. Ozboya*, University of Miami

Session 2B: Instabilities

Chairperson: *H. W. Hoffman*, Oak Ridge National Laboratory, Oak Ridge, TN, USA

Co-Chairperson: *S. Ridenour*, University of Miami

Session 2C: Experimental Techniques I

Chairperson: *J. Weisman*, University of Cincinnati, Cincinnati, OH, USA

Co-Chairperson: *K. Akyuzlu*, University of Miami

Session 3A: Multi-phase Flow Phenomena I

Chairperson: *A. Gokhman*, EDS Nuclear, Inc., San Francisco, CA, USA

Co-Chairperson: *C. R. Lee*, University of Miami

Session 3B: Safety Applications I

Chairperson: *J. W. Rose*, University of London, London, England

Co-Chairperson: *L. G. Phadke*, University of Miami

Session 3C: Experimental Techniques II

Chairperson: *W. Aung*, National Science Foundation, Washington, DC, USA

Co-Chairperson: *T. Dogan*, University of Miami

Session 4A: Multi-phase Flow Phenomena II

Chairperson: *L. Hays*, BiPhase Energy Systems, Santa Monica, CA, USA

Co-Chairperson: *V. Ganesan*, Indian Institute of Technology, Madras, India

Session 4B: Multi-phase Flow Heat Transfer
Chairperson: *S. Kakaç*, Middle East Technical University
Co-Chairperson: *J. W. Sheffield*, University of Miami

Session 4C: Fluidized Beds
Chairperson: *T. Ariman*, University of Notre Dame, Notre Dame, IN, USA
Co-Chairperson: *T. Dogan*, University of Miami

Session 5A: Boiling
Chairperson: *S. G. Bankoff*, Northwestern University, Evanston, IL, USA
Co-Chairperson: *N. M. Ozboya*, University of Miami

Session 5B: Safety Applications II
Chairperson: *Y. Bayazitoglu*, Rice University, Houston, TX, USA
Co-Chairperson: *K. Akyuzlu*, University of Miami

Session 5C: Gas-Particle Systems
Chairperson: *R. W. Lyczlowski*, Lawrence Livermore Laboratory
Co-Chairperson: *A. Gokhman*, EDS Nuclear, Inc.

Session 6A: Condensation
Chairperson: *E. Rhodes*, University of Waterloo, Waterloo, Ontario, Canada
Co-Chairperson: *J. W. Sheffield*, University of Miami

Session 6B: Mathematical Modelling
Chairperson: *R. E. Nieman*, Atomic Energy of Canada, Ltd., Pinawa, Manitoba, Canada
Co-Chairperson: *K. F. Wong*, University of Miami

Session 6C: Porous Media Two-Phase Flows
Chairperson: *S. S. Lee*, University of Miami
Co-Chairperson: *C. R. Lee*, University of Miami

Session 7: Workshops
MATHEMATICAL MODELLING AND COMPUTATIONAL TECHNIQUES
Moderator: *D. B. Spalding*, CHAM of North America, Inc., Huntsville, AL, USA

BOILING
Moderator: *S. G. Bankoff*, Northwestern University

CONDENSATION
Moderator: *J. W. Rose*, University of London

TRANSIENTS AND SUSTAINED INSTABILITIES IN MULTI-PHASE FLOWS
Moderator: *R. T. Lahey, Jr.*, Rensselaer Polytechnic Institute, Troy, NY, USA

INSTRUMENTATION AND MEASUREMENT TECHNIQUES
Moderator: *O. C. Jones, Jr.*, Brookhaven National Laboratory, Upton, NY, USA

AVAILABLE DATA BASES AND THEIR CORRELATIONS AND EVALUATION
Moderator: *C. W. Solbrig*, Commonwealth Edison, Chicago, IL, USA

NEW PROBLEMS IN POWER AND PROCESS INDUSTRIES
Moderator: *A. E. Bergles*, Iowa State University

Session 8: Final Plenary Session

Chairperson: *W. M. Rohsenow*, Massachusetts Institute of Technology, Cambridge, MA, USA

Co-Chairperson: *S. Kakaç*, Middle East Technical University

SYMPOSIUM STAFF

Arrangements: *James Poisant*

Coordinators: *Lucille Walter* and *Carol Pascalis Vogt*

Special Assistants: *Helen M. Hooper, Barbara Berman, Marlene Pernas, Tahsin Dogan, Kazim Akyuzlu,* and *Ranga Samudrala*

INSTABILITIES

Self-Induced Pressure Oscillation
in an Electrical Heating Boiler

S. LIN and P.M. LEE
Concordia University
Montreal, Quebec H3G 1M8, Canada

R.L. WANG
Montreal Engineering Company, Ltd.
St. Catherines, Ontario L2R 7J9, Canada

ABSTRACT

An investigation of water vapor produced from a small vertical experimental boiler, flowing across a throttling valve, through a bend-tube and into ambient atmosphere has been conducted. Sustained pressure oscillations in the system can be induced either quickly by opening and closing the throttling valve repeatedly for several times or slowly by the system itself. The preliminary experimental results of the self-induced sustained pressure oscillations are presented. The perturbation method is used for the formulation of the oscillations in the system. Oscillation modes and phase angles between the oscillations of the different thermal and fluid quantities are discussed.

INTRODUCTION

An investigation of water vapor produced from a small vertical experimental boiler, flowing across a throttling valve, A, through a bend-tube, E, into an ambient atmosphere has been conducted as shown in Fig. 1. Due to the heat transferred from the vapor in the tube to its ambient air, a part of the vapor condenses and becomes water.

Sustained pressure oscillations can be induced either quickly by opening and closing the throttling valve (A, Fig. 1), repeatedly for several times [1] or slowly by the system itself. Experimental results show that the frequency of the self-induced vapor-pressure oscillation is the same as that of the artificially induced one. Furthermore, the amplitude of the former remains in the same range as that of the latter.

In the present paper, the preliminary experimental results and a mathematical formulation of the self-induced sustained pressure oscillation in the vertical experimental boiler will be reported.

EXPERIMENTAL PROCEDURES AND RESULTS

The vertical cylindrical experimental boiler having an inside
diameter of 11.1 cm and a height of 30.5 cm has been used for
investigation of sustained pressure oscillations inside the
boiler. An electric heater having an outside diameter of 5.1
cm is located at the axis of the boiler. The electric power
of the heater is 500 watts which is used to heat water in the
boiler. A schematic diagram of the boiler is shown in Fig. 1,
which includes the layout of the tubing system. Tube E has a
total length of 390 cm, measured from the throttling valve, A,
to the exit end, with a height of 194 cm. Tube F has a length
of 25.4 cm and a height of 17.8 cm.

The experimental procedure for obtaining a self-induced sustained pressure oscillation in the boiler can be described as
follows:

1.   Open valves A and B, and close valve C (Fig. 1).
     Let water pass through the boiler. Then close valves
     A and B.

2.   Open valve C and let the water level drop to a certain
     distance from the top of the boiler. Close valve C.

3.   Supply electric power to the heater to heat the water
     inside the boiler.

4.   Open the throttling valve A. Keep the ratio of the
     open area to the total area of valve A equal to
     0.0224. Fig. 2 shows the geometric configuration of
     the open area of valve A.

Sustained pressure oscillations will take place after about 30
minutes. During the experimental test, the distance, H,
between the water-free surface and the top of the boiler varied, while the open area of valve A was fixed.

Fig. 3a shows an experimental record of the pressure oscillations in the boiler (top one) and in the tube (bottom one) with
H = 6.35 cm. The two pressure oscillations were measured by
two pressure transducers shown in Fig. 1. During the experimental test, one transducer received the pressure signal at
its positive terminal and the other at the negative terminal.
Therefore, the two pressure oscillations shown in Fig. 3a present a real case of 180° out of phase. Fig. 3b shows the
corresponding experimental record of oscillations of the vapor

temperature in the boiler (top one), the heating surface
temperature in the water in the boiler (middle one) and the
water temperature in the boiler (bottom one). The locations
of the three thermal couples measuring the above-mentioned
temperatures are shown in Fig. 1. It is shown that during the
oscillation, the lower pressure limit in the boiler and in the
tube are below the atmospheric level. The lower limit of the
vapor temperature in the boiler is also below the saturated
temperature corresponding to atmospheric pressure. The temperature of the heating surface oscillates irregularly due to
unsteady convection and unsteady bubble formation. The thermal couple, C, measuring the water temperature, is located
0.5 cm from the wall of the boiler. Due to heat losses through
the wall of the boiler to the ambient, the water temperature
measured is below the saturated temperature corresponding to
atmospheric pressure. Because water has a large thermal capacity, the variation of the water temperature is therefore
relatively small.

Fig. 4a shows the amplitudes of the pressure oscillations in
the boiler and in the tube, and Fig. 4b shows the amplitudes
of the oscillations of the vapor temperature, the heating surface temperature and the water temperature in the boiler as
functions of the distance, H, between the water level and the
top of the boiler. It is seen that the average amplitude of
the pressure oscillation in the boiler is nearly double that
in the tube. In the boiler, the amplitude of oscillation of
the vapor temperature is the largest, that of the water temperature is the smallest, and that of the heating surface temperature is in between.

MATHEMATICAL FORMULATION

A mathematical formulation of the artificially induced pressure
oscillations in the boiler system was conducted [2]. The
physical phenomena of the self-induced oscillations should be
similar to that of the artificially induced ones. In the
following a method similar to that used in [2] will be utilized. The difference between the two methods is that, in the
present paper, all the constants introduced to formulate the
oscillations of the thermal and fluid variables have positive
values, while in [2] some of them may be positive and some
of them may be negative. The advantage of having all positive
values of the constants is that the physical mechanism of the
oscillations can be more clearly presented.

For mathematical formulation, the boiler system is divided into four regions (Fig.5a): the horizontal water column in the
exit tube (region 1), the vapor region on the right-hand side
of the throttling valve, A (region 2), the vapor region

on the left-hand side of the throttling valve inside the boiler (region 3), and the water in the boiler (region 4).

Thermodynamic properties of the water and vapor in each of
these regions are designated by the corresponding subscripts
1,2,3 and 4.

In developing the mathematical formulation of the oscillations
in the boiler system, the following assumptions are made:

1. The oscillations of the thermal and fluid variables
    in the boiler system are considered to be small and
    hence can be treated as perturbations of a known
    steady-state condition.

2. The heat transfer processes arising in the system are
    not affected by the perturbations.

3. The changes of potential and kinetic energy caused by
    the perturbations may be neglected.

4. The frictional resistance in the throttling valve and
    tube in unsteady flow is the same as for the steady
    flow at the same velocity.

5. There is no variation of the ambient condition, and
    the electric power supplied to the heater is constant.

In the following, the perturbation theory is utilized for the
formulation of the oscillations in the boiler system. Perturbation quantities are expressed with reference to their steady-
state data. The steady-state condition in region 3 is designated by subscript 30.

The Equation of Motion for the Water Column in Region 1

Euler's equation of motion applied along the horizontal water
column (Fig. 5a) gives [3]

$$\frac{\partial v}{\partial t} + v\frac{\partial v}{\partial x} + \frac{1}{\rho}\frac{\partial p}{\partial x} + \frac{4\tau_0}{\rho D} = 0 \tag{1}$$

For a small displacement of the water column, it is assumed
that the flow is laminar; hence the shear stress at the wall
of a tube is

$$\tau_0 = \frac{8\mu v}{D}$$

After making the substitution for τ_0 in equation (1), integrating with respect to x from x_a to x_b and letting

$$L = x_b - x_a \text{ and } v_a = v_b,$$

equation (1) becomes

$$L\frac{\partial v}{\partial t} + \frac{32\mu L}{\rho D^2} v = \frac{1}{\rho} p_2. \tag{2}$$

Changing $\partial v/\partial t$ to dv/dt, and replacing v by dx/dt, we obtain from equation (2)

$$L\frac{d^2x}{dt^2} + \frac{32\mu L}{\rho D^2} \frac{dx}{dt} = \frac{1}{\rho} p_2. \tag{3}$$

The Energy Equation for the Vapor in Region 3

Referring to Fig. 5b and considering region 3 as a distinct control volume, in time dt, there is a perturbation mass, dm_{43}, flowing into the control volume from region 4, with its enthalphy h_{30}, and a further perturbation mass, dm_{32}, flowing out of the control volume with the same enthalphy h_{30} through valve A into region 2. At the same time, there is also a change of the internal energy, $(M c_p)_{30} dT_3$, in the control volume, where M_{30} and $c_{p,30}$ are the total vapor mass and the specific heat at constant pressure in the control volume at the steady-state condition. The law of conservation of energy yields

$$h_{30}\frac{dm_{43}}{dt} = (Mc_p)_{30}\frac{dT_3}{dt} + h_{30}\frac{dm_{32}}{dt}. \tag{4}$$

In equation (4) dm_{43}/dt and dm_{32}/dt have to be expressed in terms of temperature or pressure in order to obtain an oscillation equation.

The perturbation vapor-mass-flow-rate, dm_{43}/dt, is certainly a function of the rate change of the vapor pressure in the boiler and its derivatives. For simplicity, it is assumed that dm_{43}/dt is a linear function of dp_3/dt and d^2p_3/dt as follows:

$$\frac{dm_{43}}{dt} = -\left(K_a \frac{d^2p_3}{dt^2} + K_b \frac{dP_3}{dt}\right), \tag{5}$$

where K_a and K_b are positive constants. The negative sign on the right-hand side of equation (5) is due to the fact that when the vapor pressure and its time rate increase, the boiling process in the boiler will be depressed. It results in a decrease of the boiling rate. In order to determine the small perturbation vapor-mass-flow-rate, dm_{32}/dt, the flow characteristic of the throttling valve A is linearized as follows:

$$\frac{dm_{32}}{dt} = K_{32}(p_3-p_2), \tag{6}$$

where K_{32} is a positive constant.

By making use of Clapeyron's equation relating the change of vapor pressure with the change of temperature at the phase equilibrium between a liquid and its vapor in a single component system [4],

$$\frac{dP}{dT} = \frac{h_{fg}}{T(v_v-v_\ell)}, \tag{7}$$

we obtain

$$\frac{dT_3}{dt} = [\frac{T(v_v-v_\ell)}{h_{fg}}]_{30}\frac{dP_3}{dt}, \tag{8}$$

where h_{fg} is the evaporation enthalpy, v_v and v_ℓ are the specific volumes of vapor and liquid, respectively. Substitution of equations (5), (6), and (8), into equation (4) yields

$$K_a\frac{d^2P_3}{dt^2} + [K_b + (\frac{Mc_p T (v_v-v_\ell)}{h\,h_{fg}})_{30}]\frac{dP_3}{dt} + K_{32}P_3 = K_{32}P_2. \tag{9}$$

Equations (3) and (9) contain the vapor pressure, p_2, in region 2, which is affected by the displacement of the water column in region 1 and the vapor pressure in region 3. For a small perturbation, it is assumed that p_2 is a linear function of the displacement, x, and the vapor pressure, p_3, as

$$p_2 = - (c_3p_3 + c_1x). \tag{10}$$

where c_1 and c_3 are positive constants. The negative sign on the right-hand side of equation (10) is to ensure that equations (11) and (12) possess the oscillation characteristics. Substituting equation (10) into equations (3) and (9), we obtain the equations of the water column oscillation in the exit tube and the vapor pressure oscillation in the boiler:

$$L \frac{d^2x}{dt^2} + \frac{32\mu L}{\rho D^2} \frac{dx}{dt} + \frac{c_1}{\rho} x = - \frac{c_3}{\rho} p_3 \tag{11}$$

and

$$K_a \frac{d^2p_3}{dt^2} + [K_b + (\frac{MC_pT(v_v-v_\ell)}{h\, h_{fg}})_{30}] \frac{dP_3}{dt} + K_{32}(1+c_3)p_3 =$$

$$= - K_{32}c_1 x \tag{12}$$

Equations (11) and (12) are of interest in the investigation. Equation (11) is a momentum equation. It describes the oscillation of the water column in the exit tube. The term on the right-hand side of equation (11) represents an external force induced by the vapor pressure in the boiler, acting on the water column and forcing it to oscillate. Equation (12) is an energy equation. It represents the vapor pressure oscillation in the boiler. The term on the right-hand side of equation (12) represents an external energy induced by the motion of the water column in the exit tube, forcing the vapor pressure in the boiler to oscillate. These two oscillation systems oscillate simultaneously. One oscillation system acts as an external source forcing the other system to oscillate. Therefore, when the oscillations of the two systems are established, they will not die out. Thus sustained oscillations exist between these two systems.

In order to obtain more information of the coupled oscillations, equations (11) and (12) are written in the following simplified form:

$$a_1 \frac{d^2x}{dt^2} + a_2 \frac{dx}{dt} + a_3x = - a_4p_3, \tag{13}$$

and

$$b_1 \frac{d^2p_3}{dt^2} + b_2 \frac{dp_3}{dt} + b_3p_3 = - b_4x, \tag{14}$$

where a_i and b_i are positive constants defined as follows:

$$a_1 = L,$$

$$a_2 = \frac{32\mu L}{\rho D^2},$$

$$a_3 = \frac{c_1}{\rho},$$

$$a_4 = \frac{c_3}{\rho},$$

$$b_1 = K_a,$$

$$b_2 = K_b + [\frac{MC_p\ T(v_v-v_\ell)}{h\ h_{fg}}]_{30},$$

$$b_3 = K_{32}(1+c_3),$$

$$b_4 = K_{32}c_1.$$

(15)

We assume that the vapor pressure in the boiler varies sinusoidally,

$$p_3 = p_{3,max}\ \sin \omega t.$$ (16)

Substitution of equation (16) into equation (14) yields

$$x = x_{max}\ \sin(\omega t+\phi_1+\pi),$$ (17)

where

$$x_{max} = \frac{p_{3,max}}{b_4}\ \sqrt{(b_3-b_1\omega^2)^2+b_2^2\omega^2},$$ (18)

and

$$\phi_1 = \tan^{-1}\frac{b_2\omega}{b_3-b_1\omega^2} = \tan^{-1}\frac{2\zeta(\omega/\beta)}{1-(\omega/\beta)^2},$$ (19)

with

$$\beta = \sqrt{b_3/b_1}$$ (20)

and

$$\zeta = \frac{b_2}{2\sqrt{b_1b_3}}$$ (21)

β and ζ are the natural frequency and the damping ratio of the oscillation [5] of the vapor pressure in the boiler, respectively. Comparing equation (16) with equation (17), it can be seen that the displacement of the water column in the exit tube, x, leads the vapor pressure in the boiler, p_3, by a phase angle $(\phi_1+\pi)$.

Similarly, the substitution of equation (17) into equation (13) gives

$$p_3 = \frac{x_{max}}{a_4} \sqrt{(a_3-a_1\omega^2)^2+a_2^2\omega^2} \ \sin(\omega t+\phi_1+\phi_3+2\pi), \qquad (22)$$

where

$$\phi_3 = \tan^{-1} \frac{a_2\omega}{a_3-a_1\omega^2} = \tan^{-1} \frac{2\zeta^*(\omega/\beta^*)}{1-(\omega/\beta^*)^2}, \qquad (23)$$

with

$$\beta^* = \sqrt{a_3/a_1}, \qquad (24)$$

and

$$\zeta^* = \frac{a_2}{2\sqrt{a_1 a_3}}, \qquad (25)$$

β^* and ζ^* are the natural frequency and the damping ratio of the oscillation of the water column in the exit tube, respectively. Comparing equation (17) with equation (22), it is seen that the vapor pressure in the boiler, p_3, leads the displacement of the water column in the exit tube, x, by a phase angle $(\phi_3+\pi)$.

The vapor pressure, p_3, obtained from equation (22) has to satisfy the condition described in equation (16). Substituting equation (18) into equation (22), and then substituting equation (22) into equation (16), we obtain

$$\frac{1}{a_4 b_4} \sqrt{[(a_3-a_1\omega^2)^2+a_2^2\omega^2][(b_3-b_1\omega^2)^2+b_2^2\omega^2]} \ \sin(\omega t+\phi_1+\phi_2) =$$
$$= \sin(\omega t). \qquad (26)$$

To satisfy equation (26), it requires that

(a) $[(a_3-a_1\omega^2)^2 + a_2^2\omega^2][(b_3-b_1\omega^2)^2 + b_2^2\omega^2] = a_4^2 b_4^2, \qquad (27)$

and

(b) $$\sin(\omega t + \phi_1 + \phi_3) = \sin(\omega t). \tag{28}$$

Equation (28) can be satisfied by one of the following cases:

Case 1: $\phi_1 = \phi_3 = 0$. $\tag{29}$

Case 2: $\phi_1 = \phi_3 = -\pi$. $\tag{30}$

Case 1 represents that the oscillation of the vapor pressure in the boiler is in the opposite direction to the oscillation of the water column in the exit tube. In Case 2, however, the oscillations take place in phase with each other.

From equations (19) and (23) it is seen that approximate solutions for the requirements of CAse 1 and Case 2 can be obtained as follows:

For Case 1: $\frac{\omega}{\beta} \ll 1$ and $\frac{\omega}{\beta*} \ll 1,$ $\tag{31}$

and

For Case 2: $\frac{\omega}{\beta} \gg 1$ and $\frac{\omega}{\beta*} \gg 1.$ $\tag{32}$

Equations (31) and (32) show that the frequency of the oscillations, ω, should be either much lower or much higher than the natural frequencies of the two oscillation systems.

The vapor pressure in region 2 is different for the different two cases. For Case 1, it can be expressed by making use of equations (16), (17) and (10),

$$p_2 = -(c_3 p_{3,max} - c_1 x_{max})\sin(\omega t). \tag{33}$$

It is seen that the vapor pressure in the tube, p_2, may oscillate either in phase with the oscillation of the vapor pressure in the boiler, when

$$c_3 p_{3,max} < c_1 x_{max}, \tag{34}$$

or in the opposite direction to the oscillation of the vapor pressure in the boiler, when

$$c_3 p_{3,max} > c_1 x_{max}. \tag{35}$$

For Case 2, it results from equations (16), (17) and (10),

$$p_2 = -(c_3 p_{3,max} + c_1 x_{max})\sin(\omega t). \tag{36}$$

In this case, the vapor pressure, p_2, can only oscillate in the direction opposite to the oscillations of the vapor pressure in the boiler.

The experimental results shown in Fig. 3a indicate that p_2 oscillates in the opposite direction to the oscillation of p_3. Therefore, it can be concluded that the experimental system oscillates either under the condition of Case 1 with

$$c_3 p_{3,max} > c_1 x_{max}$$

or under the condition of Case 2. Because the frequency of the experimental oscillations obtained is very low, $f = 0.8$ Hz, it is expected that the system oscillates under the condition of Case 1 with

$$c_3 p_{3,max} > c_1 x_{max}.$$

The rate of the vapor-mass-flow across the throttling valve A, dm_{32}/dt, for the condition of Case 1 with

$$c_3 p_{3,max} > c_1 x_{max},$$

can be determined by substituting equations (16), (17) and (10) into equation (6),

$$\frac{dm_{32}}{dt} = K_{32}\left[(1+c_3)p_{3,max}-c_1 x_{max}\right]\sin \omega t. \qquad (37)$$

It is seen that dm_{32}/dt oscillates only in phase with the oscillation of the vapor pressure in the boiler.

The variation of the rate of the vapor-mass-flow across the boundary between region 4 and region 3, dm_{43}/dt, can be determined by substituting equation (16) into equation (5),

$$\frac{dm_{43}}{dt} = A \sin(\omega t-\phi_4), \qquad (38)$$

where

$$A = K_b \omega p_{3max}/\sin\phi_4 \text{ and } \phi_4 = \tan^{-1}(K_b/\omega K_a). \qquad (39)$$

Equation (38) represents the oscillation of the vapor-mass-flow-rate, dm_{43}/dt, which has the same frequency as the vapor pressure in the boiler. The phase angle by which the vapor pressure in the boiler leads the vapor-mass-flow-rate, dm_{43}/dt, is the angle ϕ_4.

DISCUSSIONS AND CONCLUSIONS

In the experimental investigation, oscillations of the vapor
pressure in the boiler and in the tube were recorded. However,
there is no record of the oscillation of the water column in the
exit tube. Therefore, the length L, and the location,x, of the
water column in the exit tube, are unknown. In the analysis,
the two constants, K_a and K_b, appearing in equation (5), and the
two constants,C_1 and C_3, introduced in equation (10) are also
unknowns. The constant, K_{32}, in equation (6) can be determined
by using the flow characteristic of the throttling valve, A,
(Fig. 1). The above analysis provides only three equations,
equations (10), (11), and (12), which may be used for the determination of the 6 unknowns. Therefore, three additional conditions are required for a general solution of the problem.

The analysis described in the previous section provides the
following useful information on the sustained oscillations in
the experimental boiler system:

1. Consider the vapor in the boiler and the water column
    in the exit tube as two oscillation systems. One system
    acts as an external source forcing the other system to
    oscillate. They adjust themselves to oscillate at the
    same frequency. Two oscillation modes are possible:
    In the first mode, they oscillate at a frequency which
    is much lower than their natural frequencies. For such
    a case, they oscillate in the opposite direction against
    each other. In the second mode, they oscillate at a
    frequency which is much higher than their natural fre-
    quencies. Under this condition, they oscillate in
    phase with each other.

2. The oscillations of the two systems are coupled by the
    oscillation of the vapor pressure in region 2 (Fig.5a),
    which has the same frequency as the two systems. When
    the two systems oscillate in the first mode, the
    oscillation of p_2 is either in phase with or in the
    opposite direction to the oscillation of the vapor
    pressure in the boiler, dependent on whether

$$c_3 p_{3max} < c_1 x_{max},$$

or

$$c_3 p_{3max} > c_1 x_{max}.$$

When the two systems oscillate in the second mode, the
oscillation of p_2 can be only in the direction opposite

to the oscillation of the two systems.

3. The experimental results shown in Fig. 3a indicate that p_2 and p_3 oscillate in the opposite direction with quite a low frequency. For such a case, the oscillation of the vapor pressure in the boiler is in the opposite direction to the oscillation of the water column in the exit tube and with the condition

$$c_3 p_{3max} > c_1 x_{max}.$$

The physical meaning of this condition is that the vapor pressure in the tube, p_2, is more affected by the vapor pressure in the boiler than by the displacement of the water column in the tube.

4. The vapor-mass-flow-rate, dm_{32}/dt, oscillates together with the vapor pressure in the boiler. They oscillate at the same frequency and in phase with each other.

5. The oscillations of the vapor-mass-flow-rate, dm_{43}/dt, and the vapor pressure in the boiler are coupled together. They oscillate at the same frequency. However, the vapor pressure in the boiler leads the vapor-mass-flow-rate, dm_{43}/dt, by a phase angle ϕ_4.

NOMENCLATURE

a_1, a_2, a_3, a_4 b_1, b_2, b_3, b_4	constants defined in equation (15)
c_1, c_3	positive constants
c_p	specific heat at constant pressure
D	diameter
h	enthalpy
h_{fg}	evaporation enthalpy
K_a, K_b, K_{32}	positive constants
L	length
m	vapor mass
M	vapor mass in boiler

p	pressure
t	time
T	temperature
v	specific volume
	velocity
x	displacement coordination
β_1, β^*	natural frequencies
ζ, ζ^*	damping ratios
μ	dynamic viscosity
ρ	density
τ_0	shear stress at a wall
ϕ_1, ϕ_2, ϕ_3	phase angles
ω	frequency

Subscripts

0	steady state condition
1,2,3,4	regions defined in Fig. 5a
ℓ	liquid
v	vapor

REFERENCES

1   Lin, S., An Investigation of Sustained Pressure Oscilla-
    tions in a Vertical Experimental Boiler. Two-
    Phase Transport and Reactor Safety, Vol.II,
    ed. T.N.Veziroglu and S.Kakaç, Hemisphere,
    Washington, 1978, pp.739-46.

2   Lin, S., Sustained Flow Oscillations in a Thermal-
    Hydraulic Coupled System. Recent Developments
    in Theoretical and Experimental Fluid Mechanics,
    ed. U. Müller, K.G.Roesner and B.Schmidt,
    Springer-Verlag, Berlin, 1979. pp.587-598.

3   Streeter, V.L., Wylie, E.B., Fluid Mechanics. 6th ed.,
          McGraw-Hill, New York, 1975, p.632.

4   Jui Sheng Hsieh, Principles of Thermodynamics.
          McGraw-Hill, New York, 1975, p. 66.

5   Vernon, T.B., Linear Vibration Theory: Generalized
          Properties and Numerical Methods. John Wiley,
          New York, 1967, pp.20-22.

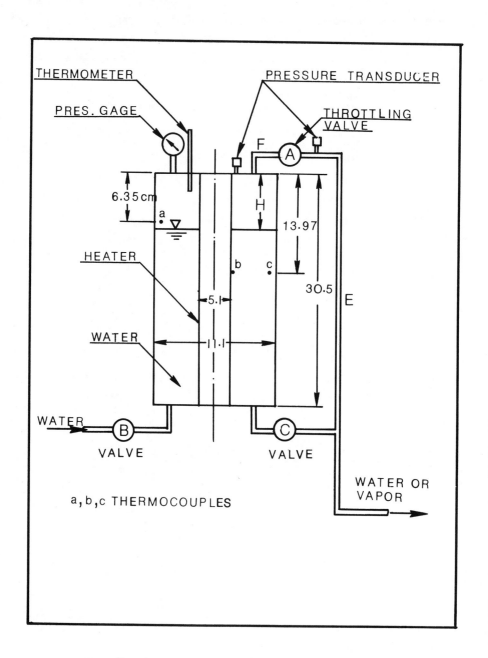

THERMOMETER

PRES. GAGE

PRESSURE TRANSDUCER

THROTTLING VALVE

6.35 cm

a

HEATER

H

13.97

F

b   c

5.1

30.5

WATER

11.1

E

WATER

B

VALVE

C

VALVE

WATER OR VAPOR

a,b,c THERMOCOUPLES

FIG 1 EXPERIMENT BOILER

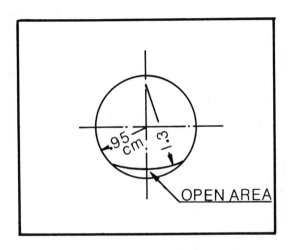

FIG 2 OPEN AREA
         OF VALVE A

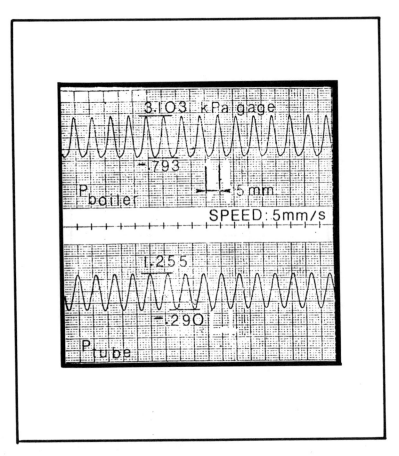

FIG. 3a   Experimental Record of Pressure oscillations in the
          boiler (top one) and in the tube (bottom one) with
          H = 6.35 cm.

Note: During the experimental test, one pressure transducer
          received the pressure signal at its positive terminal
          and the other at the negative terminal. Therefore the
          two pressure oscillations present a real case of 180°
          out of phase.

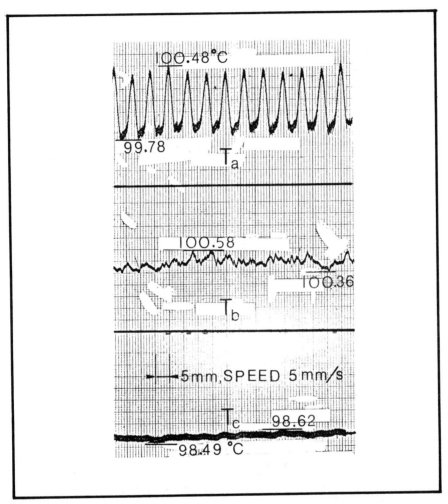

FIG. 3b Experimental Record of the vapor temperature in the
boiler (top one), the heating surface temperature in
the water in the boiler (middle one) and the water
temperature in the boiler (bottom one) with
H = 6.35 cm.

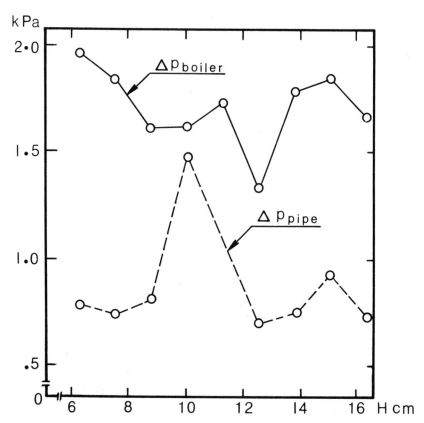

FIG. 4a   Amplitudes of the Pressure Oscillations in the boiler
and the tube as functions of the distance between the
water level and the top of the boiler

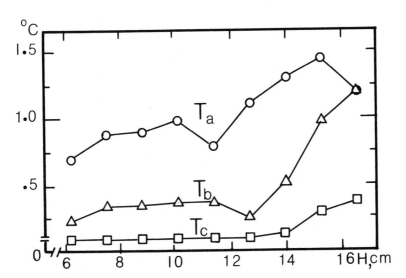

FIG. 4b Amplitudes of the oscillations of the vapor temperature, the heating surface temperature and the water
temperature in the boiler as functions of the distance
between the water level and the top of the boiler

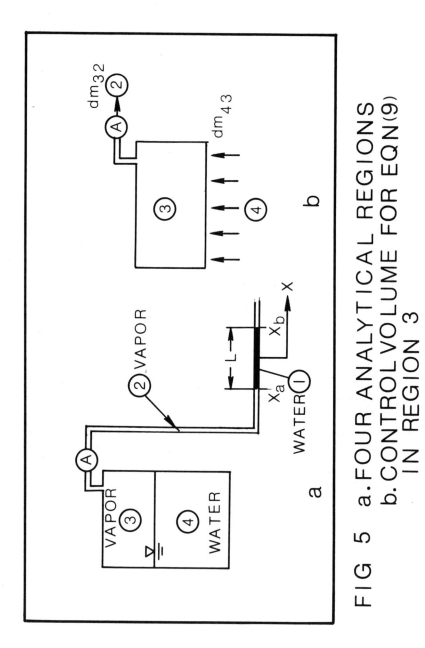

FIG 5 a. FOUR ANALYTICAL REGIONS
b. CONTROL VOLUME FOR EQN(9)
IN REGION 3

Prediction of Density-Wave Stability Limits for Evaporators—Sensitivity to Model Assumptions

P.O. AKINJIOLA and J.C. FRIEDLY
Department of Chemical Engineering
University of Rochester
Rochester, New York 14627, USA

ABSTRACT

Theoretical computations have been performed to determine how sensitive predicted stability limits are to the details of the models used. The dimensionless form of a homogeneous fluid model with uniform heat input is used as a base case. Predictions from this model are compared successively with models which include slip flow, nonuniform energy input and subcooled boiling. Conditions are chosen to be in the parameter range corresponding to several sets of data available in the literature and for which the homogeneous model assumptions might be expected to be invalid. For each comparison, results have been obtained in three cases: when the base case model is used; when the more detailed model is used for the steady state computation of pressure drops, but not used directly in the perturbation and stability analysis; when it is used both for the steady state and the dynamic analysis. It is found in some cases that the stability predictions are nearly correct when the steady state pressure drops are computed with the more detailed model but the stability limits computed with the simple model. On the other hand, details of the model are quite important in determining stability limits when subcooled boiling is important and when nonuniform heating introduces a significant time delay before the dominant pressure drop. It is concluded that it may be feasible under suitable circumstances to use simpler models for stability limit computations if more detailed codes are used to model the steady state characteristics accurately.

INTRODUCTION

The prominence of boiling heat transfer in power generation has prompted numerous studies of flow oscillation problems which frequently occur. Of the many types known [1-5], density-wave oscillations have received the most theoretical attention. The qualitative nature of density-wave oscillations is well described by the relatively simple homogeneous fluid model suggested by Bouré [6-7]. However, a number of

1229

computer codes have been developed based on these same ideas
[8-11], but incorporating detailed equipment models, correlations of the two-phase flow and heat transfer characteristics.

In spite of work for over 15 years, it is still not clear to
what extent the details of models have been verified experimentally. Most experiments have been conducted under conditions where a relatively large number of parameters have been
important. Data on the dynamic behavior, such as the oscillation threshold, are too scarce to verify that void fraction
correlations, for example, apply in the unsteady state
problem. Most often the detailed correlations used in computer codes are developed from extensive steady state experiments, and merely assumed to apply also for the dynamic case.
Of course, this need not be the case.

The question of how much detail is essential in a model is a
controversial one. To gain better insight into this question,
data taken near the oscillation threshold in nine different
studies in the literature [12-20] were recently reexamined
[21,22]. In experimental conditions ranging from cryogenic
to high temperatures and for fluids ranging from helium to
water, it was found that the simple homogeneous two-phase
fluid model was able to predict the data to within an average
error (in dimensionless parameters) of about 40%. The results
suggest that many of these data sets may not require more
detailed models, but they also suggest that it is rather
difficult to design oscillation experiments to test the
validity of details in the model.

The question of how sensitive predicted stability limits are
to the details of the dynamic models used can be looked at
from several points of view. More detailed models may provide refinements to the basic results obtained from a simple
model, as may be the case with the data analyzed recently
[21,22]. Model details may be quite important in determining
steady state conditions such as flow rate, exit quality and
pressure drop distributions, but given the steady state
behavior, the detail may not be important in the unsteady
state model. Finally the model detail may well be vital in
the dynamic problem as well as the steady state problem. It
is likely that all three of these points of view (as well as
others) will be valid in some regions of the rather high
dimensional parameter space applicable to density-wave
oscillations. However, it is not at all clear where. In
this paper we present some results designed to shed light on
the question of sensitivity to model assumptions. We have
chosen to consider the effects of using four different refinements to the basic homogeneous two-phase flow model
suggested by Bouré, including 1) a slip flow correlation,

2) a two-phase flow pressure drop correlation, 3) nonuniform heat flux, and 4) a subcooled boiling correlation. Conditions for evaluation of these assumptions have been chosen based on both published experimental results and expectations of when each should be most important.

ANALYSIS

Virtually all analyses of the problem consider a heated test section contained between two pressures determined externally. It is often convenient to write the total (dimensionless) pressure drop

$$\Delta p_{total} = \Delta p_i + \Delta p_f + \Delta p_g + \Delta p_{I-a} + \Delta p_e \tag{1}$$

in terms of conveniently computed Δp's, for example, an inlet valve, test section friction, gravity, acceleration, and an exit valve. The stability problem is then solved by a linear analysis in terms of perturbation variables, writing each variable as the steady state value plus a Laplace transformed perturbation $\Delta p = \Delta \overline{p} + \mathcal{L}^{-1}\{\delta\Delta p(s)\}$. The response in the dimensionless inlet flow rate perturbation $\delta M_1(s)$ to a change in external pressure, or total pressure drop, can be written immediately from Eq. 1.

$$\frac{\delta M_1}{\delta\Delta p_{total}}(s) = \frac{1}{\frac{\delta\Delta p_i}{\delta M_1}(s) + \frac{\delta\Delta p_f}{\delta M_1}(s) + \frac{\delta\Delta p_g}{\delta M_1}(s) + \frac{\delta\Delta p_{I-a}}{\delta M_1}(s) + \frac{\delta\Delta p_e}{\delta M_1}(s)} \tag{2}$$

Eq. 2 is valid for all models provided all pressure drops are included. Models differ only in the expressions used for the various pressure drops and in the forms of the continuity and energy equations used to solve for the transfer functions, $\frac{\delta\Delta p_i}{\delta M_1}$, etc.

Homogeneous Fluid Model

The basic homogeneous two-phase model used for the stability analysis takes on the following form in dimensionless variables continuity

$$\frac{\partial(1/V)}{\partial\tau} + \frac{\partial M}{\partial\xi} = 0 \tag{3}$$

at $\xi=0$, $1/V = 1$

energy

$$\frac{1}{V}\frac{\partial X}{\partial\tau} + M\frac{\partial X}{\partial\xi} = \left\{\begin{matrix} 0 &, & \xi<0 \text{ and } 1<\xi \\ 1 &, & 0<\xi<1 \end{matrix}\right. \tag{4}$$

at $\xi=0$, $X=-Ja$

equation of state

$$V = \left\{\begin{matrix} 1 &, & X<0 \\ 1+X &, & 0<X \end{matrix}\right. \tag{5}$$

Here V is the bulk specific volume, M the mass flow rate and X a form of the thermodynamic quality parameter. The momentum equation commonly used has the following expressions for the pressure drops in Eq. 1

$$\Delta p_i = k_i M_1^2 \quad, \quad \Delta p_f = \phi\int_0^1 VM^2 d\xi \quad, \quad \Delta p_g = \frac{1}{Fr'}\int_0^1\frac{d\xi}{V}$$

$$\Delta p_{I-a} = \int_0^1 [\frac{\partial M}{\partial\tau} + \frac{\partial(VM)}{\partial\xi}]\, d\xi \quad, \quad \Delta p_e = k_e V_3 M_3^2 \tag{6}$$

The solution to Eqs. 3-5 is characterized in terms of two parameters, the Jakob number, Ja, which represents the inlet subcooling and X_3 the exit quality parameter. It can be shown [22] that the stability limit determined from Eqs. 2 and 6 is characterized in terms of $n-1$ other parameters, where n is the total number of pressure drops important in Eq. 1 or 2. It is convenient to take these as the ratios of steady state pressure drops, $\frac{\Delta\overline{p}_f}{\Delta\overline{p}_i}$, etc. It is important to realize that we have chosen the particular dimensionless variables used here in such a way that they are relatively independent of the particular model used. The inlet sub-cooling Ja, the exit quality parameter X_3, and the pressure drop ratios are all physically meaningful quantities and it is reasonable to be able to compute them in many cases directly from experimentally measured quantities. Alternatively, their values can be determined from more detailed models of steady state performance. This should not be interpreted to imply, however, that the simple quality and void fraction profiles predicted from this model are not used in evaluating stability limits from the model.

Equations 3-6 represent the simplest model commonly used. Its predictions of stability limits will be compared with those of four different more detailed models. The detailed models have been chosen so that we can isolate the effect of relaxing one assumption at a time in the simple model. It is implicitly assumed for the purpose of this comparison that each more detailed model will give a more accurate description of the problem than the simplest model.

Slip Flow Model

The slip flow model used here is the drift flux model [23] used previously on this problem by Zuber [24]. Written in terms of dimensionless bulk fluid variables, this model consists of equations of the form of Eqs. 3-5 except for the following changes. Eq. 4 has the following term added to the left side $- \frac{\partial}{\partial \tau} [\frac{M_d(V-1)}{MV}]$; Eq. 5 has X on the right side replaced by $X M/(M+M_d)$; and Eq. 2 includes an additional slip pressure drop $\Delta p_s = \int_0^1 \frac{d}{d\xi} [M_d^2(\frac{V^2-V}{1-rV})]d\xi$, where M_d is the drift velocity and r the specific volume ratio v_f/v_g. The drift velocity correlation of Zuber and Findlay [25] is of the form

$$M_d = c \ (\frac{1-r}{WeFr})^{1/4} \ M \qquad (7)$$

The constant c is flow regime dependent, but was chosen to be 1.41 for bubbly flow for the computations here.

Martinelli-Nelson Pressure Drop Correlation

In this model modification only the expression for the friction pressure drop in Eq. 6 is changed, using the standard Martinelli-Nelson expression

$$\Delta p_f = \int_1^\lambda \phi M_1^2 d\xi + \int_\lambda^1 \phi M_1^2 (1-X \ \frac{r}{1-r})^{1.75} \ \phi_{tt}^2 d\xi \qquad (8)$$

where Φ_{tt}^{2} is the two-phase multiplier expressed graphically as a function of X (as well as fluid properties) by Martinelli and Nelson [26].

Nonuniform Energy Input

In order to make this modification extreme, we have chosen to make the energy input a step function, concentrating all of the energy flux in the initial part of the test section. In Eq. 4 the right side was replaced by $\begin{cases} 0 & , \xi<0 \text{ and } \xi>\lambda_h \\ 1/\lambda_h & , 0<\xi<\lambda_h \end{cases}$ where λ_h is the fraction of the test section in which the heating takes place.

Subcooled Boiling

The modifications here take into account the fact that the bulk fluid may not be in thermal equilibrium with the wall. The analysis used comes directly from Saha [19]. In terms of these model equations the following changes need to be made. The right side of the equation of state Eq. 5 is replaced by

$\begin{cases} 1 & , \xi<\lambda_s \\ 1 + \int_{\lambda_s}^{\xi} \Gamma_g \, d\xi & , \lambda_s<\xi \end{cases}$ where λ_s is the point of net vapor

generation which can now occur when $X \leq 0$ and Γ_g is the vapor generation rate. Γ_g is assumed to take the form

$$\Gamma_g = \begin{cases} 0 & \xi<\lambda_s \\ \dfrac{\xi-\lambda_s}{\lambda-\lambda_s} & \lambda_s<\xi<\lambda_m \\ \dfrac{\lambda_m-\lambda_s}{\lambda-\lambda_s} & \lambda_m<\xi<1 \end{cases} \qquad (9)$$

where λ_m is chosen such that $\int_{\lambda_s}^{1} \Gamma_g \, d\xi = X_3$. The point of net vapor generation was determined from the correlation [19]

$$\lambda-\lambda_s = \begin{cases} 0.00173 \text{ M a Pe} & , \text{Pe} < 70,000 \\ 38.5 \text{ a} & , 70,000 < \text{Pe} \end{cases} \qquad (10)$$

where a is the aspect ratio D/ℓ.

Details of the steady state solutions and perturbation solutions are available in the cited references and will not be repeated here. Stability and stability limits were determined by standard techniques.

RESULTS

Results have been obtained by comparing each of the four model
modifications separately with the basic homogeneous fluid
model predictions. In all cases comparisons were made in
terms of dimensionless parameters. In order to select
meaningful parameter values on which we can base our conclusions, we have looked at each of the data sets analyzed in
References 21 and 22. For each model assumption investigated,
typical conditions for the data points showing the maximum
effect of the model modification are reported in Table 1.
The values of the exit quality parameter X_3 and the inlet
subcooling parameter Ja in the first two lines are computed
from the experimental data and are left unchanged for the
comparisons. Each data point is then treated in three ways.
First, the model with the appropriate modification is used
to compute the steady state pressure drop distribution and
then the position in state space of the data point relative
to the stability limit. We have chosen to use a stability

number defined as $N_{st} = \dfrac{\Delta p_{ratio} - \Delta p^*_{ratio}}{\Delta p^*_{ratio}}$ where Δp^*_{ratio}

is the value of the ratio of the dominant system pressure
drop to the inlet pressure drop at the stability limit.
Physically this stability number reflects the fractional
change in the inlet pressure drop required to stabilize the
data point, keeping all other pressure drops, X_3 and Ja the
same. Second, the data are analyzed again, using the basic
homogeneous fluid model to yield a different pressure drop
distribution and a different stability number. Finally the
stability number is computed from the transfer functions of
the basic model using the steady state pressure drop distribution previously computed from the more detailed model.

The results in Table 1 can be interpreted in terms of two
levels of approximation to a more detailed model. If we
assume that the detailed model gives the accurate assessment
of the data point relative to the stability limit, the basic
model prediction gives an extreme case in which all of the
detail is omitted for both the steady state and the unsteady
state computation. The last line then gives the prediction
if the detailed model is used for the steady state computations and these results then used in the perturbed form of
the basic model for the stability determinations. (It must
be remembered though that only the values of X_3, Ja and the
Δp_{ratio}'s come from the detailed model; the basic $1/V$ and X
profiles are still in the integrations in Eq. 6.) The

differences among the three stability numbers determined in
this way can be used to judge how sensitive the results are
to model assumptions.

In the first column of Table 1 the effect of the slip flow
assumption in the model is investigated. From Eq. 7 it can
be seen that the drift flux model yields a drift velocity
dependent on fluid properties but not on operating characteristics. Therefore the drift is most important when the
mass flow rate is small, generally at the higher values of
the exit quality parameter. The data point analyzed from
Carver's work [14] had a slip ratio $\frac{Md}{M}$ = 0.56. The results
show that the effect of slip in determining the pressure
drop distribution is rather significant and the stability
limit (stability number) computed from the basic model is
perhaps 50% off from the slip flow model predictions.
However, the last line indicates that by simply using the
correct pressure drop distribution the predictions can be
improved quite substantially. Therefore it would appear
that the effect of slip flow here is primarily one of
influencing the steady state pressure drop distribution.
There is little additional dynamic effect contributed by the
slip flow model.

This same information is conveyed in more general terms on
the stability plane shown in Fig. 1. This figure shows the
pressure drop ratio-exit quality parameter plane when the
gravitational pressure drop is dominant. This is when one
might expect the drift flux to have the greatest effect.
The inlet subcooling, Ja, and the pressure drop distribution,

$\frac{\Delta p_a}{\Delta p_g}$, are both fixed. All other Δp's have been assumed zero.

The proximity of the three curves indicate that the dynamic
behavior of the drift flux model and that of the basic homogeneous fluid model are not greatly different, provided the
accurate pressure drop distribution is used. Therefore, it
can be concluded that slip flow tends to be primarily a steady
state effect in the range of parameters considered here.

The second column of Table 1 indicates similar results for the
effect of using a more detailed two-phase flow friction
pressure drop correlation. This model differs from the previous one in that here only the more detailed two-phase
friction pressure drop expression in Eq. 8 is used. In the
previous case the appropriate drift flux contributions in the
model equations were assumed but no change in the form of the
friction pressure drop was included. The results, however,
tend to be quite different.The data point from Solberg

[13], representative of the maximum effect of the friction
pressure drop, shows that the correct steady state pressure
drop distribution doesn't improve the predictions at all.
The stability plane in Fig. 2 shows that the results vary
widely with conditions, showing both good agreement and poor.
Here the test section friction is the dominant pressure drop,
all other Δp's in the test section being assumed zero. A
relatively low Ja was assumed so that the two-phase pressure
drop in the test section would certainly dominate.

In the third column of Table 1 the effect of concentrating
the heat flux into the first half of the test section is
shown. For the two experimental runs analyzed the heat flux
was actually very nearly uniform. These two runs were chosen
simply to provide typical data, the second being typical of
those runs in which the maximum effect is obtained. They
differ in that the first has the test section friction as the
dominant pressure drop and the second has dominating exit
pressure drop. When there is little exit pressure drop, the
result is pretty much as in the first case. Using the
appropriate pressure drop distribution gives a stability
limit approaching that of the more detailed model. On the
other hand, when the exit pressure drop is dominant, significant differences remain. Figures 3 and 4 show the same
effect when the friction pressure drop and when the exit
pressure drop is dominant. On these figures the broken curve
for the basic model is independent of the fraction of the
test section λ_h in which the heat is concentrated because
this is ignored in the simple model. The more detailed model
gives results which differ more the smaller λ_h is. Although
the simple model does less well at lower values of X, the
percentage error in X is reasonable when friction is the
dominant pressure drop. However, it does significantly worse
when the exit pressure drop is dominant. Therefore, there
appears to be a significant dynamic effect in the problem
when the dominant pressure drop is downstream from the test
section and when the quality is low. This effect is attributed to the fact that there is a significant delay time introduced between the end of the heated section and the exit pressure drop. The delay does not enter into the steady state
problem, and it is much less significant (although not negligible) when the test section friction is dominant.

The final example considers the effect of subcooled boiling,
following the work of Saha [19]. Again two experimental data
points are considered in Table 1. The first is from Yadigaroglu
[12] and has a Peclet number of about 61,000. The subcooled
boiling correlation in Eq. 10 has very little effect on the
stability. This was found to be typical of all experimental
data for Pe < 70,000. The second data point from Saha [19]

was for a significantly higher Peclet number. It shows a
relatively large effect of subcooled boiling. More significantly, there is not much improvement when the more correct
pressure drop distribution is used. Therefore, the effect is
a purely dynamic one. Fig. 5 shows the same type of thing
when friction is the dominant pressure drop. The parameter
is the Peclet number. The computed stability limits show
that there is a discontinuous effect of subcooled boiling
occurring at Pe = 70,000. Above that value the dynamic
effect is quite significant, but it is small at lower Pe.
This effect is certainly due to the discontinuous nature of
the particular correlation used in Eq. 10. It enters the
dynamic problem in the perturbation of the position of the
boiling boundary, clearly a dynamic effect only.

CONCLUSION

The computational results reported here were made to shed
additional light on the detail required in models used to
predict stability. Based on literature data, ranges of
parameters in which each effect considered tends to be
important have been identified. The effects of four separate
model assumptions were considered. It was found that the
basic homogeneous two-phase fluid model could differ significantly from the more detailed models. However, stability
predictions using the simple model could be improved by using
the steady state pressure drop distribution computed from a
more detailed model. The slip flow approximation is a model
modification which has its primary effect on the steady state
pressure drop distributions. Using these pressure drops in
the perturbed basic model gives results nearly as good as
the detailed models. On the other hand, the subcooled boiling
correlation used shows a purely dynamic effect, quite significant for Pe > 70,000. The simple model cannot be used
with any accuracy. The nonuniform heat flux approximation
shows an effect which is primarily on the steady state when
the test section friction pressure drop dominates, but which
is primarily dynamic at low exit qualities when there is a
delay between the end of the heated section and a dominant exit
pressure drop. The two-phase friction pressure drop correlation also gives results highly dependent on the parameters.
These results show that in many important cases it may be
possible to use the simple homogeneous two-phase fluid model
to predict stability limits. However, it is important to use
dimensionless parameters obtained from accurate steady state
information, obtained either from experimental measurements
or a reliable steady state model.

REFERENCES

1. Bouré, J. A., Bergles, A. E. and Tong, L. S., "Review of Two-Phase Flow Instability," ASME paper No. 71-HT-42 (1971).

2. Bergles, A. E., Proc. Euro. Two-Phase Flow Group, Rome (6/72).

3. Bouré, J. A., Bergles, A. E., Tong, L. S., Nucl. Eng. Design, 25, #2, 165 (1973).

4. Bergles, A. E., Proc. Nato Advanced Study Inst., Two-Phase Flow and Heat Transfer, Istanbul (8/76).

5. Ishii, M., "Study on flow instabilities in two-phase mixtures," ANL-76-23, ERDA Contract W-31-109-ENG 38 (1976).

6. Bouré, J., These de Docteur-Ingenieur, Universite de Grenoble, France, (1965).

7. Bouré, J., "The oscillatory behavior of heated channels. An analysis of density effect," CEAR3049, Centre d'Etude Nucleaires de Grenoble, France (1966).

8. Davies, A. L., Potter, R., Proc. Symp. on Two-Phase Flow Dynamics, Eindhoven (9/67).

9. Deam, R., Murray, J., Proc. Euro. Two-Phase Flow Meeting, Erlangen (6/76).

10. Suzuoki, A., Yamakawa, N., Bull. JSME 19, #132, 619, (1976).

11. Matausek, M. R., Nucl. Sci. Eng., 53, #4, 440 (1974).

12. Yadigaroglu, G. and Bergles, A. E., "An experimental and theoretical study of density wave oscillations in two-phase flow," MIT Report No. DSR 74629-3 (1969).

13. Solberg, K., "Results des essais d'instabilities sur la boucle "Culine" et comparisons avec un code de calcul," CEG, Note 225, Centre d'Etude Nucleaires de Grenoble, France (1966).

14. Carver, M. B., "An analytic model for the prediction of hydrodynamic instability in parallel heated channels," AECL-2681 (1968).

15. Aritomi, M., Aoki, S. and Inoe, A., "Instabilities in parallel channel of forced convection boiling upflow system," Journal of Nuclear Science and Tech. 14 [2], 88 (1977).

16. Quandt, E. R., "Analysis and measurement of flow oscillations," AIChE-ASME Joint Heat Transfer Conference, Buffalo, N.Y. (1960).

17. Harvie, J. D., "An experimental investigation of flow instability in Freon-12 and comparison with water data," Symp. Multi-phase Flow Systems, U. Strathclyde, Paper No. E1 (1974).

18. Fleming, R. B. and Staub, F. W., "Investigation of the nature of cryogenic fluid flow instabilities in heat exchangers," Final Report NAS8-11422, May 25, 1966.

19. Saha, P., "Thermally induced flow instability including the effects of thermal non-equilibrium between phases," Ph.D. thesis, Georgia Inst. of Tech., Atlanta, (1974).

20. Daney, D. E., P. R. Ludke and M. C. Jones, "An experimental study of thermally-induced flow oscillations in supercritical helium," J. Heat Transfer 101, 9 (1979).

21. Akinjiola, P. O., "Flow instability thresholds in once-through heat exchanger systems," M.S. Thesis, University of Rochester (1978).

22. Friedly, J. C., Akinjiola, P. O., and Robertson, J. M., "Flow oscillations in boiling channels," paper to be presented at 18th National Heat Transfer Conference, San Diego (8/79).

23. Wallis, G. B., One-Dimensional Two-Phase Flow, McGraw-Hill, NY (1969), Chapter 4.

24. Zuber, N., "Flow excursion and oscillations in boiling two-phase flow systems with heat additions," Proc. Symp. Two-phase Flow Dynamics, Eindhoven,vol. 1, p. 1071 (1967).

25. Zuber, N. and Findlay, J., J. Heat Transfer 87, 453 (1965).

26. Martinelli, R. C., and Nelson, D. B., Trans. ASME, 70, 695 (1948).

NOMENCLATURE

a   aspect ratio, diameter to length

c   constant in Eq. 7

D   test section diameter, [m]

Fr   Froude number, $\dfrac{u^2}{g\ell}$; $Fr' = Fr/\overline{M}_1^2$

Ja   Jakob number for inlet subcooling, $\dfrac{h_f - h_1}{h_{fg}}\dfrac{v_{fg}}{v_f}$

k   valve or orifice coefficient

$\mathcal{L}\{\cdot\}$ Laplace transform

ℓ test section length, [m]

M   flow rate; M_1 at inlet; M_d drift flow rate

N_{st} stability number, $\dfrac{\Delta p_{ratio} - \Delta p^{*}_{ratio}}{\Delta p^{*}_{ratio}}$

r   ratio of specific volumes, liquid to vapor

s   Laplace transform parameter

V   bulk fluid specific volume; V_3 at exit

v_f, v_g specific volume of liquid, vapor $[m^3/g]$

We   Weber number, $\dfrac{\ell u^2}{v_f \sigma}$

X   quality parameter, $x\, v_{fg}/v_f$; X_3 at exit

<u>Greek</u>

Γ_g vapor generation rate

Δp pressure drop; subscripts i - inlet valve, f - friction, g - gravity, I-a - inertia-acceleration, e - exit valve, s - slip acceleration

Δp_{ratio} ratio of any specific pressure drop (usually the dominant one) to the inlet pressure drop

$\delta(\cdot)$ perturbation variable

λ position at which the quality is zero; λ_h - position where nonuniform heating stops; λ_m - position at which maximum vapor generation rate is attained; λ_s - position of start of subcooled boiling.

ξ position coordinate

Φ_{tt}^2 two-phase multiplier in Fig. 8

ϕ friction coefficient

τ time

Superscripts

$\overline{(\cdot)}$ steady state value

$(\cdot)^*$ value of Δp_{ratio} at the stability limit

Subscripts

1   at test section inlet

3   at test section exit

e   exit value or orifice

f   liquid, or friction with Δp

g   vapor, or gravity with Δp

h   end of heated length

I-a   inertia plus acceleration

i   inlet valve or orifice

m   point of maximum vapor generation rate

s   point of net vapor generation, or slip with Δp

total   total pressure drop between externally determined pressures

TABLE 1

Comparison of Model Predictions

	Slip Flow	Two-Phase Δp	Nonuniform Heating		Subcooled Boiling	
Source of Data	[14]	[13]	[17]	[22]	[12]	[19]
Inlet subcooling, Ja	1.1	3.3	5.5	6.9	21.3	2.4
Exit quality, X_3	8.9	10.3	7.5	6.0	33.4	3.6
Detailed Model Predictions						
$\Delta p_f/\Delta p_i$	1.71	2.52	3.58	0.04	1.57	4.26
$\Delta p_g/\Delta p_i$	2.35	0.51	1.58	0.03	1.88	6.04
$\Delta p_a/\Delta p_i$	0.22	0.58	0.25	0.00	.53	1.26
$\Delta p_e/\Delta p_i$	1.15	0.02	2.08	3.7	.00	3.27
other parameter values	$\frac{M_d}{M}=0.56$ $r=0.037$	$r=0.037$	$\lambda=0.5$	0.5	Pe= 306,000 61,000	
Stability number, N_{st}	-0.31	0.05	0.25	1.47	-0.03	3.93
Basic Model Predictions						
$\Delta p_f/\Delta p_i$	2.40	3.04	2.08	0.02	1.38	3.98
$\Delta p_g/\Delta p_i$	1.96	0.51	2.69	0.04	2.39	6.52
$\Delta p_a/\Delta p_i$	0.34	0.58	0.25	0.00	0.53	1.26
$\Delta p_e/\Delta p_i$	1.71	0.02	1.45	3.7	0.0	3.27
Stability number, N_{st}	-0.04	0.04	1.45	0.23	-0.12	-.28
Basic Model Predictions using pressure drop distribution from detailed model Stability number, N_{st}	-0.35	- .01	-0.04	0.23	-.05	-.26

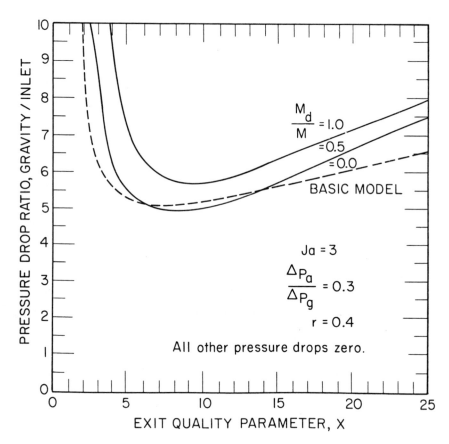

Figure I. Effect of slip flow model

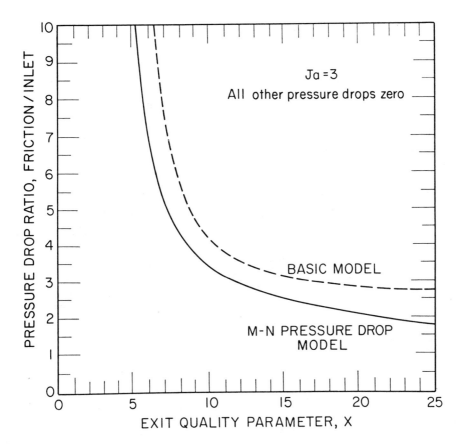

Figure 2. Effect of Martinelli-Nelson friction pressure
drop model

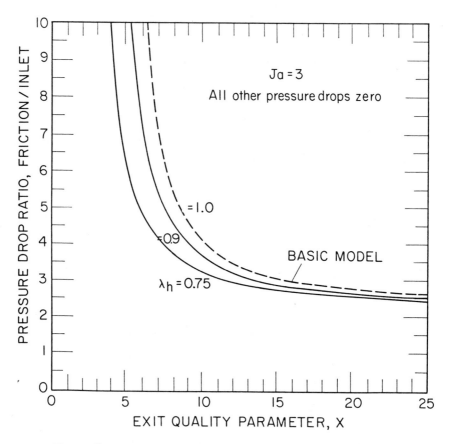

Figure 3. Nonuniform heating with dominant friction
pressure drop

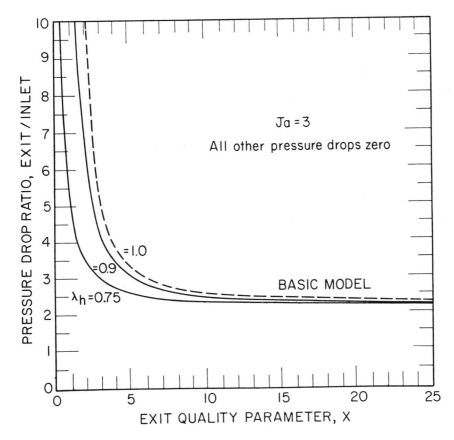

Figure 4. Nonuiform heating with dominant exit pressure
drop

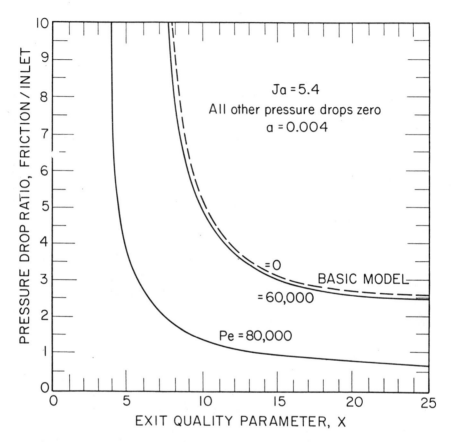

Figure 5. Effect of subcooled boiling model

A Numerical Approach for the Analysis of Boiling Flow Instabilities

T. DOGAN, T.N. VEZIROĞLU, S. KAKAÇ,* K. AKYUZLU
University of Miami
Coral Gables, Florida 33124, USA

ABSTRACT

Self-sustained oscillations in a forced convection, boiling two-phase flow system have been investigated. A numerical technique, for the solution in the time domain, has been developed and the results are compared with our experimental data. The technique is based on homogeneous flow assumption and thermodynamic equilibrium of the saturated phases. Compressibility effects of the two-phase region, thermal capacity of the heater wall and the motion of the bulk boiling boundary have been included.

The model has been applied to a flow system which comprises a subcooled liquid region, a heated section where boiling takes place and a vapor exit region. Stable and unstable operating conditions have been identified and the mode and character of oscillations have been determined for ranges of heat flux, inlet temperature and mass flow rate.

NOMENCLATURE

A	area	P	pressure
a	heat transfer coefficient	Pr	Prandtl number
b	boiling length	q	heat input per unit length
c	speed of sound in two-phase mixture	$\dot{q}$	heat generation per unit volume
c_p	specific heat	Re	Reynolds number
D	diameter	S	subcooled length
e	internal energy	t	time
f	friction factor	T	temperature
G	mass flux	U	velocity
g	gravitational acceleration	x	flow quality
h	enthalpy	z	axial distance
k	thermal conductivity		

---

* S. Kakaç, Middle East Technical University, Ankara, Turkey

Greek letters

α	void fraction
μ	viscosity
ρ	density
σ	surface tension

Subscripts

b	boiling
c	convective
e	exit
f	saturated liquid
g	saturated vapor, vapor
i	inlet, spatial index
j	temporal index
ℓ	liquid
o	steady state

INTRODUCTION

Two-phase flow instabilities, in general, refer to periodic or
aperiodic variation of the flow conditions in a system that involves simultaneous flow of different phases. The instabilities
can originate from different effects such as, two-phase pressure
drop, compressibility of the two-phase mixture, flow regime transition, acceleration due to vapor generation, etc. A detailed
discussion of the types and mechanism of these instabilities is
given in References [1,2,3]. They are undesirable from the operational and safety point of view and are critical to the power
industry, heat exchangers, evaporators, chemical process units,
etc.

For the purpose of this study the two most commonly observed instabilities, pressure-drop and density-wave instabilities, will
be discussed. These are self-sustained periodic oscillations.
Hence, the words "instability" and "oscillation" are used inter-
changably. Analysis of these oscillations require solution of
the governing differential equations subject to specific initial
and boundary conditions. Due to the complicated non-linear
nature of these equations numerical methods are inevitably used
[4,5].

In the present study a numerical method is used by which the
transient response of a general two-phase flow system can be
predicted with reasonable accuracy. The flow system under consideration is a forced convection boiling flow system which includes a subcooled liquid inlet section, a boiling (two-phase)
region and an exit vapor region (Fig. 1). Flow is established
by pressurizing the supply tank and the fluid flows through a
surge tank, a heater section and an exit tubing fitted with a
flow restriction. The system exit at the recovery tank is
vented to the atmosphere. The analysis is based on equilibrium

homogeneous flow assumption and uses a lumped parameter approach
for the numerical solution. The study also involves experimental
work for the verification of the model. The results that are
presented are for Freon-11. The digital program, however, is
flexible enough to handle different fluids, flow geometries and
boundary conditions. A detailed presentation of the solution
method, experimental program and results is given in Reference
[6].

MATHEMATICAL FORMULATION

Under the assumptions of homogeneous flow and thermodynamic
equilibrium, the conservation equations become identical in form
with the single phase equations:

Continuity

$$\frac{\partial \rho}{\partial t} + \frac{\partial G}{\partial z} = 0 \tag{1}$$

Momentum

$$\frac{\partial G}{\partial t} + \frac{\partial}{\partial z}\left(\frac{G^2}{\rho}\right) = -\frac{\partial P}{\partial z} - \rho g - 2\frac{f}{D}\frac{G^2}{\rho} \tag{2}$$

Energy

$$\frac{\partial}{\partial t}(\rho h) + \frac{\partial}{\partial z}(Gh) = \frac{4}{D}a(T_w - T) \tag{3}$$

with

$$\rho = \rho_f \Big/ \left[1 + (1-x)\frac{\rho_\ell}{\rho_g}\right] \tag{3}$$

$$h = (1-x)h_\ell + xh_g \tag{4}$$

The subscripts ℓ and g refer to the liquid and vapor phases respectively. G is the mass flux and a is the effective heat
transfer coefficient. The flow quality, x, is identical with
the thermodynamic quality. The equations are written for uniform flow area and the kinetic and potential energy terms have
been neglected. Furthermore, in the energy equation $\frac{\partial e}{\partial t} \approx \frac{\partial h}{\partial t}$
has been assumed.

The above set of equations are closed by adding the constitutive
equations for,

Friction coefficient

$$f = (1-\alpha)\frac{\rho_\ell}{\rho} \cdot f_\ell + \alpha \frac{\rho_g}{\rho} \cdot f_g \tag{5}$$

$$f_i = 0.079 \left(\frac{\rho_i UD}{\mu_i} \right)^{-.25} \quad , \quad i = \ell, g \tag{5}$$

Heat transfer coefficient

$$a = a_c + a_m \tag{6}$$

$$a_c = (1-\alpha)a_\ell + \alpha a_g$$

$$a_i = 0.0023 \, [Re_i]^{0.8} \cdot Pr_i^{0.4} \cdot \frac{k_i}{D} \quad , \quad i = \ell, g$$

$$a_m = 0.00122 \, \frac{k^{0.79} c_p^{0.45} \rho^{0.49} g_c^{0.25}}{\sigma^{0.5} \mu^{0.29} h_{fg}^{0.24} \rho_g^{0.24}} \left(\frac{\partial P_f}{\partial T} \right)^{0.75} \cdot \Delta T \cdot s$$

and the equation of state

$$P = f(\rho, h) \tag{7}$$

The overall heat transfer coefficient is assumed to be composed of a macroconvective term, a_c, and microconvective term, a_m, based on Chen's correlation [7]. The macroconvective term is assumed to be contributed proportionately from the liquid and vapor wetted areas. A similar logic has been used for the wall friction coefficient, that is, the flow has been assumed to be composed of alternate slices of liquid and vapor regions and the average friction coefficient is based on the total frictional force as contributed by individual phase contact areas. Regarding the equation of state it must be noted that an explicit expression as implied by eq. (7) is not generally possible. An iterative scheme using the differential form of this has therefore been used.

The heater wall temperature, T_w, in eq. (3) is obtained from an energy balance of the heater itself,

$$\frac{dT_w}{dt} = \frac{A_c}{\rho c} \, \dot{q} - a(T_w - T) \tag{8}$$

where $\dot{q}$ is the heat generation rate per unit volume of the tube material, A_c is the wall cross-sectional area, and ρ and c are the density and specific heat, respectively, of the tube material.

In applying the avove set of equations distinction must be made between the two-phase and liquid regions. This is done by defining a bulk boiling boundary i.e., the point where the bulk liquid temperature reaches the local saturation temperature. The change in subcooled length, Δs, then, referring to Fig. 2 is,

$$\Delta s = (\Delta h_f - \Delta h) / \left(\frac{\partial h}{\partial z} - \frac{\partial h_f}{\partial z} \right) \Bigg|_{s,t} \tag{9}$$

with

$$\frac{\partial h}{\partial z} \Bigg|_{s,t} = \frac{\partial h}{\partial z} \Bigg|_{U, \ t - t_o} \tag{10}$$

$$\frac{\partial h_f}{\partial z} \Bigg|_{s,t} = \frac{dh_f}{dP} \cdot \frac{\partial P}{\partial z} \Bigg|_{s,t} \tag{11}$$

where $t - t_o$ represents the residence time of the fluid particle in the subcooled region of the heater. It is given implicitly by,

$$s = \int_{t - t_o}^{t} U(t) \cdot dt \tag{12}$$

The flow system of Fig. 1 contains two additional elements that must be considered. The first element is the surge tank that provides a compressible volume at the upstream section. The second element is a flow restriction fitted at the system exit to provide additional pressure drop. The surge tank is part-ially filled with pressurized air and its action is described by a single equation obtained from the continuity and ideal gas equations (vapor pressure of the liquid neglected).

$$P = P_o / \left[1 + \frac{1}{V_o} \int_0^t (Q_e - Q_i) \ dt \right] \tag{13}$$

The exit restriction, having a very short length and a negligible volume, enters into the system through the momentum equation only. The pressure drop through this element is obtained fol-lowing the assumption of homogeneous flow [8] and is given be-low.

$$\Delta P = 24.9 \cdot \left(1 + x \frac{v_{fg}}{v_f} \right) \cdot \frac{G^2}{\rho} \tag{14}$$

Equations 1 through 14 completes the set of equations necessary to describe the flow system of Fig. 1. Steady state versions of these equations are used to establish the initial conditions for the transient case. The boundary conditions are:

1. Constant flow rate into the surge tank
2. Constant heat generation within the heater
3. Adiabatic conditions outside the heater
4. Constant exit pressure.

METHODS OF SOLUTION

The governing equations of the previous section are solved using
a lumped-parameter approach. The basic idea of the method is to
view the flow system to be composed of some finite number of
lumps or segments. The flow variables, then are assumed to be
represented by appropriate average values over each segment.
Fig. 3 shows a section of the actural flow channel and its equivalent lumped representation. This representation is sometimes
called "fluid transmission line", because it is analogous to a
transmission line with capacitance, inductance and resistance.
Energy and mass conservation equations are applied for the tank
and momentum equation for the tube. Finite difference form of
the basic equations, then, are:

$$\left(\frac{\partial \rho}{\partial t}\right)_i = \left(G^j_{i-1} - G^j_i\right)/L_i \tag{15}$$

$$\left(\frac{\partial G}{\partial t}\right)_i = \left(P^j_i - P^j_{i+1}\right)/L_i - g\rho^j_i - \frac{2}{D}f^j_i \cdot \frac{\left(G^j_i\right)^2}{\rho_i}$$
$$- \left(v^j_{i-1} - v^j_i\right) \cdot \left(G^j_i\right)^2/L_i \tag{16}$$

$$\frac{\partial}{\partial t}(\rho h)_i = \left[(Gh)^j_{i-1} - (Gh)^j_i + L_i q^j_i/A\right]/L_i \tag{17}$$

where

$$\frac{\partial}{\partial t}[\ ] = \frac{[\ ]^{j+1} - [\ ]^j}{\Delta t} \tag{18}$$

The equation of state takes the form,

$$P^j_i = f(\rho,h)^j_i \tag{19}$$

In this study the test section of Fig. 1 is represented by five
lumps. Under the conditions of boiling the segment in which the
boiling occurs is further divided into two segments to separate
the liquid region from the two-phase region. The resulting
lumped parameter representation of the system is shown in Fig. 4.
Of particular interest is the boiling segment b, the two-phase
region next to the boiling boundary. This segment requires
special consideration because of the volume change caused by
boundary movement. Using the proper forms of the conservation
equations for deformable control volumes one has:

$$\frac{\partial \rho}{\partial t} = \left(G_{in} - G_{ex}\right)/b \tag{20}$$

$$\frac{\partial}{\partial t}(\rho h) = \left[G_{in}h_{i-1} - G_{ex}h_i\right]/b + q/A \tag{21}$$

with

$$G_{in} = G_{i-1} - Ub \cdot \rho_{i-1} \tag{22}$$

$$G_{ex} = G_i - Ub \cdot \rho_i \tag{23}$$

where Ub is the velocity of the boiling boundary, $\Delta b/\Delta t$, and $\Delta b = -\Delta s$ as given by Eq. (9). It may be noted that since the region "b - 1" is incompressible, the form of the energy equation is unaffected by the motion of the boundary and Eq. (17) still applies to this region.

In the incompressible liquid region the continuity equation is eliminated and a single momentum equation, as given below, is solved to find the flow rate:

$$\frac{\partial G}{\partial t} = \left[\left(P_1^j - P_b^j\right) - \sum_1^b \rho \, gL_i - \sum_1^b 2f_i \frac{L_i}{D} \frac{\left(G^j\right)^2}{\rho}\right] / \sum_1^b L_i \tag{24}$$

with

$$G = G_1 = G_2 = \ldots = G_b \tag{25}$$

and

$$\frac{\partial G}{\partial t} = \left(G^{j+1} - G^j\right)/\Delta t \tag{26}$$

for the computational time step, Δt, the criteria

$$\Delta t \leqslant \Delta L/(c + |U|) \tag{27}$$

has been safely used for the conditions of interest

Digital program scheme for the solution of the above set of equations first establishes the steady state solution (P, ρ, h) at each segment and also the heater wall temperature. This solution is then perturbed slightly changing the surge tank pressure, P_i, and the transient conditions are calculated at each segment for a suitable period of time.

RESULTS AND CONCLUSIONS

Typical results of the study are illustrated in Figs. 5 through
9.   Fig. 5 shows the steady state pressure drop characteristics
of the system.   Each cruve on this figure corresponds to a different inlet temperature.   The negative slope region, which is
typical of many two-phase flow systems, is obvious especially
at low inlet temperatures.   Fig. 6 illustrates fully developed
pressure-drop oscillations.   Also shown in this figure are the
experimetnal results under comparable conditions.   A further decrease in mass flow rate results in a smooth transient to equilibrium conditions.   This is illustrated in Fig. 7.   Fig. 8 is
another transient in the stable region, but close to the density-
wave boundary.   Fully developed density-wave oscillations are
illustrated in Fig. 9.   Examination of these figures indicates
that:

1.   The study confirms the general mechanism of oscillations.

A negative slope region on the ΔP versus $\dot{m}$ curve, and an upstream compressible volume is essential for the existance of
pressure-drop oscillations.   The inlet and exit flow rates are
nearly in phase with each other and have comparable amplitudes.
Because of this fact quasi-steady formulation of pressure-drop
oscillations can be quite realistic.

Density-wave oscillations are originated and sustained by the
feed-back effects between the liquid inlet region and two-phase
exit region.   Flow rates are out of phase and the amplitude is
considerably smaller at the exit.   This is due to the large frictional resistance of the exit region in comparison to inlet region.

2.   Steady state pressure-drop curve (ΔP versus $\dot{m}$) can not be
used singly as the stability criteria.   Equation of state
has a marked effect on the stability of the system.   This can
be seen by differentiating the equation of state $P = f(\rho, h)$,

$$\Delta P = \frac{\partial P}{\partial \rho} \Delta \rho + \frac{\partial P}{\partial h} \Delta h \qquad (28)$$

The partial derivatives $\frac{\partial P}{\partial \rho}$ and $\frac{\partial P}{\partial h}$ are strong functions of thermodynamic quality x.   At low mixture qualities $\frac{\partial P}{\partial h}$ is do-
minant.   At high qualities and in the superheat region $\frac{\partial P}{\partial \rho}$
becomes dominant.   The differentials $\Delta \rho$ and Δh, in turn are
determined from the local continuity and energy equations.
Therefore, consideration must be given to the following additional factors:
             i.   Type of the fluid and operating pressure
          ii.   Heat intensity and heater wall capacity

     iii.   Compressible volumes at the upstream and down-
           stream regions
     iv.   Relative magnitudes of frictional resistance in
           the liquid and two-phase (or vapor) regions.

The fact that pressure-drop oscillations are not observed in the
whole range of the negative slope region can be explained in
terms of the complex interaction among these factors.

3. The model's prediction, qualitatively, is in very good
agreement with the experimental data. Stable and unstable regions with respect to both types of oscillations are predicted
correctly. Quantitatively, however, the model is more stable
than the actual system; sharp changes are diffused out and amplitudes are predicted low. The model is more successfully applied
to density-wave oscillations than to pressure-drop oscillations.

REFERENCES

1. Boure, J.A., Bergles, A.E. and Tong, L.S., "Review of Two-
Phase Flow Instability", Nuclear Engineering and Design,
25, 165-192, 1973.

2. Bergles, A.E., "Review of Instabilities in Two-Phase Systems", Proc. NATO Advanced Study Institute, Vol. 1,
383-422, Hemisphere Publishing Co., Washington, D.C., 1977.

3. Veziroglu, T.N. and Kakac, S. (ed.), Two-Phase Transport
and Reactor Safety, Proc. of Two-Phase Flow and Heat Transfer Symposium, Vol. 2, Hemisphere Publishing Co., Washington, D.C., 1977.

4. Lyckowski, R.W., "Numerical Techniques for the Computation
of Transient Unequal Phase Velocity, Unequal Phase Temperature, Two-Phase Flow and Heat Transfer", Two-Phase Transport and Reactor Safety, Proc. of Two-Phase Flow and Heat
Transfer Symposium, Vol. 2, 839-888, Hemisphere Publishing
Co., Washington, D.C., 1977.

5. Lyckowski, R.W., Gidaspow, A., Solbrig, C.W., Hughes, E.D.,
"Characteristics and Stability Analysis of Transient One-
Dimensional Two-Phase Flow Equations and Their Finite Dif-
ference Approximations", ASME paper No. 75-WA/HT-23.

6. Dogan, T., "Lumped-Parameter Analysis of Two-Phase Flow
Instabilities", Ph.D. Thesis, University of Miami, Coral
Gables, Florida, May 1979.

7. Chen, J.C., "A Correlation for Boiling Heat Transfer to
Saturated Fluids in Convective Flow", ASME paper No. 63-HT-34.

8. Hewitt, G.F. and Hall-Taylor, N.S., Annular Two-Phase Flow,
36-49, Pergamon Press, Oxford, England, 1970.

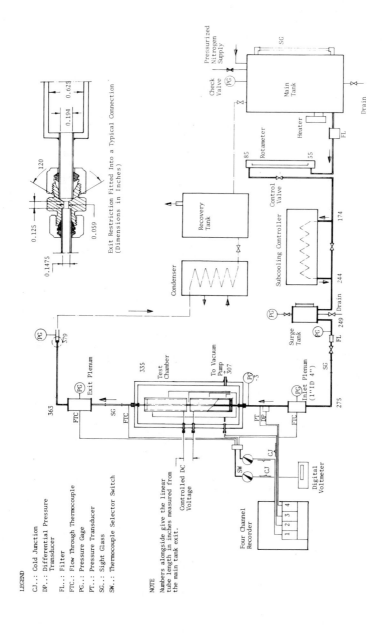

Fig. 1 – Schematic Diagram of the Experimental Apparatus.

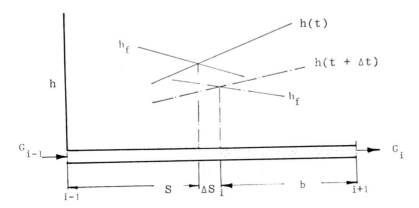

Fig. 2 - Transient Enthalpy Profiles at the Boiling Boundary.

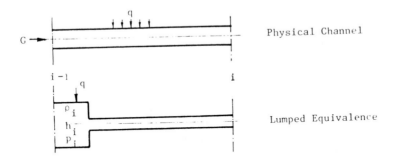

Fig. 3 - Lumped Representation of a Channel Segment.

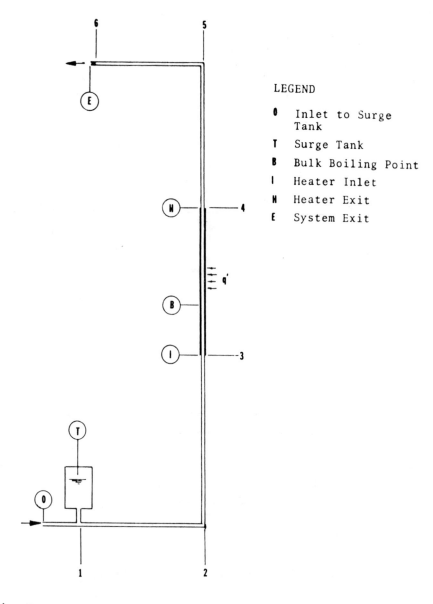

Fig. 4 - Lumped-Parameter Equivalence of the Actual Flow System

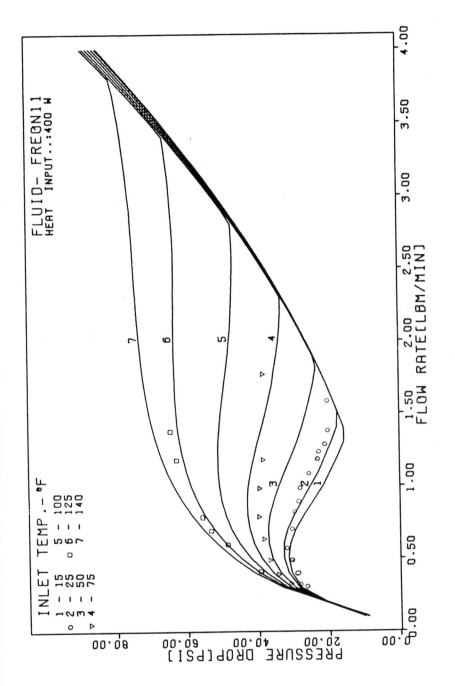

Fig. 5 - Steady State Pressure-Drop Characteristics.

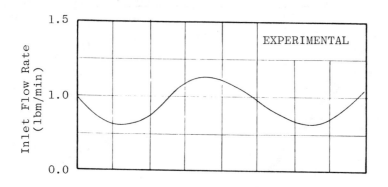

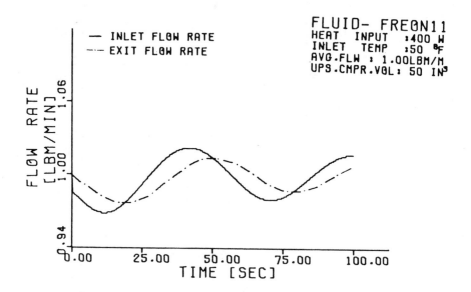

Fig. 6 - Fully Developed Pressure-Drop Oscillations
(Bottom Figure Theoretical)

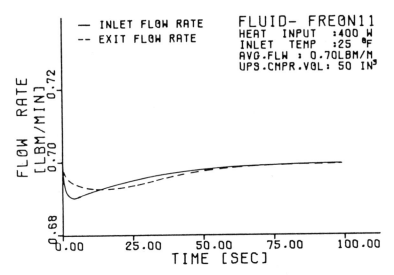

Fig. 7 - Transient Response in the Stable Region

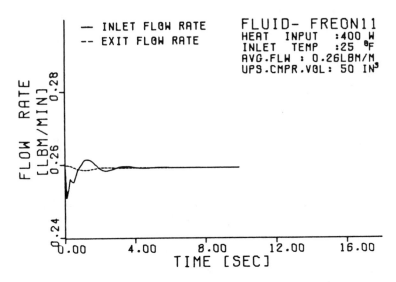

Fig. 8 - Transient Response in the Stable Region
(Density-Wave Boundary)

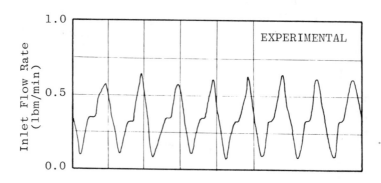

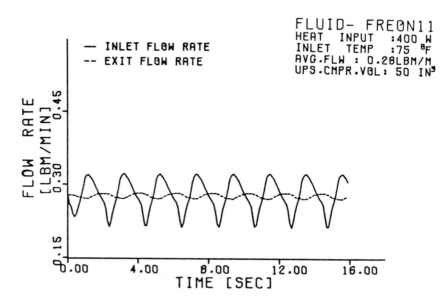

Fig. 9 - Fully Developed Density-Wave Oscillations
(Bottom Figure Theoretical).

DYMEL: A Computer Code for the Prediction of Dynamic Stability in Steam Generators

R. T. DEAM, J. MURRAY, and B. CHOJNOWSKI
Central Electricity Generating Board
Marchwood Engineering Laboratories
Southampton SO4 4ZB, England

ABSTRACT

Theoretical and Experimental Studies of Parallel Channel Stability Limits
were undertaken to resolve the uncertainty surrounding existing codes
which were applied to establish the stability of AGR boilers during the
start-up stage at the time of their commissioning.   Theoretical studies
included examination of the then existing codes and in the light of encountered discrepancies development of the DYMEL Code was undertaken.
The method of analysis adopted relies on linearisation of the conservation
equations and application of an analytical solution technique which was
preferred to the iterative integration schemes that are frequently used.
Other main features of DYMEL are incorporation of slip between phases in
the basic equations and flux/flow coupling on the primary/secondary side.
Validation of DYMEL was carried out in the first instance against experimental data generated on a test section comprising three full size (200
metres long) A.G.R. Boiler tubes mounted on the Boiler Dynamics Rig
which forms part of the Boiling Water Test Facility located at the
Marchwood Engineering Laboratories, CEGB.   Close agreement obtained
between the theoretical and experimental results is reported.   Reference
is also made to the subsequent validation of Dymel against data from
other electrically heated steam generating tubes, AGR Boiler plant
measurement, Sodium heated and Gas heated steam generating tube.

INTRODUCTION

This paper is concerned with the prediction of parallel channel instability thresholds in boilers, and reviews briefly the stability work done
at Marchwood Engineering Laboratories (MEL) over the past five years.

Many other theoretical and experimental investigations have been undertaken and there are a number of reviews of the field, Bergles [1],
Boure et al. [2], and Bailey et al. [3] for instance.

The phenomena of boiler instability may be briefly described as follows.
Contained within part of the possible operating regime of a steam
generator, there often exists conditions where it is impossible to control
the water feed flow.   These manifest themselves as self-sustained
oscillations of the feed flow (dynamic instability) or a drift away from
the desired feed flow (static instability).   The term dynamic in this

paper will be used to encompass both dynamic and static instability.
The steam generator is said to be hydrodynamically unstable if it is in
the part of the operating regime where its flow, to individual channels,
is uncontrollable.   Determining the location of a boiler's threshold to
the unstable part of its operating regime is important, because instability can lead to degradation of boiler performance, excessive tube metal
temperatures, thermal fatigue and enhanced corrosion rates.

Any method used to predict instability thresholds has to rely on an
accurate knowledge of the steady state profile from the boiler under consideration; the distribution of the pressure drop is particularly important.   In the past, predictive methods that were to be applied to
different boilers over a wide range of conditions have relied on the
computer.   The reason for this is easy to understand.   Account has to
be taken of the many complex correlations used, steam tables and the man
made complications of the geometric layout of the boiler.

MEL PROGRAM OF WORK

At MEL, the locations of the instability thresholds for Advanced Gas
Cooled Reactor (AGR) boilers, particularly under start-up conditions, was
the object of intensive study, both experimental and theoretical.   Full-
scale experiments were carried out so that accurate steady states could
be generated for use by other computer codes [4, 5, 6, 7], to predict the
instability thresholds.   Discrepancies between the predictions from
these codes and experimental data have led to the development of a more
complete code, DYMEL, for the prediction of dynamic instability.   The
reason for the success of DYMEL in predicting the MEL data where other
codes have failed is discussed and the application of DYMEL to plant and
stability data generated outside MEL is also presented.

DESCRIPTION OF THE MEL RIG

The experiments were carried out using the Boiler Dynamics rig which forms
part of the Boiling Water Test Facility of the Marchwood Engineering
Laboratories.   This rig was specially designed for studies of the steam
generation process in once-through boilers under dynamic conditions.

A schematic diagram of the rig, which is of once-through design, is shown
in Figure 1.   Feed water from the demineralisation plant storage tanks
is fed into a 45,000 litre, nitrogen blanketed, de-aerator tank where it
is boiled and dosed to obtain a specified purity level.   Feed water is
drawn from the de-aerator, via a cooler, by a three plunger, reciprocating
pump driven by a variable speed motor.   A pulsation damper is fitted at
outlet to reduce pressure oscillations to about 0.1 bar at 290 bar.
Feed is delivered to the test section at the required pressure and temperature via a variable 750 kW electric preheater.   Steam generated in
the test section passes through two pressure control valves, arranged in
series, which provide means of controlling pressure down to atmospheric

level, the steam being then vented via a silencer to atmosphere.   All
the pipework and the main components except for the pump and the test
section (described below), are manufactured from stainless steel.

Test Section

The test section consists of three steam generating channels, each closely
resembling a complete element of an AGR once-through boiler.   Each
channel is of serpentine geometry having 64 electrically heated horizontal
passes, connected by vertical 180° bends, which are electrically shorted
by low resistance links to minimise the heat input.   Direct current is
used for heating, and the connections are arranged so that the ends of
the channels are earthed at their inlet and outlet manifolds, thus eliminating the need for electrically insulated joints in the pipework.
Connections are provided for shunt resistors across passes or pairs of
passes; this allows fixed heat flux profiles, each comprising 34 sections,
to be set up along each channel.   The test section is made of Nimonic 75
to minimise the change of heat flux profiles with changing metal temperatures.

Each channel has an adjustable throttle valve at inlet and a restrictor
tube at outlet.   The steam generated at the outlet to the channels
enters a common header before being vented to atmosphere via the pressure
controller.   Thus the flow to all three channels can be held constant.

EXPERIMENTAL PROCEDURE

In the experiments described here three heat flux profiles were used.
The first was typical of that expected during the full load operation of
the boilers while the second and third were typical of that expected
during the start-up procedure.   All three channels had the same power
input and flow.   The experiments began by allowing the rig to come into
thermal equilibrium under stable conditions by choosing the system
pressure high enough to suppress any instability.   The pressure was then
reduced by steps until an oscillation on the inlet flows with a well
defined period was observed.   Oscillations became visible when their
amplitude was about 5% of the mean value.   The period and rate of growth
of the oscillations stayed sensibly constant while their amplitudes increased by a factor of about 20.   Having determined the threshold conditions, the power flow and temperature measurements were recorded and
used to produce the steady state data required as input to the Dynamic
Stability models.   An example of the agreement obtained between the
temperature measurements along the channel and the temperatures computed
from a heat balance is given in Figure 2.   The steady states are used by
the computer models to predict the period of the oscillation and the
throttle pressure drop required to just stabilise the rig.

EXPERIMENTAL RESULTS

The instability thresholds for three different power profiles were
investigated (**Figure 3**).

Profile I

This was similar to a full load power profile expected on an AGR boiler.
The thresholds were predicted by DYMEL and the other available codes.
Table I gives the experimental results and the theoretical predictions
for the full load profile experiments.   **For these cases feed flow and
power input was less than at full load.**   All the models predicted the
throttling to within the experimental accuracy.   They are also within
the accuracy (10%) on all the periods except for run 323.   It may be
significant that this experiment was at a lower pressure than the others
and therefore slip between the phases may be expected to have a larger
effect in this case.   However the discrepancy is not large enough to
allow definitive conclusions to be drawn.

Profile II & III

These were two different approximations to the expected boiler start-up
power profile, with nearly all the power concentrated in the first 12
passes.   Profile III thresholds were predicted by DYMEL (see Table 3)
but not the other codes.   The profile II have proved elusive to prediction by any code (see Table 2).   The reason for this seems to lie in
the fact that although Profile II and Profile III are very similar
conditions, the threshold pressures in Profile II are in the region 40
to 70 bars whilst those of Profile III are approximately doubled, lying
in the range 80 to 150 bars.   This is the experimental evidence that,
for these particular conditions, the power profile is a sensitive parameter and is confirmed by DYMEL.   The reason for the Profile II test
being elusive is thought to be because of the lack of reliable data on
slip ratio in a serpentine.   At lower pressures slip is greater.   An
experimental program is now underway to rectify this lack of data.   DYMEL
predicts that the slip ratio is a sensitive parameter for Profile II tests
(see Table 4).

DYMEL ANALYSIS

The analysis is quite straightforward.   The three averaged, one-dimensional, conservation equations of mass, energy and momentum for the
waterside are linearized together with the tube wall equation.   Heat
flux or temperature controlled heating are allowed.   The full equations
are solved on the waterside, allowing for interphase slip.   The primary
side fluid is assumed incompressible and temperature perturbations can be
allowed or the primary fluid temperature "frozen" if desired.   The
equations are Laplace transformed from time to frequency space.   On the
waterside the resultant equations reduce to 3 simultaneous ordinary
differential equations in distance, relating mass flux perturbations,

pressure perturbations and density perturbations. These are combined to
give one third order differential equation for the mass flux perturbations
using the linearized equation of state and a slip correlation. This is
solved by splitting the boiler up into sections, small enough so that over
each section the coefficients in the differential equation can be approximated by constants. The interpretation of this approximation is that,
for a given frequency, there are three wavelengths that propagate information through the boiler. These wavelengths vary only slowly over a
section. This is known as the W.K.B. approximation in physics. If
small enough sections are taken, the solution converges to the exact one.
In practice not many sections are required for convergence, about 50
being more than adequate. Applying this solution, all the Transfer
Functions of the boiler may be built up by matching boundary conditions
at each mesh point. Thus, the inlet pressure response to the boiler
just downstream of the throttle may be calculated for a given inlet flow
oscillation. The Nyquist criterion is applied to find the required
stabilising throttle.

The main difference between DYMEL and the other codes then available is
that each section of the boiler has the same form of transfer function,
with different coefficients. Even the boiling and superheat boundaries
are catered for automatically when they are put in small enough sections.
The other codes had different transfer functions for each of the three
regions subcooled, boiling and superheated. This, to a large degree,
explains the success of DYMEL over the other codes in predicting the MEL
data, some of which is generated near the critical pressure where each
region is beginning to take on the character of its neighbour.

A brief guide to the solution of the one dimensional flow equations is
given in the Appendix and a more detailed treatment by Holder and Owen
[8].

APPLICATION TO PLANT

The electrically heated rig had given confidence in DYMEL to accurately
model the waterside dynamics. Gas heated modelling was then applied to
give a forward prediction of a minimum start-up pressure, to avoid instability in the AGR power station boilers. Data collected from the
specially instrumented boiler during commissioning supported this
prediction. Due regard of the uncertainties in modelling the steady
state was taken. Since the plant was not run to generate threshold data,
DYMEL was used to confirm when the boiler had operated unstably, the results
show broad agreement with the plant data both at long periods (40 secs)
and short periods (less than 8 secs). In spite of the difficulties
associated with defining the steady state for the plant under these vastly
oversurfaced conditions experienced at start-up. (Superheat is about
80% of the boiler length). Unlike electrically heated rigs, steady
states are always going to be difficult to define accurately for dynamic
stability calculations under these conditions. Even if tube banking and
gas mixing is taken into account, the actual crossflow for a serpentine

geometry would cast doubt on the counterflow calculation done in the available steady state codes, although this is perfectly adequate for other applications.

A good example of the difficulties encountered can be gauged by comparing the results obtained with and without subcooled boiling heat transfer as set out in Table 5. This had two effects which changed the results. The steady state heat flux profile is changed and so are the dynamics of the wall in the subcooled boiling region. Correct modelling of this region just prior to the boiling boundary is important under these conditions. This is because the enthalpy perturbations, as they are generated locally in the subcooled region, are damped away as they move downstream. A damping length can be associated with this process, which depends on the wall dynamics. Any enthalpy perturbations generated further upstream than this length will be unimportant locally. The enthalpy perturbations will be dominated by the local heat flux profile for this distance upstream. The conditions presented here have a damping length of about one metre, for the case of no subcooled boiling heat transfer and about two metres with subcooled boiling heat transfer. Thus it is important to correctly model the heat flux profile to better than a third of a pass accuracy near the boiling boundary in the subcooled region. (A pass is about 3 metres).

From the various runs done it was obvious that "better" agreement with the plant data could have been produced by the tuning of the steady state. However, in spite of the steady state uncertainties the conclusion can be drawn that DYMEL predictions are in line with plant operating experience.

A more detailed report of this work is given by Deam [9].

APPLICATION OF DYMEL TO OTHER DATA

Full Size Electrical Simulation of a Fast Reactor U-Tube Boiler

The U.K.A.E.A., Winfrith, have carried out sponsored research into heat transfer, flow and dynamic stability limits in U-tubes intended for the commercial Fast Reactor boilers. Part of this work is reported by Bailey et al. [10]. Sufficient data was supplied by the A.E.A. to MEL so that "blind" predictions could be made by DYMEL on six selected sets of conditions.

The rig consisted of two U-tubes in parallel that were electrically heated, the shape of the power profile being fixed by machining the outside diameter of the tube. The experimental results were obtained by fixing the inlet water flow and temperature for a given pressure and increasing the power until the instability was observed. The heated section was 28.2 metres in length and was represented in DYMEL by 35 sections. The heat transfer coefficients and pressure drop were calculated using correlations verified at MEL for AGR boilers. The inlet and outlet pipe-work to the heated section was not represented. A nominal 100% power

profile was given and this percentage was varied for each set of inlet
conditions given to DYMEL, so that the computer runs were done in a
similar manner to the experiments. The results were then presented
graphically for each set of inlet conditions as a plot of throttle required to stabilise the tubes against percentage of nominal full power
delivered to the rig. The predicted percentage power could then be
read off against the throttle which was given for each set of conditions.

The results of the "blind" predictions are set out in Table 6 and, as
can be seen, agreement is quite good except for Run 16.

In order to identify the sensitive features of the U-tube configuration
a further selection of runs were done on DYMEL. The sensitivity analysis covered variation in pressure, tube roughness (friction factors),
slip, tube metal conductivity and specific heat. From the sensitivity
runs some tentative conclusions could be drawn as to the controlling
features of the modes of these instabilities at different periods. For
instance, the balance of gravity to frictional pressure drop is particularly important for long period modes (i.e. static instability) and the
representation of the tube wall for the short periods (about 10 secs).
Increasing operating pressure stabilises all periods. A slip correlation for a U-tube configuration will have to be investigated (i.e. one
that works for up flow and down flow). This work is more fully reported
by Deam [11].

1.5 MW Sodium Heated Helical Boiler

Experimental results from a 1.5 MW sodium heated rig obtained by
Electricite de France were compared with dynamic stability predictions
of DYMEL. The data was taken from a report by Llory [12] which was
written within the context of a collaboration exercise between EdF and
the CEGB. The results of four experiments were given. The experiments
were performed on a rig which has 3 helical coils of about 80 m developed
length and 0.0197 m bore. The secondary mass velocity varied between
.114 and .190 kg/sec while the pressure was between 87 and 115 bar.

The EdF report gave heat flux profiles as well as the geometric details
and heat transfer correlations. It was therefore possible to prepare
input data for DYMEL without recourse to a heat exchanger code. When
however this was done it became quite apparent, see Table 7, that the
model predictions and the experimental results were in serious disagreement. A sensitivity analysis indicated that the discrepancy could only
be explained if the heat flux profile was in error. The EdF heat flux
profile had been deduced on the basis of theoretical calculations and
was not based on any direct experimental measurements. A second
opinion on the heat exchanger calculation was sought and a different heat
flux profile was obtained [13] which indicated that the evaporator was
shorter by about 80%. The heat flux profile was produced entirely
independently of the dynamic stability work.

The experimental results and the revised predictions of the DYMEL

computer program are given in Table 7.   Experiments 16 and 20 used
three channels while 27 and 29 used only two.   The channel pressure drop
was about ten times that across the inlet throttling.   Therefore large
percentage differences between the measured and predicted throttling may
be expected and will not cause concern.   The most significant result is
the large differences between the predictions when the different steady
states are used.   The agreement with the experimental results when using
the EdF profile is very poor.   In particular a long period resonance
(the fundamental) is predicted to be the least damped.   No evidence for
this mode appeared in the flow traces.   The agreement with experiment
using the revised profile is very encouraging and for three of the experiments is well within the uncertainties that a sensitivity analysis has
shown to be present.

Murray [14] has reported this work in more detail.

Gas Heated Simulation of an AGR Boiler

Work sponsored by the CEGB has been carried out at Babcock and Wilcox,
Renfrew, Scotland by Anglesea and King [15].   In this work, DYMEL was
used to predict threshold data from measurements made on a gas heated,
single circuit plus by-pass experimental simulation of a full sized
helical AGR boiler.   The steady states, used for the prediction of the
instability thresholds, were generated by means of a specially developed
computer program called HETHA.   This program optimises the fit between
the calculated steady state and all the measured data, thereby increasing
the reliability of the steady state determination.   The agreement between measured and predicted results is summarised in Table 8.   Sensitivity analyses performed using DYMEL also showed that slip ratio,
secondary fluid heat transfer coefficients in the subcooled liquid
region, friction factor correlations, the overall power profile and the
local power profile in the economiser near the boiling boundary were all
parameters that had the most influence on the predicted thresholds.

CONCLUSIONS

A computer code called DYMEL has been developed to predict dynamic instability thresholds for once-through boilers.   The code has been validated
against several sets of data.   The success of the code is largely due to
the philosophy of doing initial validation work against electrically
heated experiments, where the steady state waterside conditions can be
reliably determined.   Thresholds for boilers with primary fluid heating
were then correlated well by DYMEL, due account having been taken of the
sensitivity of the threshold to the uncertainty in the knowledge of the
steady states.

ACKNOWLEDGEMENTS

The authors wish to acknowledge the contribution to this work given by

members of the Heat Transfer Section at MEL, both past and present.
Also members of the T.A.S. Division at A.E.E. Winfrith and the Thermal
Analysis Section at B & W, Renfrew.

This work was carried out at the Marchwood Engineering Laboratories and
is published by permission of the Central Electricity Generating Board.

REFERENCES

1. BERGLES, A. E. "Review of Instabilities in Two Phase Systems".
    Two Phase Flow and Heat Transfer, NATO Advanced Study Institute,
    Istanbul, Turkey (1976).

2. BOURNE, J. A., BERGLES, A.E., TONG, L. S. "Review of Two Phase Flow
    Instability". Nuclear Engineering Design Vol. 25, No. 2 pp 165-194
    (1973).

3. BAILEY, N. A., DAVIES, A.L. et al. "Instabilities in Two Phase
    Flow Systems". H.T.F.S. Design Report 17.

4. MOXON, D. ASME Reprint 73-WA/HT-24 (1973).

5. PRESTON, R. Internal CEGB Report RD/L/N187/75 (1975)

6. DAVIES, A. L. & POTTER, R. UKAEA Report AEEW-R446 (1966)

7. HOPE, J. H. Internal CEGB Report PKR/SE/94 (1973)

8. HOLDER, S. J., OWEN, R. G. "Oscillatory Instabilities in Two Phase
    Flow Systems". H.T.F.S. Design Report 12.

9. DEAM, R. T. Internal CEGB Memorandum MM/COMB/TL65 (1977).

10. BAILEY, N. A., HOWE, W. D., SUTTON, C. United Kingdom Atomic
    Energy Authority Report AEEW-R1175 (1978).

11. DEAM, R. T. Internal CEGB Memorandum MM/COMB/TL3 (1976).

12. LLORY, M. 68th Conference of A.I.Ch.E. Los Angeles (1975).

13. RUFFEL, A. E. Private Communication.

14. MURRAY, J. Internal CEGB Memorandum MRM268 (1976).

15. KING, J. L., ANGLESEA, W. T. Babcock & Wilcox Report No. 1/78/808
    (1978).

16. ABRAMOWITZ, M. & STEGUN, I. A. Handbook of Mathematical Functions
    pp 17. Dover.

Nomenclature

Cp	specific heat at constant pressure
Cm	ρCp for tube metal
D	internal tube diameter
f	friction factor
G	mass flux
g^*	normalized mass flux perturbation $g^* = \dfrac{G^*}{G_o}$
H_c	convective heat transfer coefficient
H_b	boiling heat transfer coefficient
h	specific enthalpy
K	conductivity of tube metal
k	gravitational acceleration times height/length
p	pressure
Q	heat flux/unit volume
R	see equation 14
r	tube wall radial space variable
T	temperature
T_s	saturation temperature
t	time
u	velocity
z	axial distance
ρ	density
τ	fluid transit time $\quad \Delta\tau = \dfrac{\Delta z}{U_o}$
s	Laplace frequency variable

Special Symbols

*	superscript denotes perturbed variable
o	subscript denotes steady state variable
$<\tau>$	denotes spatial average of τ
$\bar{\tau}$	denotes flow average of τ
in	subscript denotes inlet of a section
g	subscript denotes gas side
m	subscript denotes tube metal
i	subscript denotes inside of tube wall
o	subscript denotes outside of tube wall

TABLE 1

PROFILE I: COMPARISON OF RIG RESULTS WITH MODEL

	EXPT				RIG		DYMEL	
Run No.	Flow kg/sec	Inlet Temp ^{o}C	Outlet Temp ^{o}C	Pressure bar	Throttle bar	Period sec	Throttle bar	Period sec
320	.128	174	513	106	1.5	270	1.5	243
323	.134	173	496	76	2.0	210	1.9	160
327	.129	143	514	141	0.5	510	0.9	545
331	.128	110	426	140	0.3	225	0.5	220
338	.129	161	520	141	1.0	480	1.3	446
341	.129	148	512	133	1.0	520	1.3	470
345	.135	112	450	111	1.0	150	1.3	134

TABLE 2

PROFILE II: COMPARISON OF RIG RESULTS WITH MODEL

	EXPT				RIG		DYMEL	
Run No.	Flow kg/sec	Inlet Temp ^{o}C	Outlet Temp ^{o}C	Pressure bar	Throttle bar	Period sec	Throttle bar	Period sec
380	.044	118	371	44	.16	150	.25	70
							.18	345
424	.064	107	366	63	.30	140	.38	79
							.02	298
474	.046	107	377	67	.20	270	.41	239
							.14	28
515	.046	94	281	43	.09	50	.29	277
							.25	32
538	.061	95	290	53	.17	48	.21	27
							.13	244
584	.052	95	314	57	.11	42	.23	32
							.20	269
595	.065	93	265	46	.42	64	.32	28
							.09	242
601	.064	95	309	48	.40	40	.46	25
							.41	212
624	.050	94	390	66	.12	270	.32	250
							.20	28

TABLE 3

PROFILE III: COMPARISON OF RIG RESULTS WITH MODEL

EXPT					RIG		DYMEL	
Run No.	Flow kg/sec	Inlet Temp °C	Outlet Temp °C	Pressure bar	Throttle bar	Period sec	Throttle bar	Period sec
643	.065	94	404	118	.22	280 75	.24 .17	271 58
664	.063	94	431	140	.16	300 75	.18 .12	290 63
671	.065	92	423	130	.19	295	.20 .14	281 60
673	.048	93	398	144	.10	420 110	.08 .07	399 94
680	.049	91	363	90	.44	300	.35 .18	293 63
690	.063	94	346	81	.82	250	.50 .31	244 52
720	.075	91	362	107	.31	255	.28 .24	58 259
721	.072	89	404	115	.29	235	.26 .23	257 56
724	.090	116	367	113	.45	210	.35 .32	47 206

TABLE 4

PROFILE II: SENSITIVITY TO SLIP

EXPT			DYMEL					
Run No.	Throttle	Period	Homogenous Throttle Period		Thom Slip Throttle Period		Smith Slip Throttle Period	
380	.16	150	.25	70	.47	101		
424	.30	140	.38	79	.50	101		
474	.20	270	.41	239	.36	244	.19	270
515	.09	50	.25	32	.25	54	.31	63
538	.17	48	.21	27	.26	37	.37	52
584	.11	42	.23	32	.23	41	.25	51
595	.42	64	.32	28	.41	48	.50	63
601	.40	40	.46	25	.38	38	.47	46
624	.12	270	.32	250	.27	250	.13 .18	278 52

TABLE 5

COMPARISON OF PREDICTED AND OBSERVED
UNSTABLE PERIODS (SECS.) FOR THE AGR BOILER

1) No Subcooled Boiling Heat Transfer

RUN I.D.	BOIL 13		BOIL 14(20.51)		BOIL 14(23.51)		BOIL 15		BOIL 16	
tube No.	Plant	DYMEL	Plant	DYMEL	Plant	DYMEL	Plant	DYMEL	Plant	DYMEL
23A	33.4	14.3	36.0	16.7	26.3	17.5			26.0	16.6
31A					stable	*	20.7	12.7	38.0	16.1
43B	18.7	16.6			23.3	16.9	19.6	12.2	18.5	15.3
44B					19.7	17.1	16.9	12.5	24.7	15.1

* threshold at 17.3 secs. throttle required to stabilize equalled predicted throttle.

2) Subcooled Boiling Heat Transfer Incorporated

tube No.	Plant	DYMEL	Plant	DYMEL	Plant	DYMEL	Plant	DYMEL	Plant	DYMEL
23A	33.4	37.8	36.0	33.6	26.3	26.3			26.0	35.4
31A					stable	25.9	20.7	24.3	38.0	33.5
43B	18.7	$\left\{\begin{array}{c}70\\28\\16\end{array}\right\}$			23.3	24.7	19.6	23.6	18.5	28.9
44B					19.7	25.4	16.9	24.1	24.7	28.8

Note :   All runs also predicted either high closed loop gains or instabilities at short periods, typically between 8 and 1 second periods. Short period noise at about these periods was observed on the plant, but since the periods are so short they are of no consequence as far as thermal cycling of the tube walls.

TABLE 6

COMPARISON OF WINFRITH EXPERIMENTAL DATA
AND DYMEL PREDICTED DYNAMIC STABILITY LIMITS

RUN I.D.	WINFRITH RIG		DYMEL	
	Power	Period	Power	Period
49	45.2%	Static Instability	43.5%	Static Instability
16	56.3%	Long Period	60/70%	30/40 seconds
55	60.8%	33 seconds	52.5%	44 seconds
42	66.0%	22 seconds	62%	28 seconds
43	50.2%	10 seconds	42%	7.5 seconds
41	26.3%	Static Instability	25.5%	Static Instability

TABLE 7

COMPARISON OF EdF RIG RESULTS WITH DYMEL

Experiments							DYMEL			
Waterside Conditions							EdF Heat Flux		Revised Heat Flux	
Ident	W kg/ sec	Tin °C	Tout °C	Pin bar	Throttle bar	Period sec	Throttle bar	Period sec	Throttle bar	Period sec
16	.114	167	510	117.4	.13	8.8	.13	21.0	–	–
							.10	9.4	.13	8.7
							.10	5.8	.10	3.0
20	.138	177	507	89.9	.21	6.4	.25	21.2	–	–
							.24	9.4	.33	9.0
							.12	5.5	.15	3.0
27	.190	191	506	94.7	.56	5.5	1.07	14.0	–	–
							.32	5.6	.69	5.6
							.13	3.5	–	–
29	.117	177	452	107.5	.15	9.1	.53	25.5	–	–
							.05	10.3	.19	9.6
							.10	6.2	.07	3.5

TABLE 8

COMPARISON OF DYMEL PREDICTIONS
AGAINST BABCOCK & WILCOX DATA

Test No.	Measured Throttle Δp (mbars)	e (mbars)	Measured Unstable Period (secs)	Predicted Unstable Period (secs)
21	146	-91	17	21
23	554	-84	16	19
24	697	-80	19	24
26	141	-18	30	37
28	74	-21	40	50

e = (DYMEL predicted throttle Δp) - (Measured throttle Δp)

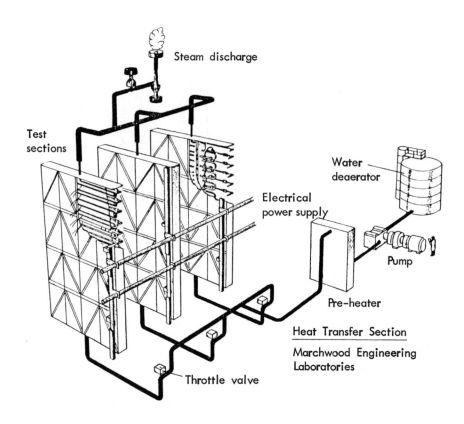

Steam discharge

Test sections

Water deaerator

Electrical power supply

Pump

Pre-heater

Heat Transfer Section

Marchwood Engineering Laboratories

Throttle valve

FIGURE 1. FLOW DIAGRAM OF THE BOILER DYNAMICS RIG

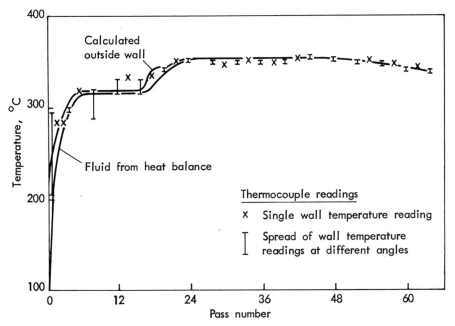

FIGURE 2. TEMPERATURE PROFILE FOR B.D.R. RUN 651

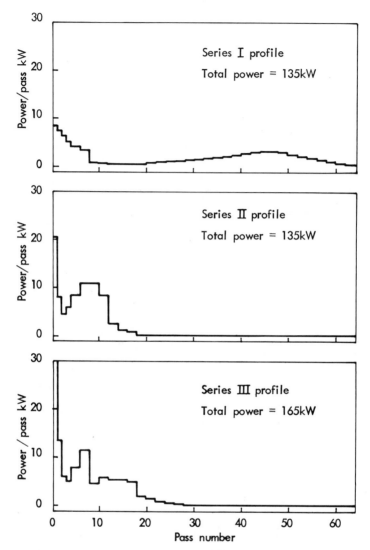

FIGURE 3. HEAT FLUX PROFILES IMPOSED ON
THE TEST CHANNELS DURING THE
DYNAMIC STABILITY INVESTIGATIONS

APPENDIX

A BRIEF GUIDE TO THE SOLUTION OF THE
1D FLOW EQUATIONS USED IN DYMEL

The following equations are solved:-

Coolant

$$\frac{\partial}{\partial t}\rho + \frac{\partial}{\partial z}G = 0 \qquad \text{Mass conservation} \qquad (1)$$

$$\frac{\partial}{\partial t}\left[\rho\left(h+\tfrac{1}{2}u^2\right)\right] + \frac{\partial}{\partial z}\left[G\left(h+\tfrac{1}{2}u^2\right)\right] + Gk = q + \frac{\partial p}{\partial t} \qquad \text{Energy conservation} \qquad (2)$$

$$\frac{\partial}{\partial t}G + \frac{\partial}{\partial z}\left(Gu\right) = -\frac{\partial p}{\partial z} - k\rho - f Gu \qquad \text{Momentum conservation} \quad (3)$$

Heat Transfer from Wall

$$q = \frac{4}{D}\left[H_c\left(T_{m_i}-T\right) + H_b\left(T_{m_i}-T_s\right)^2\right] = \frac{4}{D}k\frac{\partial}{\partial r}T_m \qquad (4\&5)$$

Heat Transfer through Wall (Diffuse Flat Plate)

$$C_m\frac{\partial}{\partial t}T_m + k\frac{\partial^2}{\partial r^2}T_m = q_m \qquad (6)$$

Heat Transfer from Gas

$$q_g = \frac{4}{D}H_g\left(T_g - T_{m_c}\right) = \frac{4}{D}k\frac{\partial}{\partial r}T_m \qquad (7\&8)$$

Gas Temperature (Fixed Gas Line, Complete Gas Mixing)

$$\frac{\partial}{\partial t}T_g = 0 \qquad (9A)$$

(No Gas Mixing)

or: $\left(\rho C_p\right)_g\frac{\partial T_g}{\partial t} + \left(u\rho C_p\right)_g\frac{\partial T_g}{\partial z} = q_g \qquad (9B)$

Rather than present a detailed derivation of the theory and solution scheme used in DYMEL, the principle results will be set out together with a guide to how they may be derived.   The advantages of the method is also discussed.

The starting point is the one dimensional flow continuity equation (1), (2) and (3).   Kinetic and Potential energy will be ignored in equation (2), the energy equation, in order to facilitate the brief analysis that follows.   From these equations, it is required to find the linear response of the boiler to an infinitesimal perturbation in any of the variables.   The response of the system to flow perturbations is particularly important.   We will therefore find it convenient to cast the equations in terms of the normalized mass flux perturbation g^*. Equations (1) to (3) are therefore written down in terms of the steady state variables plus a small perturbation from the steady state (i.e. $G = G_0 + G^*$, $\rho = \rho_0 + \rho^*$ etc.   The steady state is denoted by a zero subscript, the perturbation by a star superscript).   The equations can then be written out for the starred (perturbed) variables.

$$\frac{\partial}{\partial t} \rho^* + \frac{\partial}{\partial z} G^* = 0 \tag{10}$$

$$\frac{\partial R^*}{\partial t} + \rho_0 \frac{\partial h^*}{\partial t} + G_0 \frac{\partial h^*}{\partial z} + G^* \frac{\partial h_0}{\partial z} = q^* + \frac{\partial p^*}{\partial t} \tag{11}$$

$$\frac{\partial G^*}{\partial t} + \frac{\partial}{\partial z} \left(G^* u_0 + G_0 u^* \right) = -\frac{\partial p^*}{\partial z} - k \rho^* - f \left(G^* u_0 + u^* G_0 \right) \tag{12}$$

Closure is obtained by the linearization of the equation of state about the steady state:-

$$\rho^* = h^* \frac{\partial \rho}{\partial h}\Big|_p + p^* \frac{\partial \rho}{\partial p}\Big|_h \tag{13}$$

The leading term in equation 5 deserves special mention.   It represents the inclusion of slip into the one-stream model adopted.   The variable R is given by:-

$$R = \langle \rho h \rangle - \langle \rho \rangle \bar{h} \tag{14}$$

$\bar{h}$ is the flow averaged enthalpy, the angular brackets denote area averaging over the tube cross-section.

Taking these definitions, no other terms appear in the energy equation.
The equation of state now has to take into account the relationship between $<\rho>$, $\bar{h}$ and $<p>$, using steam tables plus a correlation for slip.
All that needs to be said about R, is that it can be expressed in terms
of the slip ratio and therefore correlations exist for it.   Other terms
with similar derivation to R exist in the momentum equation.   We shall
ignore them.

Equations (10), (11), (12) and (13) are now Laplace Transformed from time
to frequency space.   A change in variable from axial distance $\bar{z}$ to fluid
transit time τ is also made.   The equation of heat flow through the tube
wall is linearized and gives an equation for Q^* in terms of g^*, $\frac{\partial g^*}{\partial \tau}$, p^*
and Tg^*.   Axial heat conduction in the wall is ignored.   The
resulting equations can then be combined to give two equations in g^* and
p^*.   Firstly,

$$\frac{\partial^2 g^*}{\partial \tau^2} + b(\tau)\frac{\partial g^*}{\partial \tau} + c(\tau)g^* = k_1(\tau)p^* + k_2(\tau)\frac{\partial p^*}{\partial \tau} + k_3(\tau)T_g^* \qquad (15)$$

which is a disguised form of the energy equation.   Secondly,

$$\alpha(\tau)\frac{\partial^2 g^*}{\partial \tau^2} + \beta(\tau)\frac{\partial g^*}{\partial \tau} + \gamma(\tau)g^* = -\frac{\partial p^*}{\partial \tau} \qquad (16)$$

which is the momentum equation.

Equation (15) is now expressed in terms of Tg_{in}^* as set out under the
paragraph below on handling the gas side perturbations.   If the gas
side temperature profile is "frozen", as would be found in a multi-tube
boiler with good gas side mixing, $k_3(\tau)$ is set equal to zero.

The problem now is to solve the simultaneous ordinary differential
equations (15) and (16).   These equations hold throughout the boiler.
The terms b, c, k_1, k_2, k_3, d, p and γ varying axially along the boiler.
It can be pointed out, that sometimes k_1 and k_2 are small enough to be
neglected.   This decouples equations (15) and (16) which simplifies the
analysis.   However we shall pursue the general case.   Equations (15)
and (16) are equivalent to one third order differential equation:-

$$\frac{\partial^3 g^*}{\partial \tau^3} + a_3(\tau)\frac{\partial^2 g^*}{\partial \tau^2} + b_3(\tau)\frac{\partial g^*}{\partial \tau} + c_3(\tau)g^* = k_4(\tau)p_{in}^* + k_5(\tau)T_{g_{in}}^* \qquad (17)$$

Solution to Equation 17

The solution scheme adopted in DYMEL is to split the boiler into sections.
The sections are made small enough, so that the coefficients in equation
(17) can be taken as constants with little error in the resultant
solution, which is built up by matching boundary conditions at each mesh

point.   Computer codes invariably split the boiler into sections.   This
is because fluid properties, steady state heat flux distribution and the
various correlations used are complicated functions.   These complications are reflected in the axial variation in a_3, b_3, c_3, k_4 and k_5.
The scheme outlined above is convenient, in that each section has transfer functions of identical form, but with different coefficients.   Even
the boiling and superheat boundaries can be allowed for within a section,
provided the section is small enough.   This has great advantage over
schemes with special transfer functions for each of the three regions
subcooled, two phase and superheated.   Near the critical pressure each
region begins to take on the character of its neighbour and so it would
be necessary to modify each region's transfer function.   The solution
to equation (17) within a section is given by:-

$$j^* = A e^{w_A \tau} + B e^{w_B \tau} + C e^{w_C \tau} + D \tag{18}$$

where w_A, w_B and w_C are the solution of the cubic equation

$$\omega^3 + a_3 \omega^2 + b_3 \omega + c_3 = 0 \tag{19}$$

The analytic solution given in Abramowitz and Stegun [16] is generalised
to allow complex coefficients as well as complex roots.   These three
w's each correspond to a complex wave number which propagates information
through the system.   The wave numbers are a function of frequency.

Handling of Gas Side Perturbations

Linearizing equation (4) we may derive:-

$$Q^* = A T_{m_i}^* + f\left(j^*, \frac{\partial g^*}{\partial \tau}, p^*\right) \tag{20}$$

and thus using equations (5) to (8) we may also derive that

$$Q^* = -\chi_m T_{m_i}^* + \chi_g T_g^* \tag{21}$$

where $\chi_m(Hg,k,\Delta r,Cm,s)$, $\chi_g(Hg,k,\Delta r,Cm,s)$, Δr being the width of the
tube wall.

$T_{m_i}^*$ can now be eliminated from equation (20) to give:-

$$Q^* = \lambda f\left(j^*, \frac{\partial g^*}{\partial \tau}, p^*\right) + A \frac{\chi_g}{\chi_m} T_g^* \tag{22}$$

(and $\quad \lambda = \dfrac{x_m}{A + x_m} \quad)$

But Tg^* is a function of τ, the fluid transit time.   Therefore to re-tain the cubic form of the solution and not go to a quartic, which has a much more complicated analytic solution, some averaging has to be done. Equations (6), (7) and (8) give us:-

$$T_{m_c}^* = 5\, T_{m_c}^* + 4\, T_g^* \tag{23}$$

and Equation 9B:-

$$T_g^* = G_1(\tau)\, T_{m_c}^* + G_2(\tau)\, T_{g_{in}}^* \tag{24}$$

The method chosen was as follows:-

Equation (24) is averaged over the transfer functions G_1 and G_2 alone.

$$\therefore \; T_g^* = \langle G_1 \rangle\, T_{m_c}^* + \langle G_2 \rangle\, T_{g_{in}}^* \tag{25}$$

$\langle G_1 \rangle$ and $\langle G_2 \rangle$ are now taken as constants, independent of τ.

From (25) and (23) we derive:-

$$T_g^* = \dfrac{\left[\langle G_1 \rangle\, 5\, T_{m_c}^* + \langle G_2 \rangle\, T_{g_{in}}^* \right]}{[1 - 4\langle G_1 \rangle]} \tag{26}$$

thus substituting (26) into (21) we get:-

$$Q^* = \left[-x_m + \dfrac{x_g \langle G_1 \rangle\, 5}{[1 - 4\langle G_1 \rangle]} \right] T_{m_c}^* + \dfrac{x_g \langle G_1 \rangle}{[1 - 4\langle G_1 \rangle]}\, T_{g_{in}}^* \tag{27}$$

This is of the desired form, which combined with equation (20) yields:-

$$Q^* = \lambda f(q^*, \tfrac{\partial q^*}{\partial t}, p^*) + \dfrac{A x_g \langle G_2 \rangle}{\left[x_m - \dfrac{x_g \langle G_1 \rangle\, 5}{[1 - 4\langle G_1 \rangle]} \right]} \cdot \dfrac{1}{(1 - 4\langle G_1 \rangle)}\, T_{g_{in}}^* \tag{28}$$

where now

$$\lambda = \cfrac{\chi_m - \cfrac{\chi_g \langle G_1 \rangle \xi}{[1 - \psi \langle G_1 \rangle]}}{A + \chi_m - \cfrac{\chi_g \langle G_1 \rangle \xi}{[1 - \psi \langle G_1 \rangle]}}$$

This equation for Q^* is now used to reformulate equation (15) in terms of Tg^*_{in} instead of Tg^*.

To calculate the gas temperature perturbation propagation, equation (24) is used with the average external wall temperature perturbation $\langle Tm\dot{o} \rangle$ which can be calculated using the solution to equation (17).

$$Tg^* = G_1(\tau) \langle Tm_c^* \rangle + G_2(\tau) Tg^*_{in} \qquad (29)$$

To summarise, Q^* is expressed in terms of the waterside conditions and Tg^*_{in} by axially averaging the transfer functions $G_1(\tau)$ and $G_2(\tau)$ from equation (24). Tg^* is propagated using equation (24) and the average external tube wall temperature calculated from the averaging of $G_1(\tau)$ and $G_2(\tau)$.

Application to Stability Analysis

Thus from a knowledge of g^* throughout the boiler, as given by the solution to equation (17) in each section, all the transfer functions of the boiler can be derived. The particular transfer function of interest for stability analysis is the inlet pressure perturbations, just downstream of the inlet throttle, relative to the inlet flow perturbations. The Nyquist stability criterion is then applied, to calculate the required stabilizing throttle and unstable frequency.

Down-Hill and Up-Hill Boiling Tests in Helicoidal Tubes (Two-Phase Instabilities)

M. DOBREMELLE, L. DUCHATELLE, P. NOGRE, and M. CHABERT
Centre d'Etudes Nucleaires de Saclay
91 Gif-sur-Yvette, France

ABSTRACT

This paper reviews the results of up-hill and down-hill boiling experiments in the steam generator test facility (5 MW) at Grand Quevilly (Zebulon Loop). A comparison is made of experimental results with calculations using the Archange (CEA, France) and Loop (HTFS, Great Britain) codes. The chief conclusion drawn is that down-hill boiling raises no particular problems with respect to startup, control, shutdown or static stability. As for dynamic stability, while both systems operate identically at normal pressure, the instability threshold at low pressure occurs at water flow rates 25 % higher for down-hill boiling than for up-hill boiling.

INTRODUCTION

The experimental work on the development of steam generators, particularly those of fast breeders in France, was carried out at the Heat Transfer Test Center of the Commissariat à l'Energie Atomique at Grand Quevilly. The main facility of this Test Center has a power capacity of 5 MW. It features two liquid metal loops and a water/steam circuit which have similar components to those of an LMFBR power plant.

In recent years, we tested the steam generator modules of components of the Phénix and Super-Phénix 1 power plants. The steam generator components of the latter are helical coils of different pitch diameters. Their similarity to those of the HTR steam generators led us to carry out stability tests on these units in up-hill boiling, as part of an agreement between General Atomic and the Commissariat à l'Energie Atomique.

The development of a French project then led us to perform down-hill boiling tests to determine the effect of flow direction on dynamic instability initiation thresholds. In actual fact, while excellent stability can be obtained, the use of steam generators with down-hill boiling allows simplification of the gas circuits of the HTR power plant, as well as savings in investment and operating costs, combined with greater reliability.

DESCRIPTION OF THE INSTALLATION

Figure 1 shows a diagram of the installation. The heat produced in the heater by heavy fuel oil combustion is transferred to the intermediate heat exchanger by the primary sodium,
which is pumped by a mechanical pump with a nominal delivery
of 57 tons per hour. The sodium/potassium alloy flow in the
secondary loop is also ensured by a mechanical pump with a
nominal delivery of 75 tons per hour. The maximum service
temperatures are 585°C in the primary loop and 550°C in the
secondary loop.

The water/steam circuit includes the following :

- a condenser drum cooled by various deionized water circuits,
- a feedwater pump which delivers 12 tons per hour at 220
  bars pressure,
- measurement systems for flow rates from 0 to 3 t/h and
  3 to 12 t/h,
- a feedwater heater supplied with steam taken after the
  high pressure desuperheater,
- a high pressure steam desuperheater,
- a low pressure steam desuperheater,
- the helical coil test cell equipped with flow control
  valves.

The overall installation is monitored and controlled from the
control room (Figure 2.)

Description of the Zebulon test loop

The Zebulon test loop consists of four steam generators shown
in Figure 3. Each steam generator features a 20 x 25 mm diameter incoloy 800 tube which conveys the water that is heated
and vaporized. The sodium/potassium (NaK) alloy flows in
countercurrent flow around the water tube in an annular space
between the water tube and an outer tube 58 x 70 mm in diameter. Stability is maintained by centering studs. The
coils have the pitch diameters 0.630 m, 0.810 m, 1.8 m and
2.7 m. The heat exchange lengths are about 63 meters.

Measurement systems

The measurement instrumentation includes the following :

- magnetic flowmeters with permanent magnets for measuring NaK alloy flow rates calibrated to ± 3 %.

- Venturi type flowmeters for measuring water flow rates calibrated to ± 2 %.

- pressure sensors for measuring absolute pressures at the water inlet and steam outlet manifolds ; the detector element is a diaphragm whose deformation is transmitted to a strain gauge bridge normally balanced to zero ; accuracy is about ± 1 bar .

- differential pressure sensors (Figure 4) with metal wave diaphragm which moves the mobile core of a differential transformer under the effect of pressure ; a demodulator transforms the a.c. voltages induced in the secondaries into d.c. voltage ; these units calibrated to ± 1 % are used to measure pressure drops between the different zones in the circuit :

  - at the terminals of the flow control valves,

  - the economizer/evaporator zone

  - the superheater zone ;

  this is carried out for each coil,

- temperature measurements are taken in the fluids at the inlet and outlet of each steam generator ; in addition, changes in the temperature of the NaK alloy are followed in each coil by means of thermocouples distributed along the annular spaces at approximately 2 m intervals.

All temperatures are measured by chromel/alumel thermocouples in 1 mm diameter austenitic steel sheaths featuring insulated junction. These thermocouples are calibrated and their accuracy depends on the temperature level :

- 100 to 200°C   ± 0.5°C,
- 200 to 400°C   ± 1°C,
- 400 to 600°C   ± 1.5°C .

All the measurement sensors feed electrical signals which are recorded at each test by means of a 400-channel centralizer scanned at a rate of one channel per second (Figure 5).

TESTS PERFORMED

Many tests were carried out in steady state up-hill boiling [7] followed by static and dynamic stability tests [7, 8].

Using the Zebalur heat transfer computation code and the loop [7, 8] dynamic stability computation code, we obtained good agreement between experiments and calculations.

With respect to down-hill boiling, we carried out a limited number of tests designed specifically to investigate dynamic stability, but which also cover steady state conditions and static stability. The theoretical analysis of the experimental results was carried out by the Archange code described in the following section.

THE ARCHANGE CODE

The Archange code [1] is a steam generator computation code with many possibilities.

The boundary conditions are the input values of the primary and secondary fluids : flow rates, enthalpies, pressures as well as geometry. Two alternatives allow setting of the ΔP at the circuit terminals or the power.

The results are the flow rate, pressure and temperature fields along the steam generator. The code carries out steady state computations as well as dynamic and thermal transient calculations. The steam compressibility is taken into account, hence the flow rate is not constant longitudinally during a single evolution.

The primary fluid may be selected among carbon dioxide, helium, air, water, steam, sodium or one of its alloys.

Several tubes or groups of tubes in parallel can be processed. However, the primary temperature is constant at a given abscissa.

The circuit may include components such as diaphragms, tubes, pumps, valves, turbines, etc.

The Archange code also makes it possible to perform dynamic stability computations for a steam generator. To do this, it was combined with the British Loop code [2].

Thermodynamic equations and assumptions

The computation model is based on the simultaneous resolution of three thermodynamic equations of conservation of energy, mass and quantity of movement. These equations are treated unidimensionally along the fluid flow axis.

Five possible flow configurations are considered in succession :

.   water,

.   local boiling,

.   clear boiling up to dryout point (critical quality),

.   boiling with dryout of liquid film,

.   dry steam.

It is considered that the liquid and vapor phases have identical speeds (homogeneous model).

The problem consists of calculating the following quantities at each abscissa x of the steam generator, as a function of time t :

.   primary fluid temperature $\theta(x,t)$,

.   wall temperature $r(x,t)$,

.   enthalpy of secondary fluid $H(x,t)$,

.   quality of secondary fluid steam $X(x,t)$,

.   secondary fluid pressure $P(x,t)$,

.   mean speed of secondary fluid (the
    liquid and steam speeds are assu-
    med to be equal $u_1 = u_v$) $u(x,t)$,

.   enthalpy of liquid and vapor phases $h_1(x,t)$, $h_v(x,t)$,

.   densities of liquid and vapor phases $\rho_e(x,t)$, $\rho_v(x,t)$,

The ten thermodynamic equations presented below correspond to these ten unknown functions :

Energy balance equations :

.   primary fluid (gas) :

$$\frac{\partial \theta}{\partial t} + u_p \frac{\partial \theta}{\partial x} = \frac{h_p X_p}{\rho_p S_p C_p} (r - \theta). \qquad (1)$$

(u_p, h_p, X_p, ρ_p, S_p, C_p represent respectively the speed, heat transfer coefficient, wetted circumference, density, passage cross-section and specific heat at constant pressure of the primary fluid.

. heat exchange wall between primary and secondary fluids :

$$\rho_m \cdot S_m \cdot C_m \frac{\partial r}{\partial t} = - h_p X_p (r - \theta) - \Phi_s .$$ (2)

(ρ_m, S_m, C_m represent the density, cross-section and specific heat of the metal heat exchange wall).

. secondary fluid (water) :

$$\frac{\partial H}{\partial t} + u \frac{\partial H}{\partial x} = \frac{1}{\rho} \cdot \frac{\partial p}{\partial t} + \frac{\Phi_s X_s}{\rho S_s} .$$ (3)

(Φ_s, X_s, S_s represent the heat flux, heat exchange circumference and passage cross-section of the secondary fluid).

The following definitions are used in the latter equation :

. mean density of water :

$$\rho = (1 - \alpha) \rho_1 + \alpha \rho_v .$$

. mean enthalpy of water :

$$H = \frac{(1 - \alpha) \rho_1 u_1 h_1 + \alpha \rho_v u_v h_v}{\rho . u} .$$

. equation of conservation of mass relative to the secondary fluid :

$$\frac{\partial \rho}{\partial t} + \frac{\partial (\rho u)}{\partial x} = 0$$ (4)

. equation of conservation of quantity of movement relative to the secondary fluid :

$$\frac{\partial p}{\partial x} = \frac{f}{2 D_H} \rho . u^2 + \rho g - \rho \left(\frac{\partial u}{\partial t} + u \frac{\partial u}{\partial x} \right) .$$ (5)

. definition of steam quality :

$$X = \frac{H - h_1}{h_v - h_1} \text{ pour } h_1 < H < h_v .$$ (6)

. state functions of the secondary fluids :

- enthalpies of liquid and vapor phases :

$$h_l(p,T), \ h_v(p,T).$$ (7, 8)

- densities of liquid and vapor phases :

$$\rho_l(p,T), \ \rho_v(p,T).$$ (9, 10)

Added to these equations are the equations defining the friction and heat transfer laws.

Numerical resolution method

The steam generator is subdivided into elementary increments of length Δx. Their discretization of time, with increment Δt, is imposed. The system of equations with partial derivatives is replaced by a system of equations with finite differences. The functions $f(x,t)$ are represented by the quantities f_i^t which are approximations of $f(x,t)$ at abscissa i and at time t.

Assuming that all the magnitudes (speeds, pressures, enthalpies, etc) concerning the primary and secondary fluids are known at instant $t - \Delta t$, it is necessary to calculate these magnitudes at instant t. The computation is carried out step by step on the abscissa from the upstream to the downstream end of the circuit.

Thus the problem at the level of one increment i is posed in the following manner :

assuming all the magnitudes with subscripts
$\begin{Bmatrix} t-\Delta t \\ i-1 \end{Bmatrix}$, $\begin{Bmatrix} t- \Delta t \\ i \end{Bmatrix}$ and $\begin{Bmatrix} t \\ i-1 \end{Bmatrix}$ to be known, let us calculate the same quantities at $\begin{Bmatrix} t \\ i \end{Bmatrix}$

The resolution of the energy balance equations applied in the increment (i - 1, i) yields the magnitudes : θ_i^t , r_i^t , H_i^t , assuming an estimate of the pressure p_i^t and the speed u_i^t of the secondary fluid.

This estimate of p_i^t and u_i^t is provided by the resolutions of the equations of mass balance and conservation of quantity of movement applied to this same increment.

The calculation is continued step by step up to the end of the circuit. If the boundary conditions are not satisfied, iterations on the overall circuit become necessary.

Correlations employed

.   Local boiling

Vaporization theoretically begins when the enthalpy of the water is equal to or exceeds the enthalpy of incipient vaporization.

However, if the wall temperature exceeds the vaporization temperature (TSAT) at the pressure considered, the bubbles formed disappear immediately, as the temperature far from the wall is lower than TSAT.

At this moment local boiling is said to occur, and the wall/water heat transfer coefficients are very different.

By setting :

$$h = h_c + h_b$$

where :

. h wall/water heat transfer coefficient,
. h_c convection heat transfer coefficient,
. h_b boiling heat transfer coefficient,

we have :

$$h_c = 0.023 \ R_e^{0.8} P_r^{0.33}$$

and :

$$h_b = \frac{\mu' r}{\sqrt{\dfrac{\sigma}{g(\rho' - \rho'')}}} \left(\frac{C'}{0.013 \ R \ Pr'} \ 1.7 \right)^3 \ \frac{(r - Tsat)^3}{r - \theta}$$

(Figure 6, reference [3])

with :

. μ' liquid viscosity at temperature TSAT
. R latent heat of evaporation,

- . σ tension of steam
- . ρ' liquid density at TSAT,
- . ρ'' vapor density at TSAT,
- . C' liquid specific heat,
- . Pr' liquid Prandtl's number,
- . r wall temperature,
- . Θ mean fluid temperature

- . Dryout quality

When we proceed from the zone in which a liquid film exists
at the wall to the zone in which the fluid is in the mist
state, a sudden drop is observed in the heat transfer coefficient. The corresponding quality is called the "critical
quality" or "dryout quality". Beyond this critical quality,
the heat transfer coefficients are calculated by means of
Miropolskiy's law (Figure 7, reference [4]).

The correlation suggested by L. Duchatelle and L. de Nucheze
(5) to determine this critical quality X_{crit} is the
following :

$$X_{crit} = 1.39 \ 10^{-4} \ \Phi^{0.732} \ G^{-0.209} \ e^{0.00246 \ P} \quad .$$

where :

- . Φ flux density W/m^2,
- . G mass flow rate $kg/m^2/s$,
- . P pressure in bars,

for :

$$375 < G < 3500$$

$$30 \ 10^4 < \Phi < 150 \ 10^4$$

$$45 < P < 175$$

(Figure 8)

Miropolskiy's law is the following :

$$N_u = N_{u'} \left[1 - 0.1 \left(\frac{\rho'}{\rho''} - 1 \right)^{0.4} \left(1-X \right)^{0.4} \right] \left[X + \frac{\rho''}{\rho'} \left(1-X \right) \right]^{0.8} \quad .$$

where :

. N_u,   Nusselt's number in steam conditions,
. X   steam quality,

.   Review of correlations in other zones

Water and steam : $N_u = 0.023 \ R_e^{0.8} P_r^{0.33}$

Double phase between nil quality and critical quality.

Jens and Lotte's law

$$T_\rho - T_{sat} = 7.9 \ \phi^{0.25} \ e^{\frac{P}{63.5}}$$

.   Correlations to calculate pressure differences

In the double phase region, the pressure drops are calculated by using the single phase laws, increased by the multiplication factors of Martinelli-Nelson (Figure 9, reference [6])

We have :

$$\Delta P = \Delta P_f + \Delta P_a + \Delta P_g$$

where :

. ΔP_f pressure difference due to friction,
. ΔP_a pressure difference due to acceleration,
. ΔP_g pressure difference due to gravity

By setting :

$$\Delta P_f = \Delta P_{fr_e} \ C_{fr}$$

$$\Delta P_a = \Delta P_{ac_e} \ C_{ac}$$

$$\Delta P_g = \Delta P_{gr_e} \ C_{gr}$$

ΔP_{fr_e} , ΔP_{ac_e} , ΔP_{gr_e} are respectively calculated as if the fluid was water at the saturation temperature. C_{fr}, C_{ac}, C_{gr}, are coefficients.

STEADY STATE CONDITIONS

The tests dealt with the usual operating conditions of steam
generators :

.   outlet pressure   about 170 bars

.   water flow rate Q_{water} $0.075 < Q_{water} < 0.3$ kg/s

    corresponding to a load ranging from 100 to 25%.

.   NaK flow rate :   about ten times greater than water flow
    rate,

.   steam outlet temperature   about 540°C

.   power W $170 < W < 620$ KW
                                                 per coil

In all the tests, startup was carried out with water-fill,
i.e. the primary circuit was first heated. The water in the
secondary circuit was then vaporized progressively. The
different parameters were brought to their predetermined values by maintaining vaporization at a given level.

In these conditions, the coils were tested in up-hill vaporization and in down-hill vaporization. The water inlet valves
were sufficiently closed to ensure good stability.

No irregularity was observed in startup and operation, despite prevailing fears concerning down-hill boiling.

In the conditions investigated, the theoretical results agree
with experimental results, both in down-hill and up-hill
boiling. Figure 10 shows one example of this good agreement.
The dotted curve representing temperature variations in the
primary circuit is experimental, and the upper solid curve
is the calculated curve.

In the following tests, before triggering the instabilities,
the temperature field was also recorded. In the case of low
operating pressures, with down-hill vaporization, less satisfactory agreement was observed between experiment and
calculations. A finer analysis must therefore be carried
out to draw the consequences at the correlations level.

STATIC STABILITY

Figure 11 gives one example of the variation in pressure
drop ΔP as a function of flow rate. Section AB is one branch
of the parabola representing the variation in ΔP when the
steam zone is very long. Section CD is obtained for a very
long water zone. Section BC is the connection zone in which
normal operating conditions prevail. It may be noted that
the intersection with the characteristic of a pump gives
three operating points causing very unstable behavior in the
unit. This was corrected by adding a pressure drop at the
inlet. The curve corresponding to the overall unit then
becomes the upper curve, which no longer exhibits a negative
slope.

Using the measured ΔP curves, the inlet pressure drop ΔP is
calculated which leads, for each coil, to a given stability
index I at the inflection point of the S curve.

The stability index I is defined as follows :

$$I = \frac{\frac{\partial \Delta P}{\Delta P o}}{\frac{\partial M}{Mo}}$$

Figures 12 and 13 show the results obtained for up-hill vaporization, and Figures 14 and 15 show the results relative to
down-hill vaporization.

Figures 12 and 14 illustrate the good agreement between experiment and calculations.

Figure 16 compares up-hill vaporization with down-hill vaporization for a given coil.

Widely different types of behavior are observed, as the
direction of ΔP is reversed in down-hill vaporization. To
obtain the same stability index, it is therefore necessary
to add a slightly larger inlet pressure drop.

DYNAMIC STABILITY TESTS

Dynamic stability tests in up-hill and down-hill flow were
performed following the procedure described below. Starting
with stable operating conditions, this involved determining
the water flow rate which leads to dynamic instability, and
the values of these flow rates obtained in up-hill and
down-hill boiling are compared.

Procedure

With the four coils supplied, for instance, with a total flow rate of 0.3 kg/s, or about 25 % of nominal flow rate, the inlet valves are regulated to balance the flow rates and to ensure good static stability. The NaK alloy flow rates are adjusted on each coil to obtain the steam outlet temperature.

Whilst the starting conditions were established, the water flow rate was decreased by increments of about 5 % until dynamic instabilities were produced.

Another type of test consists of increasing the NaK flow rate until instabilities are initiated.

These operations are carried out at several pressure levels.

Figure 17 shows a test recording in which static type instabilities (period 40 min) are observed to be superimposed on dynamic type instabilities (period about 2 seconds).

Test results

. At 70 bars pressure

The operating conditions at which dynamic instabilities are initiated in up-hill boiling are the following :

. water flow rate	$859 \text{ kg/m}^2/\text{s}$,
. NaK inlet temperature	523°C,
. water inlet temperature	185°C,
. steam outlet temperature	521°C.

The same tests, performed in similar conditions in down-hill boiling, shows that dynamic oscillations occur at a water flow rate 25 % greater than that indicated above.

Furthermore, it may be noted that these instabilities occur at 70 bars pressure, and disappear when the pressure reaches about 78 bars.

. At 106 bars pressure

The operating conditions at which dynamic instabilities are initiated are the following :

. water flow rate	$796 \text{ kg/m}^2/\text{s}$,
. NaK inlet temperature	530°C,

- water inlet temperature   182°C,
- steam outlet temperature   528°C.

The same observations apply as at 70 bars pressure.

- At 140 bars pressure

The dynamic instability conditions in up-hill boiling are the following :

- water flow rate   461 kg/m^2/s,
- NaK inlet temperature   527°C,
- water inlet temperature   183°C,
- steam outlet temperature   522°C.

In this case, the conditions in which dynamic instabilities are initiated are closely comparable in down-hill boiling.

This appears to indicate that a high pressure, above 140 bars, the operating conditions provoking dynamic instabilities are substantially identical in down-hill boiling and up-hill boiling. At lower pressures, however, down-hill boiling is more sensitive to dynamic instabilities, and these occur at water flow rates 25 % higher than those for up-hill boiling.

Note also that at high pressure, instabilities occur at very low water flow rates (461 kg/m^2/s), i.e. at an operating rate lower than 15 %.

Comparison of experiments and calculations

The Loop code was applied with the data corresponding to the different tests. Stability was estimated by means of the Nyquist diagram (Figure 18).

In the case of up-hill boiling, very good agreement was observed between experiment and calculations, and the instability initiation thresholds were correctly determined by the Loop code.

As for down-hill boiling, the analysis was not completed, but the initial results appear to indicate that good agreement can be obtained after rectification of some correlations of the Archange code.

REFERENCES

1   J.C. Rousseau, P. Barber, M. Dobremelle and B. Villard
     Etude de la cinétique du circuit secondaire d'une cen-
     trale nucléaire refroidie par gaz.
     CEA Report No.R-4012.

2   Davies and Potter
     Code Loop, Instabilities in two-phase flow systems.
     HTFS Design Report, AERER 456.

3   W.M. Rosenhow and J.A. Clark
     Heat transfer and pressure drop data for high heat flux
     densities to water at high sub-critical pressures.
     Heat transfer and Fluid Mechanics Inst., pp. 193-207,
     Stanford University Press (1951).

4   Z.L. Miropolskiy
     Heat transfer in film boiling of a steam/water mixture
     in steam generating tubes.
     Teploenergetika pp. 49-52, Vol.10, No.5 (1963), Faraday
     Translations 6032 (1963).

5   L. Duchatelle, L. de Nucheze and M.G. Robin
     Departure from nucleate boiling in helical tubes of li-
     quid metal heated steam generator.
     ASEM.AICHE, Heat Transfer Conference, Atlanta, Georgia,
     5/8 August 1973.

6   R.C. Martinelli and D.B. Nelson
     Prediction of pressure drop during forced circulation
     boiling of water.
     Trans. ASME, August 1948.

7   L. Duchatelle and L. de Nucheze
     Calcul et mesure du transfert de chaleur et des pertes
     de pression dans les générateurs de vapeur à serpentins
     hélicoïdaux chauffés par métal liquide.
     DRNR/STRS R 40, November 1974.

8   L. Duchatelle, M. Chabert, Y. Grandcollot, L. de Nucheze
     Etude de stabilité dynamique et statique de générateurs
     de vapeur à tubes hélicoïdaux.
     DRNR/STRS R 43, (March 1976).

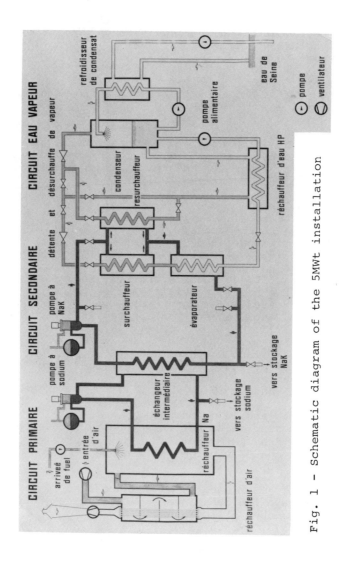

Fig. 1 - Schematic diagram of the 5MWt installation

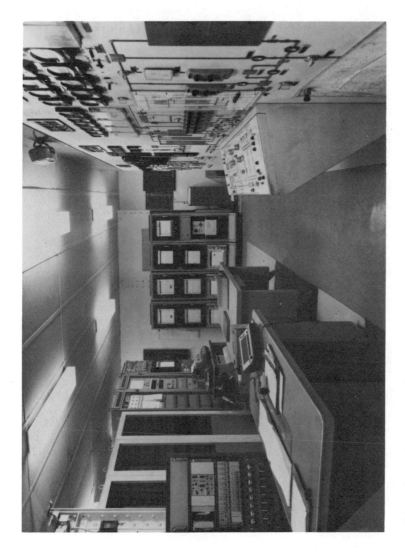

Fig. 2 - The control room

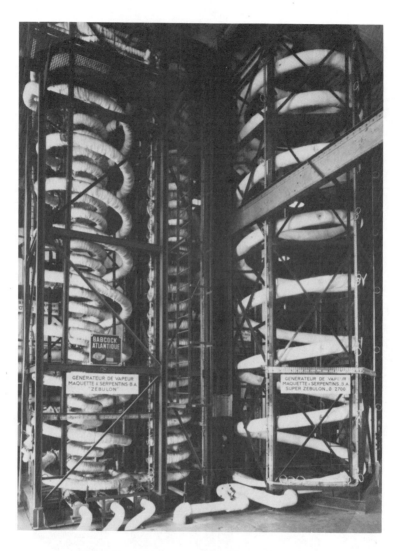

Fig. 3 - Steam generators for the
Zebulon test loop

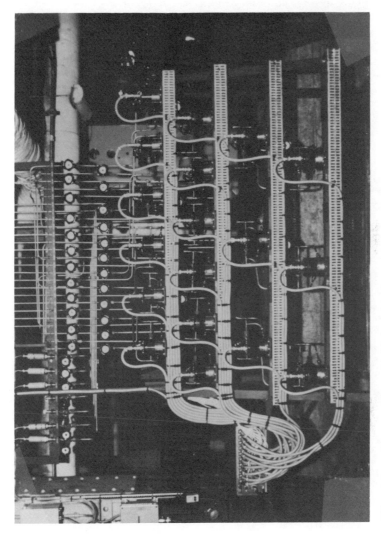

Fig. 4 - Set up for differential pressure sensors

Fig. 5 - 400 channel centralizer

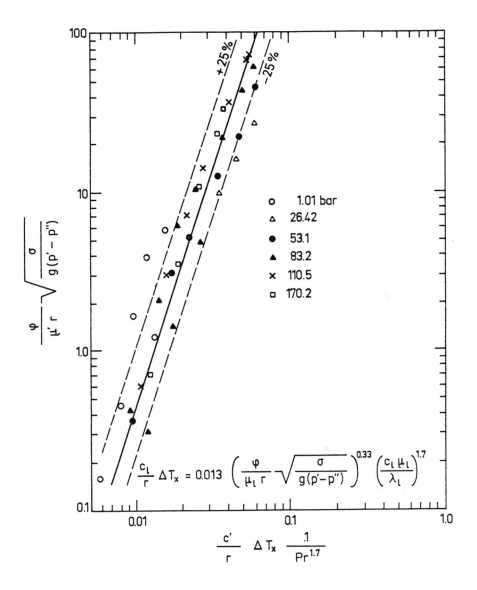

Fig. 6 - Nucleate boiling in tubes
(water) Ref. [3]

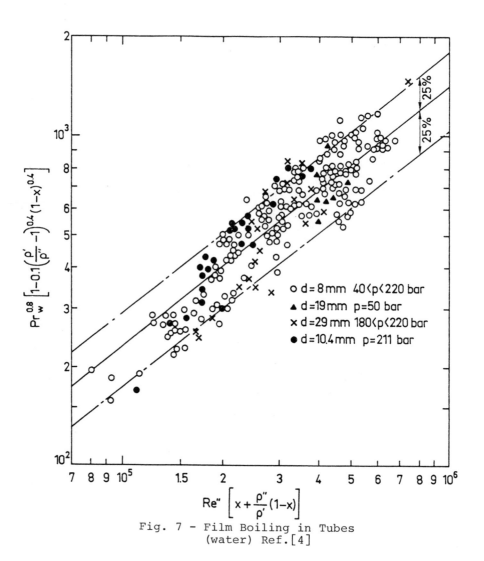

Fig. 7 - Film Boiling in Tubes
(water) Ref.[4]

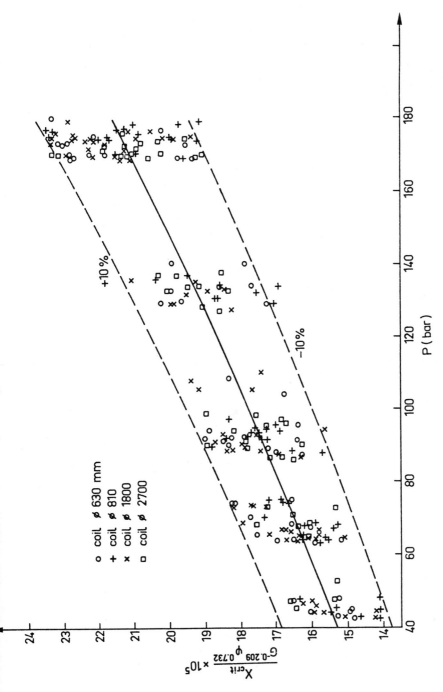

Fig. 8 – Effect of the pressure on the dry out quality Ref. [5]

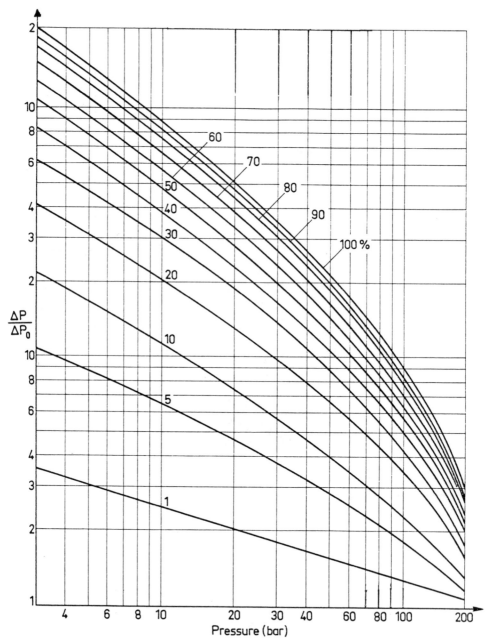

Fig. 9 - Multiplying coeffieient of
the pressure drop Ref. [6]

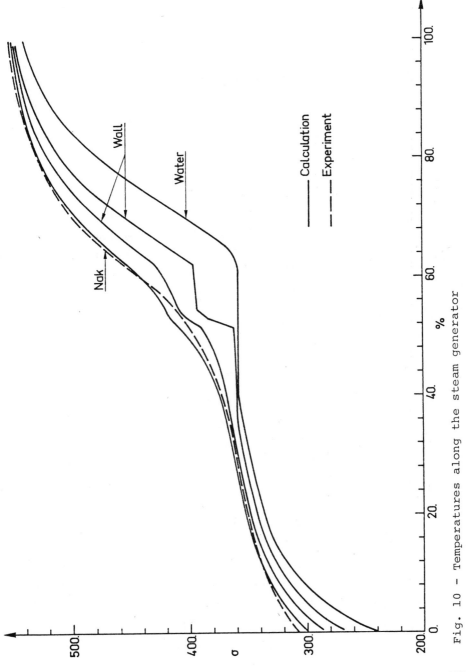

Fig. 10 - Temperatures along the steam generator

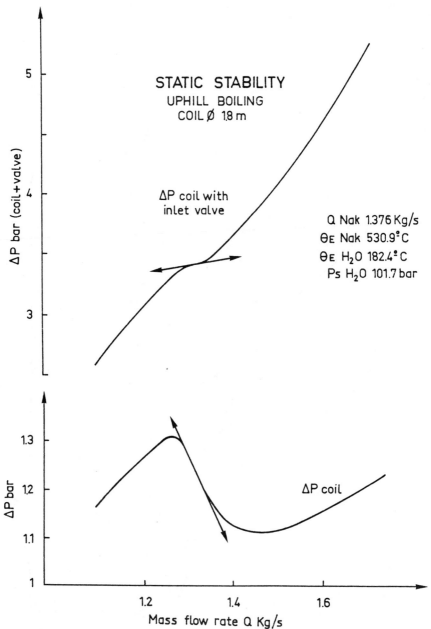

Fig. 11 - Variation of pressure drop
vs. the flow rate

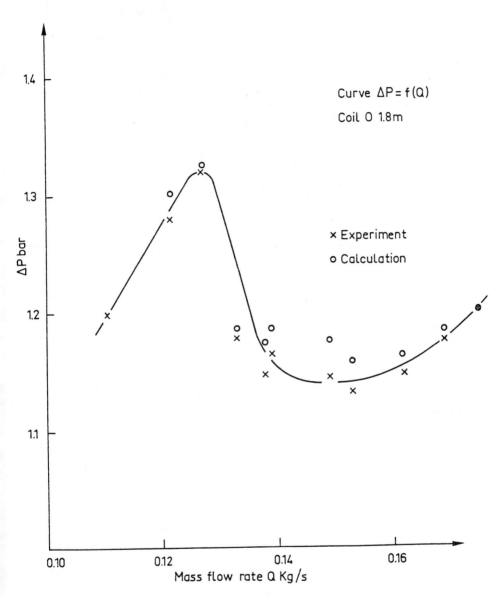

Fig. 12 - The stability index for uphill vaporization

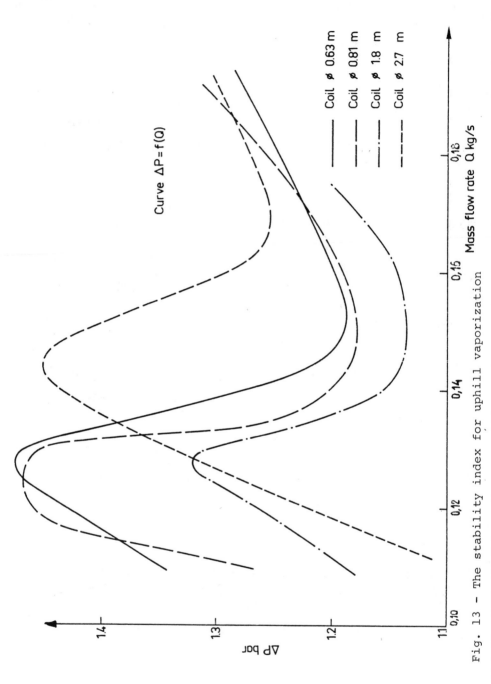

Curve $\Delta P = f(Q)$

—————— Coil ⌀ 0.63 m
—·—·— Coil ⌀ 0.81 m
—··—··— Coil ⌀ 1.8 m
— — — Coil ⌀ 2.7 m

ΔP bar

Mass flow rate Q kg/s

Fig. 13 - The stability index for uphill vaporization

1316

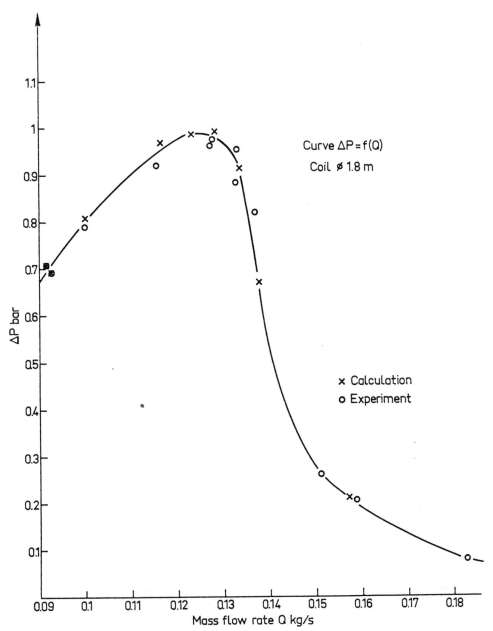

Fig. 14 - The stability index for downhill vaporization

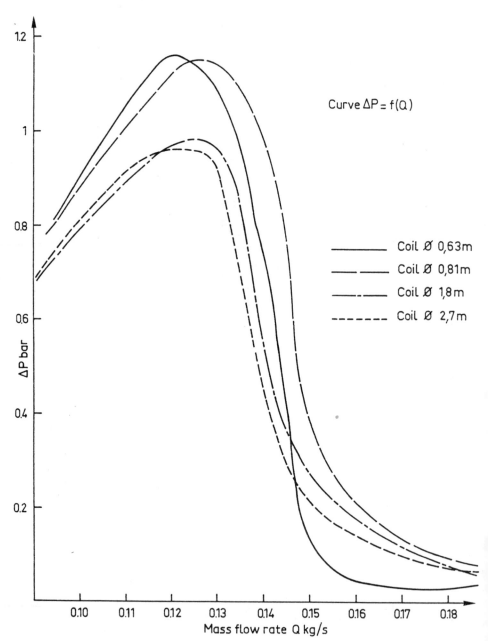

Fig. 15 - The stability index for downhill vaporization

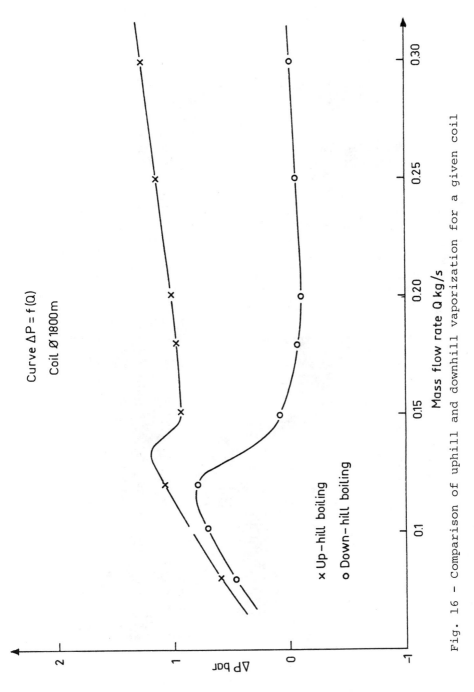

Fig. 16 – Comparison of uphill and downhill vaporization for a given coil

1319

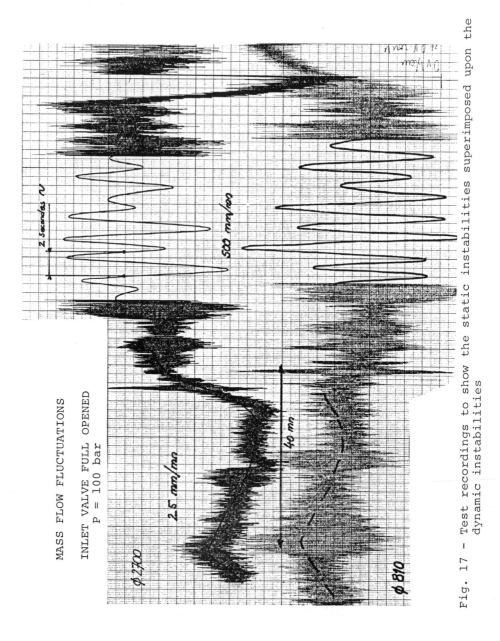

Fig. 17 - Test recordings to show the static instabilities superimposed upon the dynamic instabilities

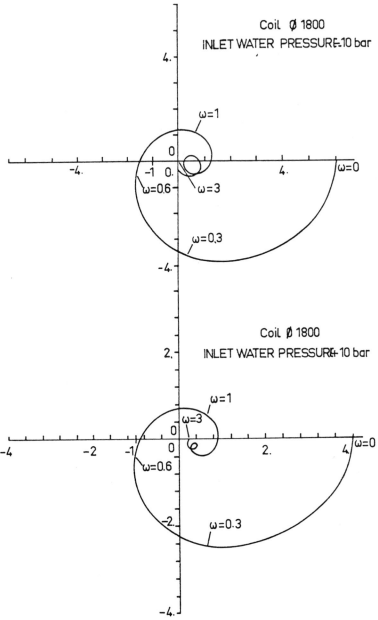

Fig. 18 - Nyquist diagrams -
static stability

Instabilities in Two-Phase Flow through Porous Media with Magnetic Field

A.P. VERMA
Department of Mathematics
S.V. Regional College of Engineering and Technology
Surat 395007, India

ABSTRACT

The paper analytically discusses the phenomenon of instabilities in displacement problems involving two immiscible
liquids through porous media with magnetic field effect. The
basic assumptions underlying the present investigation are
that the injected liquid is conducting and less viscous while
the native liquid is nonconducting and relatively more viscous, and the behaviour of the instabilities is governed by
a statistical treatment. The basic equations of the flow
system coupled with analytical consideration for additional
physical effects yield a nonlinear differential equation
whose approximate mathematical solution has been obtained by
a perturbation method. It is found that there is no stabilization of the instabilities in this case.

INTRODUCTION

The paper deals with the phenomenon of fingering viz., instabilities in displacement problems involving two immiscible
liquids through porous media with magnetic field. The underlying assumptions made in the present analysis are that the
injected liquid is conducting and less viscous while the
native liquid is nonconducting and relatively more viscous
viz., water injection in an oil formation, a statistical
treatment determines the behaviour of the instabilities and
the effect of magnetic field is to increase the injected

1323

liquid pressure by $\mu H^2/8\pi$, where μ is the permeability of
the magnetic field H.

It is a well known physical phenomenon that when a field
contained in a porous medium is displaced by another of less-
er viscosity then instead of a regular displacement of the
whole front, protuberances (fingers [1]) may arise which
shoots through the porous medium at relatively great speed.
These protuberances which represent instabilities in the
displacement problem are called fingers. The displacement
problems of this type coupled with allied flow systems in the
porous medium have gained much current importance particularly
in petroleum technology and hydrogeology, and many authors
have analysed these problems from different view points; for
example, Scheidegger [2,3], Verma [4-8], Chavent [9-10].

In the statistical treatment of fingers, we consider only the
average cross-sectional area occupied by the fingers, and
disregard their individual size and shape (see FIG. 1 (a) and
(b)). This treatment of fingers [3], with the notion of
fictitious relative permeability, becomes formally identical
to the Buckley-Leverett description of the double phase immiscible fluid flow in porous media. In this case, the saturation of ith fluid (S_i) is defined as the average cross-
sectional area occupied by it at the level x, i.e., $S_i = S_i(x,t)$,
and thus the saturation of the displacing fluid in the porous
medium represents the average cross-sectional area occupied
by the fingers.

Here we investigate the phenomenon of instabilities through
homogeneous porous media in the presence of a variable magnetic field which has not been considered so far by the earlier
authors. The mathematical formulation of the basic flow equations, under the assumptions stated above, yield a nonlinear
differential equation whose approximate solution by a

perturbation method gives an analytical expression for the average cross-sectional area occupied by the fingers. It is found that the fingers do not stabilize in the present case.

NOMENCLATURE

K = Permeability of the Medium
K_i = Relative permeability of injected liquid
K_n = Relative permeability of resident liquid
P = Porosity of the medium
P_i = Pressure of the injected liquid
P_n = Pressure of the resident liquid
p_c = Capillary pressure
S_i = Saturation of the injected liquid
S_n = Saturation of the resident liquid
t = Time
V_i = Seepage velocity of injected liquid
V_n = Seepage velocity of resident liquid
x = Linear coordinate
β = Capillary pressure coefficient
δ_i = Viscosity of the injected liquid
δ_n = Viscosity of the resident liquid
λ = Constant.

Those symbols which are defined in the text are not included in the table.

THE PROBLEM AND ITS MATHEMATICAL FORMULATION

We consider here that there is a uniform injection of liquid (i) into a homogeneous porous media saturated with native liquid (n) such that the invading liquid cuts through the native liquid formation and gives rise to protuberances (fingers). This furnishes a problem of well developed finger flow. Since the entire native liquid at the initial boundary, $x = 0$ (x being measured in the direction of displacement, is displaced through a small distance as a result of liquid injection, therefore, it is further assumed that complete water saturation exists at the initial boundary.

Our particular interest in the present paper is to obtain an analytical expression for the average cross-sectional area occupied by the fingers and discuss the possibility for finger stabilization in the investigated case. For the mathematical formulation of the above model we assume that the flow is governed by Darcy's law and assume further that the macroscopic behaviour of fingers is governed by a statistical treatment (Scheidegger [3]).

Thus, assuming the validity of Darcy's law in the investigated case, we may write the basic flow equations governing instabilities phenomenon as

$$V_i = - (K_i / \delta_i) \ K [(\partial p_i / \partial x) + (\mu / 4\pi)H \ \partial H / \partial x] \qquad (1)$$

$$V_n = - (K_n / \delta_n) \ K(\partial p_n / \partial x) \qquad (2)$$

$$P(\partial S_i / \partial t) + (\partial V_i / \partial x) \ = \ 0 \qquad (3)$$

$$P(\partial S_n / \partial t) + (\partial V_n / \partial x) \ = \ 0 \qquad (4)$$

$$S_i + S_n \ = \ 1 \qquad (5)$$

$$p_c = p_n - p_i \qquad (6)$$

where equations (1) and (2) give the filtration velocity from Darcy's law, (3) and (4) are the continuity equations of the two phases, (5) states that the sum of saturation is unity and (6) defines the pressure discontinuity in the flow of two immiscible liquids across the interface, that is, at finger tips. It may be mentioned that the second term in equation (1) is due to the variable magnetic field whose effect is to increase the pressure of the injecting phase by $\mu H^2 / 8\pi$.

Further we may add that only a one dimensional mathematical model has been discussed here.

From equations (1) – (4) we get the equations of motion as

$$P(\partial S_i/\partial t) - (\partial/\partial x)\left[(K_i/\delta_i)K\{(\partial p_i/\partial x)+(\not{M}/4\pi)H\ \partial H/\partial x\}\right] = 0 \quad (7)$$

$$P(\partial S_n/\partial t) - (\partial/\partial x)\left[(K_n/\delta_n)\ K(\partial p_n/\partial x)\right] = 0 \qquad (8)$$

Eliminating the time derivative by combining equations (7) and (8), using equations (5) and (6), and integrating with respect to x, we get

$$\left[(K_i/\delta_i)K + (K_n/\delta_n)K\right](\partial p_n/\partial x) - (K_i/\delta_i)\ K(\partial p_c/\partial x) \quad (9)$$

$$+ (\not{M}K_i/4\pi\delta_i)K\ H\ \partial H/\partial x = V$$

where V is a constant of integration which can be evaluated later on. The pressure of resident liquid (p_n) may be expressed in terms of the mean pressure $\bar{p}$ as

$$p_n = \bar{p} + (p_c/2), \quad \bar{p} = (p_i + p_n)/2 . \tag{10}$$

By regarding the mean pressure as constant [11], we have from equations (9) and (10) :

$$\frac{\partial p_i}{\partial x} = - \frac{(K_n/\delta_n \cdot K)}{[K_i/\delta_i \cdot K + K_n/\delta_n \cdot K]}(\partial p_c/\partial x) \tag{11}$$

$$- \frac{\not{M}(K_i/4\pi\delta_i)\ KH}{[K_i/\delta_i \cdot K + K_n/\delta_n \cdot K]}(\partial H/\partial X) + \frac{V}{[K_i/\delta_i \cdot K + K_n/\delta_n \cdot K]}$$

$$V = \frac{1}{2}(K_n/\delta_n \cdot K - K_i/\delta_i \cdot K)\frac{\partial p_c}{\partial x} + (K_i/\mathcal{E}_i \cdot K)(\not{M}/4\pi)H\frac{\partial H}{\partial X} \tag{12}$$

Plugging in these values in equation (7) and simplifying

we get,

$$P(\partial S_i/\partial t) + (\frac{\partial}{\partial x}) \left[(K_i/\delta_i)K \left\{ \frac{1}{2} (dp_c/dS_i)(\partial S_i/\partial x) \right. \right. \tag{13}$$

$$\left. \left. - (\mathcal{M}/4\pi)H \frac{\partial H}{\partial x} \right\} \right] = 0$$

For definiteness we assume at this stage the following relationships for the relative permeabilities and capillary pressure which are quoted in standard literature [3,8].

$$K_i = S_i, \quad K_n = (1 - S_i), \quad p_c = \beta\, g(S_i) \tag{14}$$

where β is the constant capillary pressure coefficient and $g(S_i)$ is some function of S_i. Substituting these values in equation (14), we obtain

$$P\frac{\partial S_i}{\partial t} + (\frac{K}{\delta_i}) \left[\frac{\beta}{2} \left\{ g'(S_i)(\frac{\partial S_i}{\partial x})^2 + S_i g''(S_i)(\frac{\partial S_i}{\partial x}) \right. \right. \tag{15}$$

$$\left. + S_i g'(S_i)\frac{\partial^2 S_i}{\partial x^2} \right\} - (\frac{\mathcal{M}}{4\pi}) \left\{ (H\frac{\partial H}{\partial x})(\frac{\partial S_i}{\partial x}) \right.$$

$$\left. \left. + S_i(\frac{\partial H}{\partial x}^2) + S_i(H\frac{\partial^2 H}{\partial x^2}) \right\} \right] = 0$$

This is the desired nonlinear differential equation governing the phenomenon of instabilities in the investigated case whose approximate mathematical solution has been discussed in the following section.

APPROXIMATE SOLUTION

Since equation (15) is highly nonlinear due to the presence of complicated terms, we attempt an approximate analytical solution by using the perturbation method. The capillary pressure coefficient β is considered to be small in the investigated case and hence it is assumed as the perturbation parameter. Thus, neglecting β in equation (15) at the first instance, we get

$$P(\partial S_i/\partial t) - (\mu K/4\pi\delta_i)\left[(H\frac{\partial H}{\partial x})(\partial S_i/\partial x) \right. \tag{16}$$

$$\left. + S_i\left\{(\partial H/\partial x)^2 + (H\frac{\partial^2 H}{\partial x^2})\right\}\right] = 0$$

Further, since the magnetic field in the present problem is considered in the x direction only, we may write the value of H as $H = \lambda/x^n$, where λ is a constant parameter and n is an integer. Substituting this value of H in equation (16), we get

$$\left(\frac{4\pi\delta_i P}{n\,k\,\lambda^2\mu}\right) x^{2n+2}\frac{\partial S_i}{\partial t} + x\frac{\partial S_i}{\partial x} = (2n+1)\,S_i \tag{17}$$

This is a first order partial differential equation of the Lagrange's type whose characteristic equations are

$$\frac{dt}{a\,x^{2n+2}} = \frac{dx}{x} = \frac{dS_i}{(2n+1)S_i} \;, \tag{18}$$

where $a = \left(\dfrac{4\pi\delta_i P}{n\,k\,\lambda^2\mu}\right)$

Integrating equation (18), we obtain

$$t + c = a\frac{x^{2n+2}}{(2n+2)}, \quad x\,D + S_i^{1/(2n+1)} \tag{19}$$

where C and D are constants of integration which may be determined by the following condition

$$S_i = 1, \quad at \quad x = L, \quad t = 0 \tag{20}$$

The condition states that initially there is full injected liquid saturation within a layer of infinitesimal width L at the injected face, x = 0. It is conceived that the resident liquid is completely displaced through a small distance due to the injection of liquid (i).

Then, combining equations (19) and (20), we get

$$S_i = \left[1 - \left(\frac{2n+2}{a} \right) \frac{t}{x^{2n+2}} \right]^{-\left(\frac{2n+1}{2n+2}\right)} \tag{21}$$

Now differentiating equation (21) with respect to x, we obtain

$$\frac{\partial S_i}{\partial x} = \frac{(2n+1)(2n+2)}{a\, x^{2n+3}}\, t \left[1 - \left(\frac{2n+2}{a} \right) \frac{t}{x^{2n+2}} \right]^{-\left(\frac{4n+3}{2n+2}\right)} \tag{22}$$

$$= \phi_1(x,t), \quad \text{say}$$

$$\frac{\partial^2 S_i}{\partial x^2} = - \frac{(2n+1)(2n+2)(2n+3)}{a\, x^{2n+4}}\, t \left[1 - \left(\frac{2n+2}{a} \right) \frac{t}{x^{2n+2}} \right]^{-\left(\frac{4n+3}{2n+2}\right)} \tag{23}$$

$$+ \frac{(2n+1)(2n+2)^2(4n+3)}{a^2\, x^{4n+6}}\, t \left[1 - \left(\frac{2n+2}{a} \right) \frac{t}{x^{2n+2}} \right]^{-\left(\frac{6n+5}{2n+2}\right)}$$

$$= \phi_2(x,t), \quad \text{say.}$$

Next, substituting the values of $(\partial S_i/\partial x)$ and $(\partial^2 S_i/\partial x^2)$ from equations (22) and (23), in the β-terms of equation (15) which were neglected at the first instance, we get

$$a\, x^{2n+2}(\partial S_i/\partial t) = x(\partial S_i/\partial x) = \psi(S_i, x, t) \tag{24}$$

where $\psi(S_i, x, t) = \left[(2n+1)S_i - (\beta K/2\delta_i)\left\{ g'(S_i)\, \phi_1^2(x,t) \right.\right.$

$$\left.\left. + S_i g''(S_i)\, \phi_1(x,t) + g'(S_i)\, \phi_2(x,t) \right\} \right]$$

Equation (24) is a quasilinear differential equation whose characteristic equations are

$$dt = a\, x^{2n+1}\, dx, \quad (dx/x) = (dS_i/\psi(S_i, x, t))$$

From equation (21), we may write

$$\frac{t}{x^{2n+2}} = \left(\frac{a}{2n+2} \right) \left[1 - S_i^{-\left(\frac{2n+2}{2n+1}\right)} \right] \tag{25}$$

Inview of the fact that the coefficient of the various terms in x within the parantheses are very small (since they are multiplied by the perturbation parameter β) it is fairly reasonable (as in Verma [8]) to assume that $\dfrac{t}{x^{2n+2}} \sim \dfrac{t}{x^{2n+1}}$, etc., where n is an integer of the order of 2 or 3. With this consideration, from equations (24) and (25), we get

$$\psi(S_i, x, t) = (2n+1) S_i \left[1 - f(S_i) \right] \tag{26}$$

where $f(S_i) = \dfrac{\beta K}{2\delta_i} \left[2(3n+2) g'(S_i) S_i^{\frac{6n+5}{2n+1}} \right.$

$$+ \left\{ g''(S_i) - (14n+11) g'(S_i) \right\} S_i^{\frac{4n+3}{2n+1}}$$

$$\left. - g''(S_i) S_i^{\frac{2n+2}{2n+1}} + (8n+5) g'(S_i) S_i \right]$$

Thus, the characteristic equations of quasilinear differential equation (24) may be written as

$$dt = a\, x^{2n+1}\, dx, \qquad \frac{dx}{x} = \frac{dS_i}{(2n+1)S_i\left[1 - f(S_i)\right]} \tag{27}$$

Simplifying the coefficient of dS_i by using binomial theorem, we may write the second equation of (27) as

$$\frac{dx}{x} = \left[\frac{1}{(2n+1)S_i} + \left(\frac{\beta K}{2(2n+1)\delta_i} \right) \left\{ 2(3n+2)g'(S_i)S_i^{\left(\frac{4n+4}{2n+1}\right)} \right. \right.$$

$$+ (g''(S_i) - (14n+11)g'(S_i))\, S_i^{\left(\frac{2n+2}{2n+1}\right)}$$

$$- g''(S_i) \ S_i^{\frac{1}{2n+1}} + (8n+5) \ g'(S_i) \ \Biggr\} \Biggr] \ dS_i$$

Performing integration of equation (27), we get

$$Ex = S_i^{\frac{1}{2n+1}} \cdot \exp \left[\left(\frac{\beta K}{2(2n+1)\delta_i} \right) G(S_i) \right] \tag{28}$$

$$t + F = a \ \frac{x^{2n+2}}{2n+2} \tag{29}$$

where E, F are constants of integration and

$$G(S_i) = \int \Biggl[2(3n+2) \ g'(S_i) \ S_i^{\left(\frac{4n+4}{2n+1}\right)}$$

$$+ \Bigl\{ g''(S_i) - (14n+11) \ g'(S_i) \Bigr\} \ S_i^{\left(\frac{2n+2}{2n+1}\right)}$$

$$- g''(S_i) S_i^{\frac{1}{2n+1}} + (8n+5) \ g'(S_i) \Biggr] \ dS_i$$

For given $g(S_i)$, we may evaluate $G(S_i)$ explicitly. A relationship between these two integrals under condition (20) gives the formal mathematical solution of the fingering problem. This analytically defines the distribution of average cross-sectional area occupied by the fingers.

CONCLUDING REMARKS

As an illustration, if we assume $g(S_i) = S_i$ [4], then $g'(S_i) = 1$, $g''(S_i) = 0$ and

$$G(S_i) = \Biggl[2\left(\frac{3n+2}{6n+5}\right) S_i^{\left(\frac{6n+5}{2n+1}\right)} - \left(\frac{14n+11}{4n+3}\right) S_i^{\left(\frac{4n+3}{2n+1}\right)} \tag{30}$$

$$+ \left(\frac{8n+5}{2n+1}\right) S_i \Biggr]$$

A relationship between the two integrals (28) and (29) under condition (20) may be written in this case as

$$\alpha(n) \; S_i^{\frac{1}{2n+1}} \; \exp\left[\left(\frac{\beta K}{2\delta_i} \right) G'(S_i) \right] = \left[\frac{a \; x^{2n+2}}{(2n+2)} - t \right]^{\frac{1}{2n+2}} \quad (31)$$

where

$$\alpha(n) = \left(\frac{a}{2n+2} \right)^{\frac{1}{2n+1}} \exp.\left[- \left(\frac{\beta K}{2\delta_i} \right) \left\{ 2\left(\frac{3n+2}{6n+5}\right) - \left(\frac{14n+11}{4n+3}\right) \right. \right.$$
$$\left. \left. + \left(\frac{8n+5}{2n+1}\right) \right\} \right]$$

Since the saturation S_i is defined as the average cross − sectional area occupied by the fingers (cf. introduction section) therefore we consider $S_i = 0$ as a criteria for investigating the stabilization of fingers. Thus, putting $S_i = 0$ in equation (30), gives

$$x = \left[\frac{2n+2}{a} \; t \right]^{\frac{1}{2n+2}} \quad (32)$$

It is evident from this equation that x grows indefinitely as $t \to \infty$ and therefore no stabilization of fingers seems possible in this case

An approximate analytical solution of a mathematical model of instabilities in displacement problems with magnetic field effect has been obtained here under certain conditions. It is found that the fingers grow indefinitely and do not stabilize in this case. Notwithstanding the limitations of a perturbation procedure and certain assumptions made in idealizing the model and giving definiteness to the mathematical analysis, we have discussed one case of the complicated fingering porous media magnetic field phenomena which may prove useful in subsequent investigations. The analytical result is well suited for small capillary pressure coefficient problems. The numerical or graphical illustrations, although not discussed, due to our present restrictive interest in analytical discussions are immediately obvious.

REFERENCES

1.   A. E. Scheidegger (1961), Canad. J. Phys. 39, 1251.
2.   A. E. Scheidegger and C. C. Chow (1972), J. Hydrology,15,1,1.
3.   A. E. Scheidegger and E. F. Johnson (1961), Canad. J. Phys.,
         39, 2, 326.
4.   A. P. Verma (1969), Canad. J. Phys. 47, 3, 319.
5.   A. P. Verma (1970), J. Appl. Phys. 41, 9, 3638.
6.   A. P. Verma (1972), In fundamentals of transport phenomena
         in porous media (ed. J. Bear), Elsevier,
         Amsterdam, p. 221.
7.   A. P. Verma, and S. K. Mishra (1973), J. Appl. Phys. 44, 4,
         1622.
8.   A. P. Verma,and S. K. Mishra (1974), Phys. Fluids, 17, 6,
         1338.
9.   G. Chavent (1976), In Applications of Methods of functio-
         nal analysis to Problems in Mechanics, Springer
         Verlag, p. 258.
10. G. Chavent (1978). In Distributed Parameter Systems Mode-
         lling and Identification, Springer-Verlag,p. 196
11. T. Oroveanu (1966), Scurgerea Fluidelor Multifazice Prin
         Medii Poroase, Ed. Acad. R. S. R., Romania,
         324-25.

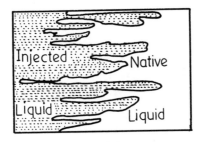

Fig. 1(a)

Displacement front showing
the actual development of
fingers.

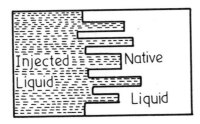

Fig. 1(b)

Schematic representation of
fingers at level x.

A Study of Hydrodynamic Instability in Natural Circulation Boiling Coolant Channels by Means of Graphical Computation

K. SVANHOLM
OECD Halden Reactor Project
Halden, Norway

ABSTRACT

Graphical computation is used for analysis of hydrodynamic instability in natural circulation, boiling coolant channels. In addition to giving results fitting reasonably well to experiments, the method clarifies the basic physics behind the channel behaviour, and gives insigth in the influence of all channel parameters. The relationship between static and dynamic characteristics is also demonstrated.

In the startpoint, gross simplifications are used. However, as the calculation is developed, the diagrams are modified by empirical values, and demonstrate thereby the influence of the simplifications onto the calculated instability point and the oscillation frequency of the channel.

The analysis covers primarily the case of saturated inlet flow and non-oscillating steam production, but leads also to determination of parametric influence in case of subcooled inlet flow with oscillating steam production. The graphical method may contain development potential for closer examination of the latter case.

INTRODUCTION

Two-phase flow has been used for many years in a variety of engineering equipement. The analysis of its behaviour has been limited to the last thirty years, and especially the understanding of instability phenomena has been limited to a relatively small group of specialists.

Because of the large group of engineers which may be confronted with the problemacy, it is not only necessary to develop experts tools for detailed examinations of spesific cases, but also to find a method for displaying the basic mechanism behind the instabilities, such that they can be conceived by engineers with only fundamental knowledge in hydraulics.

In engineering the combination of calculation and displaying in diagrams has a long tradition. One can only consider analysis of thermal power machines where pressure-volume diagrams together with diagrams of temperature, entropy and enthalpy displays the fundamental process, serves for comparison of the theoretical process and measurements, and also show the influence of the simplifications applied.

In this paper, coolant channels are analysed in diagrams displaying the most important physical magnitudes. Gross simplifications, for which the experimental evidence is shown, are inserted. This leads to good agreement to observations in the region where the simplifications are most valid, namely the high quality, high void region, while the agreement is poorer in the other end of the scale.

THE EXPERIMENTS

The experiments to be analyzed first were executed in the Halden Boiling Water Reactor. This reactor is cooled and moderated by heavy water, and the normal flow mode in the coolant channels is natural circulation.

In 1966 experiments with Instrumented Fuel Assembly no. 40, (IFA - 40), were carried out for determination of operational limitations for the coolant channels in this reactor. The experiments are extensively reported in [1], so only a brief description will be given here. In addition, observations from an earlier experiment are also used. They are reported in [2].

Fig. 1 shows in principle the IFA - 40, and its main data. Of special importance for this analysis is the fact that the channel was equipped not only with inlet turbine flow meter, but also with turbine flow meter at the outlet. The channel also contained an inlet throttle valve, which could be controlled remotely over a very wide range of inlet pressure drops, giving data from an accordingly wide range of flow parameters.

The main, and very valuable results from the experiments, are shown in the Fig. 2 and Fig 3. These are the operation characteristics of the channel for two different system temperatures, showing the inlet velocity behaviour as function of channel power, with inlet loss coefficient as parameter. Results from the earlier experiment (IFA - 4), are also included. The figures show t wo boundaries for safe operation of the channel :
- A lower limit for inlet velocity. Reduction of the inlet velocity below this limit will lead to change in the heat transfer from boiling to film cooling, with great danger for destruction of the heater elements.
- A high limit for inlet velocity, where the combination of high power and small inlet loss coefficient leads to periodic oscillations in the inlet velocity.

The most direct influence onto the operation of the Halden Reactor, was the knowledge that with an inlet loss coefficient of 50 (at 230° C), one channel could be operated at 6-700 kW power, safe from both limitations. Other observations of particular interest for the analysis of this channel are shown in the Figs. 4 and 5. Fig. 4 shows that the outlet velocity is, somewhat simplified, proportional to the power, and equal to the velocity the steam would have if being alone in the channel. The Fig. 5 shows that the outlet velocity is largely independant of the inlet velocity.

CALCULATION OF THE IFA-40 CHANNEL

Definitions

The main and very important parameter inlet velocity is governed by the pressure difference, or head, over the inlet section, both statically and dynamically. What is left of the flow potential is consumed by the two-phase section, and variations in this head will again influence the head available for inlet flow.

In Fig. 6 the IFA-40 channel is drawn. Imaginary water column manometers are illustrated. In the diagram to the rigth their readings are marked horizontally on the vertical distance scale.

For total flow potential is in this analysis used the water column from the free surface of the coolant outside the channel, and down to the lower end of the heater elements. It materializes as head over the inlet section if the inlet port is fully closed, and the channel is permitted to boil away all water above the lower end of the heater elements. All manometers will then read zero. Closing the outlet in the same situation will make all manometers read equal to the total head, which is then consumed by the outlet. An other extreme the zero power situation. The channel is then filled with stagnant water, and all manometers will then read equal to the distance from the moderator level and down to the point of measurement. This means that the total head is consumed by the weigth of the water.

Since no such manometers were available in the Halden Reactor experiments, the knowledge of the head function is limited. But the values for one, and the most important point, can be calculated from the data in the Figs. 2 and 3, using the equation :

$$h_{in} = \frac{V_{in}^{2}}{2 g} K_{in} \qquad (1)$$

The results are shown for 230° C and 200° C in Fig. 7.
The most important information the figures demonstrates, is that the head over the two-phase section is proportional to inlet velocity (visualized in Fig. 7 b) Thit relationship is approximately valid in the total area examined, containing a wide range of flow and power values. It can therefore be assumed that this proportionality also is valid locally in the channel.

Data from IFA-4 are also included in the Figs. 8 and 9. There is some uncertainty about its inlet loss coefficient. The calculations are made for two alternative values, 4 and 7.

The diagrams in Fig. 7 are also suitable for extrapolating the characteristics for the channel to the situation where the inlet head is zero. The results are marked in the Fig. 8 , for 200° C , and shows another limitation for the channel, the inlet flow for which the total flow potential is consumed by the two-phase section. This also means that the instability problemacy only exists inside the relatively narrow area shaded in the Fig. 8 , the region above this area is inacessible, and can only be made available for operation by reduction in the head requirement for the two-phase section.

The Static Gain of the Channel.

The principle of this analysis is to examine the head variation in the interface between the one-phase (inlet) section and the two-phase section of the channel, integrated to this boundary, both downstream in the one-phase section from outside the inlet, and upstream from outside the outlet. The first use of this calculation is made in the determination of the static gain of the channel.

In Fig. 9 is shown the head function for a natural circulation channel. If the inlet flow is increased 1 % , the increase in inlet head will be 2% , because of the square relationship (equ. 1). The head over the two-phase section will increase with 1 % , because of the proportionality demonstrated in the Fig. 7. These responses are opposite in direction.

Regarding the increase in inlet head of 2 % as original disturbance, and the increase in the two-phase head as response, the ratio between these can be defined as the static gain of the channel :

$$\text{Static gain} = \frac{\text{Response}}{\text{Original disturbance}} = \frac{1 \text{ \% of } h_2}{2 \text{ \% of } h_{in}} = \frac{h_2}{2 \cdot h_{in}} \qquad (2)$$

This static gain is unit when the inlet head is one third of the total head. When the inlet head is reduced by increase in channel power, its value will increase. Throttling will reduce it.

Since the head function is continous, the response from the two-phase section onto the increase in inlet flow will reduce the inlet head and thereby the inlet flow towards the original value. The channel can therefore be described as a feed-back stabilized amplifier, which reacts onto a disturbance by restoring the original situation.

When this static gain is above unit, it means that the channel overreacts. This overreaction is not exerted immediately, but comes to expression after the increase in flow has been transported into a conciderable part of the two-phase section. The oscillations will then develope as a consequence of overreaction after a time delay. Illustration and calculation of this process will be given below.

Th static gain of the IFA-40 channel is shown in the Fig. 10 , in Fig. 11 the line for static gain equal to unit is drawn in the hydraulic characteristics for the channel (200°C).

The components of the Two-Phase Head.

The head over the two-phase section is consumed by three components :

- 1. Weight of the water in the channel.
- 2. Acceleration of the water.
- 3. Two-phase friction losses.

In the following simplified expressions will be developed for these three components :

- 1. Weight of the water:

The head gradient over a length element of the channel can be expressed :

$$\frac{dh_w}{dL} = \frac{V_{in}}{V_{local}} \tag{3}$$

- 2. Acceleration of the water:

$$\frac{dh_a}{dL} = \frac{V_{in}}{g} \left(\frac{dV}{dL} \right) \tag{4}$$

- 3. Two-phase friction losses :

The equation for frictional losses in tubes for one-phase flow can be written :

$$\frac{dh_f}{dL} = \frac{V^2}{2g} \lambda \frac{1}{D_h} \tag{5}$$

In case of evaporation in the channel, inlet velocity is used for V , and the equation is multiplied by a two-phase operator. In this case is used :

$$n_2 = \left(1 + 2400 \left(\frac{x}{P}\right)^{0.96} \right) , \quad (\text{Becker}) \tag{6}$$

The dominant structure of the product of (5) and (6) is :

$$\frac{dh_f}{dL} = V_{in}^2 \cdot x \cdot \text{constant} \tag{7}$$

Inserting :

$$Q = V_{in} \cdot x \cdot \text{constant} \tag{8}$$

gives :

$$\frac{dh_f}{dL} = V_{in} \cdot Q \cdot \text{constant} = V_{in} \cdot V_p \cdot \text{constant} \qquad (9)$$

This simplification limits the numerical accuracy, but greatly simplifies a logical examination of the channel. The inaccuracies are largest for the smallest values for quality, which is also the region where the frictional losses are of the smallest importance for the channel behaviour.

Closer evaluation of the equations shows that the constant in equ. (9) is

negligible. Therefore all later examination of this channel is made only for the 200°C case, because this part of the experiment contains data for the highest relative power.

It is also here shown that all three components of the two-phase head can be expressed by the velocities. This explains why the hydraulic characteristics of the channel for 200 and 230°C becomes identical when they are scaled over produced steam volume instead of over power.

All three components are proportional to inlet velocity. This explains the observations in the diagrams in Fig. 7 , where this simple relationship is demonstrated.

This influence of inlet velocity is indirect, the direct influence is by density. But it is very convenient for the graphical calculations to let changes in inlet velocity represent the changes in local densities, time point and position taken into account.

Dynamic Head over the Inlet Section

The examination of the dynamic properties of the channel is made by superimposing an oscillation in inlet velocity onto its static value. Numerically the calculations will be made with an amplitude of 1 % of the static value.

The calculations are demonstrated in Fig. 12. Fig. 12 A shows the calculation of the frictional component, and as above, one percent change in inlet velocity gives two percent change in inlet head. The amplitudes are in phase.

The accelleration component is calculated in Fig. 12 B. This component has its maximum amplitude when the change in inlet velocity has its maximum. This means that it is shifted 90 relative to the amplitudes of the inlet velocity and inlet frictional head.

Fig. 12 C shows the adding of the two components, after the same principles as adding the voltage over resistor and inductance when alternating current is applied.

Dynamic Head over the Two-Phase Section

The first example selected for calculations is one where the steam data are so extreme that good agreement to the observations is ensured. It is the point in Fig. 3 at 600 kW , and where the inlet loss coefficient is 150 (on the instability line). These data are extrapolations.

In Fig. 13 A is shown the IFA - 40 channel, together with the axial power profile. In Fig. 13 B axially integrated power and local velocity along the channel are shown. In Fig. 13 C the transport time from the start of the two-phase section is shown.

In Fig. 14 A the three components of the two-phase head are calculated. They are added, and transferred to Fig. 14 B , which show the head function.

The term outlet head is determined as what is left of the total flow potential when all the other terms have been determined. This means that the static characteristic of the channel has been adjusted to the observed by this term only. The value of outlet head for one power level will be examined later.

In Fig. 15 A the head function and transport time function are drawn to unit scale. In Fig. 15 B is drawn a sine wave, representing an oscillation of one percent in inlet velocity.

Projecting values for the amplitude in inlet velocity up to the transport time function and horizontally (to the left) produces a diagram, Fig. 15 C, which reflects the percentual variations in local densities along the channel. The local changes in the head function is obtained by projecting the density variations horizontally onto the head function and up to the diagram Fig. 15 D.

It is now possible to calculate the amplitude in the two-phase head :

A static increase in the inlet velocity of one percent means that the upper half of the diagram Fig. 15 D will be filled. This means that the two-phase head is increased with one percent. The two-phase head is in this case 1.50 meters, the integral value of the function in Fig. 15 D is 0.77 percent, and :

$$\Delta h_2 \quad = \quad 1.50 \cdot 0.77 \% \quad = \quad 0.0115 \text{ m} \quad = \quad 1.15 \text{ cm} \quad\quad (10)$$

One should specificly note that the wave in inlet velocity is positioned to fulfill a dual requirement :

- 1 : In the actual time point, the inlet velocity is minimum, which also gives inlet head minimum.
- 2 : The length of the wave in inlet velocity is chosen to maximize the integral in Fig. 15 D, to give the maximum amplitude in the two-phase head.

The amplitude in the inlet head is simple to calculate : The inlet head is 0.55 meters, and two percent equals 1.1 cm., closely equal to the amplitude in the two-phase head. The dynamic gain is :

$$\text{Gain} = \Delta h_2 / \Delta h_{in} = 1.15 / 1.10 = 1.05 \qquad (11)$$

This means that as a con sequence of an oscillation in inlet velocity of one percent, the response in the two-phase section is equal to the head oscillation necessary to create this oscillation in inlet velocity. The channel is therefore at the stability limit. Increasing the inlet loss coefficient will increase the amplitude necessary to maintain the oscillation to above what the two-phase section can exert, and the channel will therefore be stable.

The agreement for the gain is good, as could be expected , but can only be obtained by fitting the static characteristic. The calculated oscillation frequency is 0.94 Hz. , the observed is ca. 1.2 Hz.

This very good agreements is only obtained by selecting an extreme parameter combination. The problems in determination of dynamic gain and frequency is more easily demonstrated when repeating the calculations for lower power.

Calculation of the 200 kW case is shown in the Figs. 16 - 18 . For velocity, data from Fig. 4 have been used. In Fig. 17 it can be seen that the head function is very similar to the one of the 600 kW case, also in absolute value, while the ratios between the three components are changed. The important change is the more linear transport time function, due to the reduced ratio between outlet and inlet velocities.

Mainly because of this change, the phase-shift coefficient is reduced to 0.57 percent. Other values are :

$$h_2 = 1.73 \text{ m}$$

$$\Delta h_2 = 1.73 \text{ m} \quad 0.57 \% = 0.99 \text{ cm}$$

$$h_{in} = 0.32 \text{ m}$$

$$\Delta h_{in} = 0.32 \text{ m} \quad 2 \% = 0.64 \text{ cm}$$

$$\text{Gain} = 0.99 / 0.64 = 1.55$$

According to this calculation, the inlet head coefficient should be increased from 20 to 31 to ensure stable operation of the channel.

The reasons for the strongly reduced requirement for inlet head coefficient (compared to the 600 kW case) are :

- Inlet velocity is larger, and the amplitude in inlet head rises to the square of the inlet velocity.

- To a smaller extent, the phase-shift coefficient is reduced, because of the
smaller ratio between outlet and inlet velocity.

One should observe that this ratio is dominating in the determination of the
phase-shift coefficient. Uncertainties in the velocity distribution in the channel
can only influence its value to a minor extent. One should also observe that
the use of measured velocities instead of steam velocity has reduced the gain.
It should further be noticed that the form of the head function has got increased
potential to influence the results (compared to the 600 kW case)

Up till here, the influence from inertia in the one-phase section has been
neglected, and its influence will be studied in the following, for the 200 kW
case.

In Fig.18 the wave in inlet velocity is also drawn for the case of inlet impe
dance being inertia only. The highest amplitude in the two-phase head will
coincide with the largest negative accelleration of the water in the one-phase
channel. The diagram demonstrates how the phase-shift coefficient is concidera-
bly increased, from 0.57 to 0.83 . This destabilizing increase is dependant
on the ratio between inlet and outlet velocity. For the 600 kW case, the
increase can only be small.

Calculations show that 15 m   of friction-free tube is necessary for creating
the described situation. The   one-phase section of the IFA-40 channel is only
0.4 meters, and the influence of this section can therefore only be small.
The calculations results in a negligible increase in inlet head, and a phase-
shift of only ca. 7°.

For this low power case, the outcome of the calculations is not numerically
satisfactory. With the inlet head coefficient of 20 , the channel was not found
unstable before 400 kW. The frequency is even worse off, being only the half
(0.49 Hz) of what was found in the experiments. This is the largest penalty
for using a too primitive description for the mass transport mechanism.

Velocity Oscillations in the Two-Phase Section of the Channel .

Up till here, the calculations have been made with a strongly simplified model
of the two-phase flow. With this model one can expect the best agreement in
the high void, high quality region.

To be able to improve the calculations the observations should be examined for
characteristic behaviour which may be incorporated in the calculations.

Recording of oscillations in both inlet and outlet velocities in the IFA-40
experiment was only made for highly developed amplitudes, while the very
beginning of the oscillations is the most important region.

Such a recording exists from the experiments with IFA-4 [2] . It is shown
in Fig. 19 , and it shows that the inlet and outlet velocities are oscillating in
phase, and with equal amplitude. This is as can be expected, when assuming
that the two-phase column is incompressible (under the very small pressure
oscillations present), and demonstrates under this assumption that the steam
production is not oscillating.

The oscillation in the velocity of the two-phase column can be incorporated into
the calculations as follows :

- Friction, which can, because of the direction of the forces, be added to the
  inlet friction. A simplified expression has been derived from the equs (5)
  and (6), and the assumption that the two-phase friction is proportional to
  the square of local velocity, when local density is constant :

$$h_{2,f,d} \quad = \quad 2\,\% \cdot \frac{V_{in}^{2}}{2\,g} \cdot K_c \cdot 2 \qquad\qquad (12)$$

The last factor of 2 should only be regarded as aproximative.

- Inertia. This effect can be accounted for by adding the mass of the two-phase
  column to the mass of the one-phase column

Final Results from the Stability Calculations

In Fig. 20 are shown the values from the calculations of dynamic gain, including the effect from the dynamic friction and inertia in the two-phase section
of the channel. There is still considerable distance between the calculated line
for dynamic gain equal to unit, and observed stability line. However, for
definition of stability line is used the point where the amplitudes sharply increases, while the Fig. 21 shows a considerable content of regular oscillations
already at 315 kW, where the calculated gain is ca. 1.5 .

Comparison Between Calculated and Observed Frequencies .

When the agreement between calculated stability line and observed oscillations
can be described as satisfactory, the disagreement is far larger for the frequencies, see Fig. 22. Some of the distance can be due to erronous velocity
calculations, but this can not account for the whole error.

To examine the channel more closely, the observed frequencies are inserted
into the diagrams, see the Fig. 23 .   . Only the two cases in the vincini-
ty of the instability point, 300 and 400 kW are shown here.

While the discrepancy in period is large, the channel length affected is relatively
small, and so is also the part of the head function. as one can see from the
diagrams, this is because so much of the period is consumed by the low void,
low velocity section of the channel. The influence on the dynamic gain is shown

in Fig. 24 . One may now judge the agreement between calculated and observed instability point as exellent.

However, it is more important to observe the relatively slow increase in the gain. Together with the gradual developement of the oscillations from 250 to 400 kW, there will always be room for subjective judgement. The most interesting result from the fitting of the observed oscillations into the diagrams, is that the start point of the density wave, for all cases from 200 to 500 kW, lies where the calculated void value is from 0.75 to 0.65 . This is possibly the point where the slug formation takes place, and leads the attention to the rôle this phenomenon may have in the formation of density waves. If slug formation is of importance in this context, it is an open question wether further refinement in theoretical treatment of this problemacy will bring one closer to the reality.

Calculation of the IFA-40 Channel with Ideal Outlet Section

In the calculation of the stability of the IFA-40 channel it is demonstrated that it is impossible to execute the calculations without utilizing the observed static data for inlet velocity. It is assumed that relatively large outlet loss is responsible for the discrepancy between the sum of the calculated components of the head function, and the total head.

The outlet loss coefficient of the channel was measured to 3.4 in cold water tests before the in-pile experiments. Calculations where the two-phase velocity and density are used (homogenous flow, orifice type of restriction) give results near this value, confirming the order of magnitude of the assumed out let loss.

Removing this outlet loss, and calculating new values for inlet velocity and gain gives results as shown in Fig. 25 . Inlet velocity increases from the point A to the point B, the gain in the point B is equal to the gain in the point C in the original channel. The figure illustrates the potential for improvement of the operational characteristic of the channel.

THE UNIFORMLY HEATED CHANNEL

The agreement between the observations and calculations for the IFA-40 channel was relatively easy to obtain, mainly because of the following reasons:

- Outlet loss is big, making the phase-shift coefficient big and easy to determine.

- Inlet loss is big and well defined, dominating over the more uncertain dynamic friction in the region of instability.

To study the problemacy of a channel without these characteristics, the experiments reported in [3] is analyzed in the following. It is of especially great
value that measurements of the head function were made by means of a multi-
manometer system, so that the calculated head function can be checked.

In Fig. 26 are shown the calculated head functions and transport time functions
for four power levels, 50 to 200 kW. Slip is set equal to unit. Half-waves,
all starting in the point where the void is calculated to 0.7 , are drawn below,
and phase-shift coefficients are derived.

It can be seen in the Fig. 26 that the changes in the head function with power
are small. In Fig. 27 the calculated head functions for 100 and 150 kW are
compared to observations. The discrepancy between calculations and observation
is small, less than 2 % of the total head.

This means that the determination of the head function and its changes causes
only small uncertainties in the stability calculations. The most important
magnitudes are the form of the transport time function, and the position of the
start point of the density wave. The phase-shift coefficient grows fast when
the length of the half-wave is about the half of the total transport time.

In Fig. 28 is shown the amplitude in the two-phase head as function of power.
Values for dynamic friction, calculated by means of equ. (12) and observed
inlet velocities, together with the amplitude in inlet head, are also shown. When
these damping terms are exeeded by the amplitude in the two-phase head, the
channel will become unstable.

The agreement between calculated and observed instability point is good. However, both dynamic friction and the amlitude in two-phase head deserves
spacious bands of uncertainty. Especially the transport time function may be
improved by application of slip correlations in calculation of local velocities.

The frequency for the 150 kW case is calculated to 1.6 Hz, observed at 160
kW was 0.95. Application of slip values larger than unity will be necessary for
better agreement, and for closer examination of the start point of the density
wave in this channel.

The main objective of this section is to demonstrate how the results of an experiment can be described :

- Head function can be measured by multi-manometer systems.
- Transport time function can be measured directely by injecting traceable
  matters into the two-phase flow.
- Observed frequencies can be used for fitting the density wave into the diagrams.
- Void gauge measurements can also contribute, especially by defining the
  position in the channel where the phase-shift is 90° relative to the upper
  section of the channel.

Computer codes may be programmed to display their calculations in identical diagrams, and a more intimate diagnostisation of possible disagreement between code and experiment is thereby possible.

STATIC CHARACTERISTIC AND INSTABILITY

Because the same parameters decide both the static characteristic and dynamic behaviour of a channel, it is possible to some extent to judge the dynamic limitation from the static characteristic.

In the Figs. 29 and 30 are shown results from experiments with natural circulation channels. In all cases instability occurs   when the inlet velocity approaches the tangent point of a hyperbola. It is easy to realize that the stability must be poor in the tangent point :
- Friction and accelleration, both being product of inlet velocity and power, are dominating.
- Hence, the weigth of the water is small, meaning that the ratio   between outlet and inlet velocity is large. The transport time function is stongly curved, and the density wave starts early.

From existing emphirical background, it may be possible to establish a percentual power level relative to the tangent point which may not be safely exceeded This can serve as a first approximative determination of the stability limit, when the static characteristic is determined.

One should also observe that the inlet velocity function versus power approaching the hyperbola when the weigth of the water in the channel diminishes, confirms that not only accelleration, but also the two-phase friction in the channel can be expressed as product of inlet velocity and power (equ. (9)).

THE INFLUENCE OF SUBCOOLING

As a basis for all previous calculations it has been assumed that the steam production is not oscillating. This will change when the water is subcooled at the inlet.

The most primitive model will assume perfect behaviour of the water, i. e. reduced inlet velocity means less power for heating the water, and more power is available for steam production. It is easy to realize from the diagrams that increased velocity in the two-phase column when the inlet velocity is at minimum value, will further reduce the stability. Increase in the subcooling so that the time for heating the water to saturation becomes a considerable part of the oscillation period, will lead to a phase-shift in the steam production away from the most destabilizing situation, which is inverse coherence with the inlet velocity.

The real boiling process, with boiling starting already when the bulk flow of water is considerably subcooled, may increase the phase-shift and reduce the amplitude in the steam production. The simplest model will therefore most probably exaggerate the destabilizing influence of subcooling.

However, the logics of the simplest model leads to the following rule for comparison of experiments made at different pressures:

 - If the steam volume is reduced by increase in the pressure, the power can be increased untill the produced steam volume is restored, both for the density wave mechanism, and for the oscillation in produced steam volume from a given amplitude in inlet velocity. This means that the subcooled power (and temperature) should be increased proportionally to the total power to make the experiments hydraulically identical. The theoretically calculated start point of bulk boiling will then also be the same.

This simple rule is demonstrated by the observations shown in Fig. 31 . [4] .

REFERENCES

1. G. Kjaerheim and E. Rolstad: "In-Pile Hydraulic Instability Experiments with a 7-Rod Natural Circulation Channel", EURATOM Report, Proc. Symp. on Two-Phase Flow Dynamics, Eindhoven, 1967.

2. O. Vapaavuori: "IFA - 4 Results Show That Instrumented Fuel Assemblies Are Needed to Determine Real Reactor Power Limits", Halden Project Report - 35, 1964.

3. C.L. Spigt: "On the Hydraulic Characteristics of a Boiling Water Channel with Natural Circulation", Report WW016 - R92, Laboratory for Heat Transfer and Reactor Engineering, Technological University of Eindhoven, 1966.

4. R.P. Mathisen: "Out of Pile Instability in the Loop Skalvan", EURATOM Report, Proc. Symp. on Two-Phase Flow Dynamics, Eindhoven, 1967.

NOMENCLATURE

f	Hz	Frequency
g	m/sec^2	Gravitation constant
h	m, cm	Head
H	M	Total head
A		Area
F		Force
K		coefficient

L	m	Length
p	bar	Pressure
P	sec	Period, ($= 1/f$)
Q	kW	Power
V	m/sec	Velocity
x		Quality (weigth fraction of water evaporated)
ψ	%	Phase - shift coefficient
λ		Hydraulic friction factor
φ		Angle
ϱ		Density

List of subscripts

in		Inlet
out		Outlet
c		Channel
d		Dynamic
f		Friction
w		Weight
1		One - phase
2		Two - phase

Prescript

| Δ | | Increment |

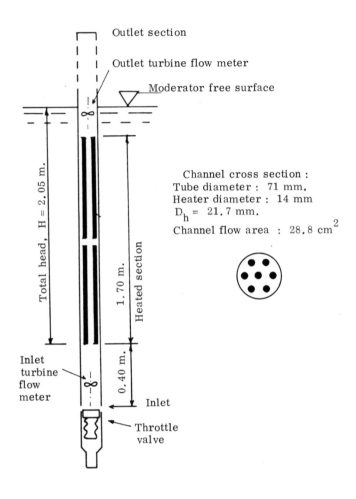

Fig. 1.   Instrumented Fuel Assembly   IFA – 40

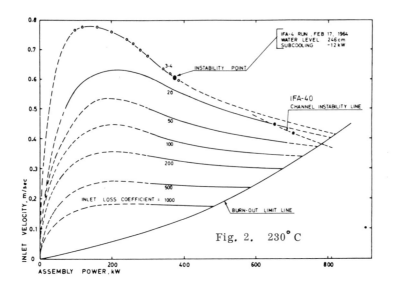

Fig. 2. 230° C

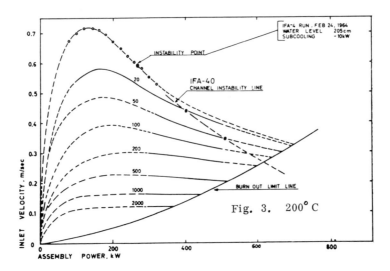

Fig. 3. 200° C

Fig. 2 and 3. Thermo-hydraulic characteristics of the
channels IFA - 40 and IFA - 4.

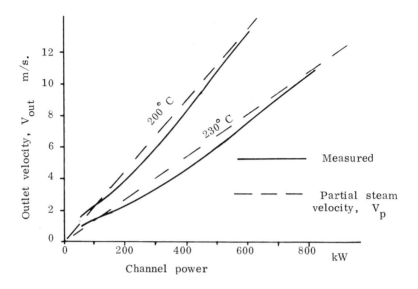

Fig. 4 .   Outlet velocities vs. power in IFA-40

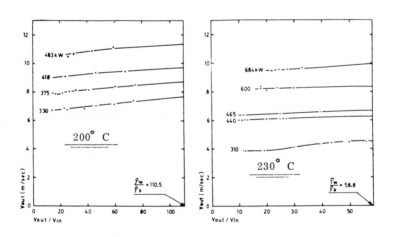

Fig. 5. V_{out} vs. V_{out}/V_{in} during throttling experiments.

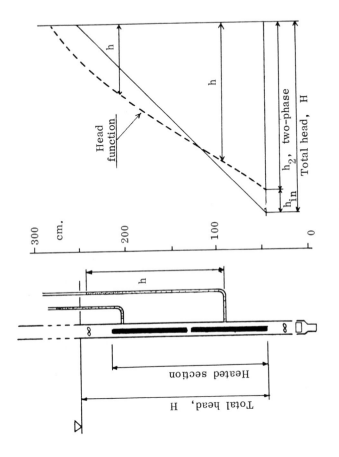

Fig. 6.   Definition of head .

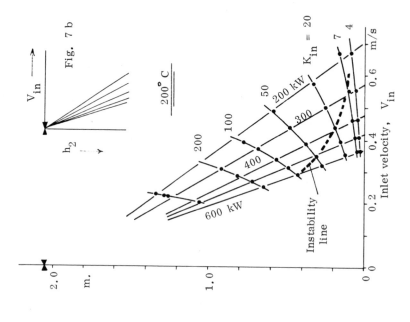

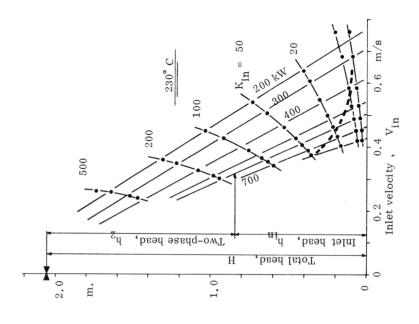

Fig. 7. Head distribution in IFA - 40 and IFA - 4 .

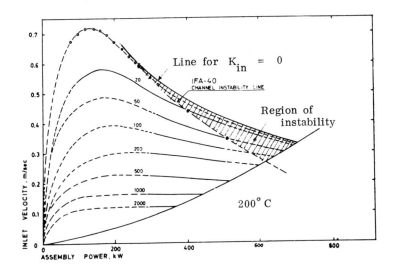

Fig. 8. Region of instability in the hydraulic characteristic of the channels IFA - 40 and IFA - 4 .

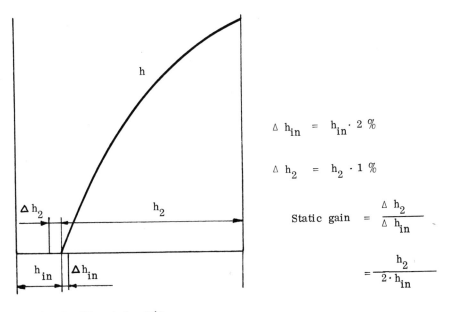

$$\Delta h_{in} = h_{in} \cdot 2\%$$

$$\Delta h_2 = h_2 \cdot 1\%$$

$$\text{Static gain} = \frac{\Delta h_2}{\Delta h_{in}}$$

$$= \frac{h_2}{2 \cdot h_{in}}$$

Fig. 9. The static gain.

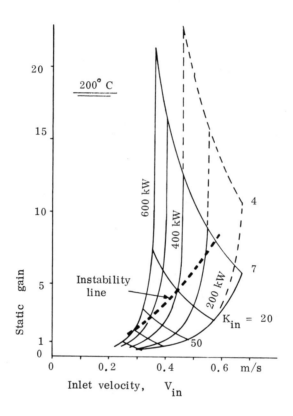

Fig. 10.   Static gain of the
            channels IFA - 40 and IFA - 4

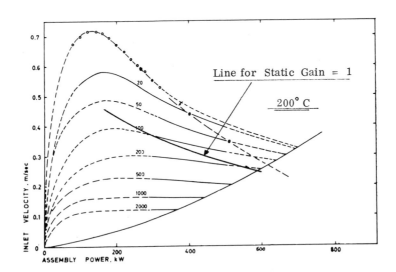

Fig. 11. Line for static gain equal to unit in the channels IFA - 40 and IFA - 4

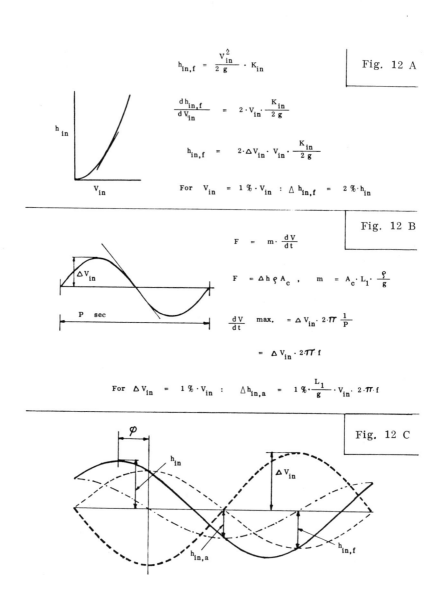

$$h_{in,f} = \frac{V_{in}^2}{2\,g} \cdot K_{in}$$

Fig. 12 A

$$\frac{d\,h_{in,f}}{d\,V_{in}} = 2 \cdot V_{in} \cdot \frac{K_{in}}{2\,g}$$

$$h_{in,f} = 2 \cdot \Delta V_{in} \cdot V_{in} \cdot \frac{K_{in}}{2\,g}$$

For $V_{in} = 1\,\% \cdot V_{in}$: $\Delta h_{in,f} = 2\,\% \cdot h_{in}$

Fig. 12 B

$$F = m \cdot \frac{d\,V}{d\,t}$$

$$F = \Delta h\,\varrho\,A_c \quad , \quad m = A_c \cdot L_1 \cdot \frac{\varrho}{g}$$

$$\frac{d\,V}{d\,t} \text{ max.} = \Delta V_{in} \cdot 2 \cdot \pi\,\frac{1}{P}$$

$$= \Delta V_{in} \cdot 2 \cdot \pi\,f$$

For $\Delta V_{in} = 1\,\% \cdot V_{in}$: $\Delta h_{in,a} = 1\,\% \cdot \frac{L_1}{g} \cdot V_{in} \cdot 2 \cdot \pi\,f$

Fig. 12 C

Fig. 12. Calculation of dynamic inlet head.

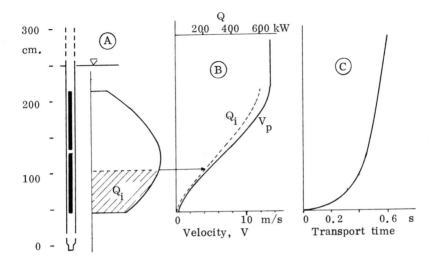

Fig. 13. Calculation of velocity and transport time in IFA – 40
200 C , $Q = 600$ kW, $V_{in} = 0.27$ m/s , $K_{in} = 150$,
$h_{in} = 0.55$ m.

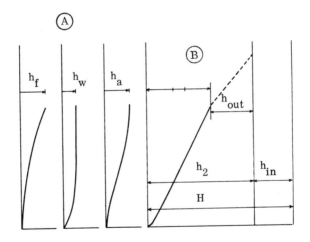

Fig. 14. Calculation of head distribution. IFA – 40
200° C , $Q = 600$ kW.

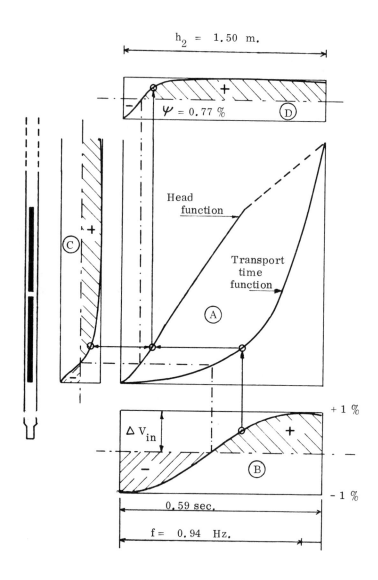

Fig. 15.   Calculation of the amplitude in the two-phase head and frequency. $200°$ C ,   Q = 600 kW.

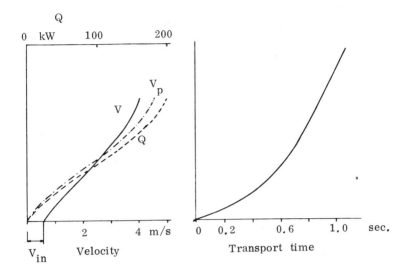

Fig. 16. Calculation of velocity and transport time. IFA -40
200° C, Q = 200 kW , V_{in} = 0.57 m/s , K_{in} = 20
h_{in} = 0.32 m.

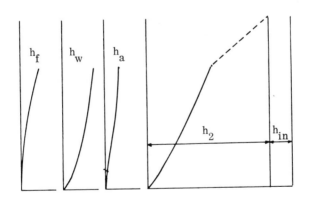

Fig. 17. Calculation of head distribution. IFA - 40
200° C , Q = 200 kW.

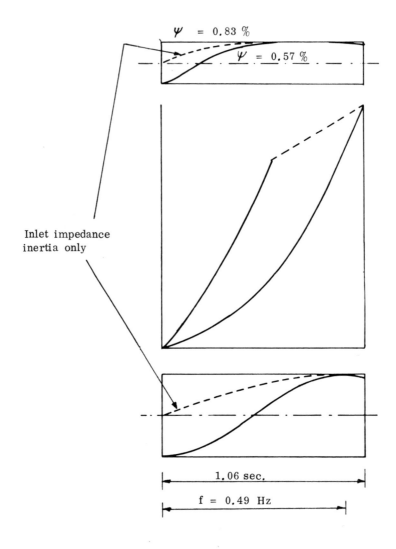

Inlet impedance
inertia only

$\psi = 0.83\ \%$

$\psi = 0.57\ \%$

1.06 sec.

f = 0.49 Hz

Fig. 18.   Calculation of the amplitude in the two-phase head
and frequency.   200° C ,   Q = 200 kW.

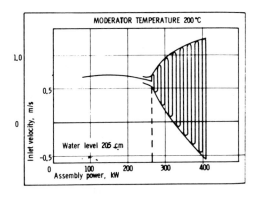

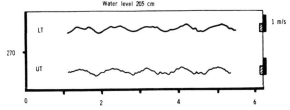

Fig. 19. Recording of coherent oscillations in
the inlet and the outlet velocity
in IFA - 4 .

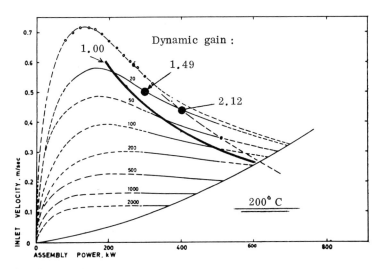

Fig. 20. Calculated dynamic gain for IFA -40

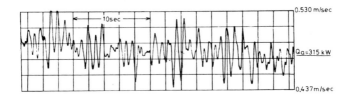

Fig. 21.   Recorded oscillations in inlet velocity.
IFA – 40 , 200° C ,   Q =   315 kW.

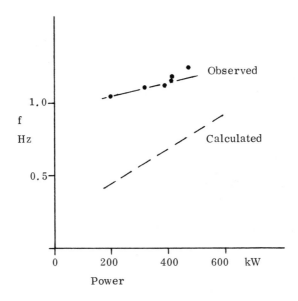

Fig. 22.   Comparison of calculated and observed frequencies.

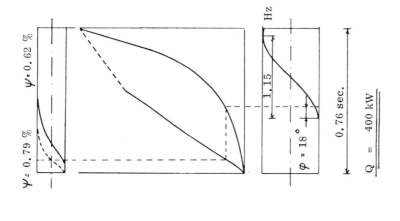

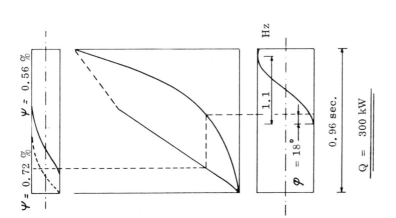

Fig. 23. Calculation of amplitude in two-phase head by inserting observed oscillation frequency.

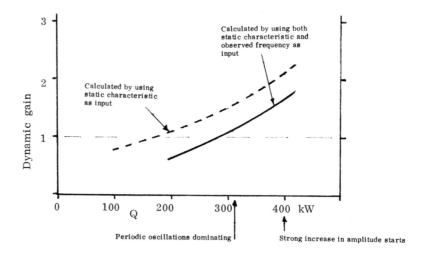

Fig. 24. Dynamic gain for the IFA - 40 channel. $K_{in} = 20$.

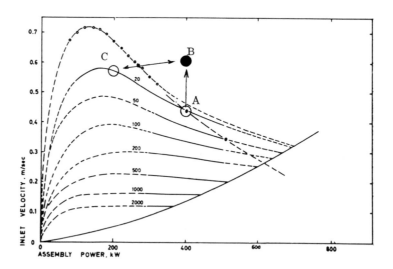

Fig. 25. Potential improvement of the hydraulic characteristic of the IFA - 40 channel.

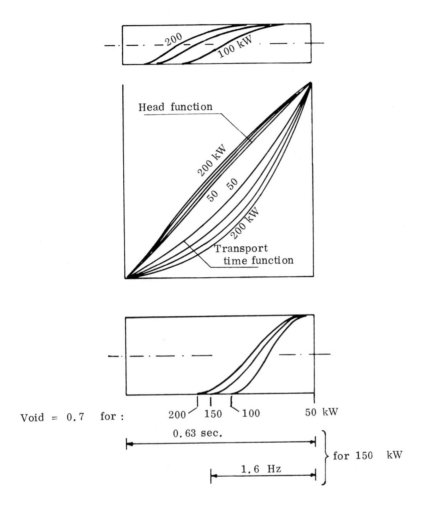

Fig. 26.   Calculation of amplitude in two-phase head and
           frequency for a channel with small inlet and outlet
           losses.

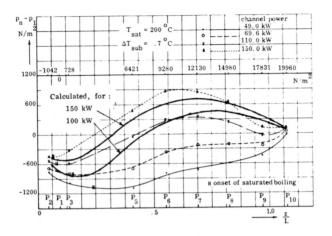

Fig. 27. The apparent longitudinal pressure distribution for various channel powers, Test section I. (Spigt)

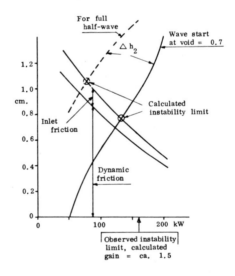

Fig. 28. Stability calculation for the channel.

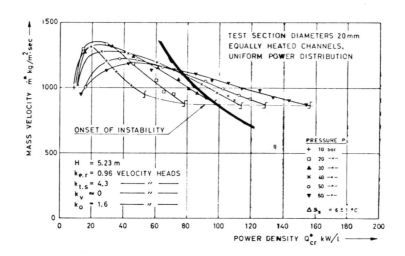

Fig. 29. Effect of pressure on the flow in parallel boiling channels. (R. P. Mathisen)

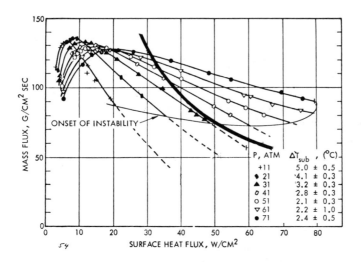

Fig. 30 . Variation of stability limit with pressure for the experiments of Becker.

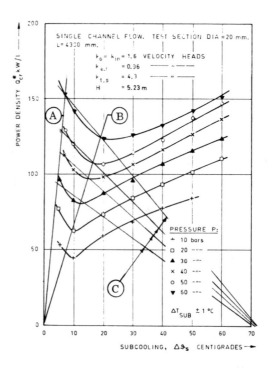

A : Line for minimum subcooling, compareable.

B : Line for Q_{cr} minimum.

C : Lines demonstrating that the relative power reduction from compareable increase in subcooling is constant

Fig. 31. Effect of subcooling and pressure in single channel boiling flow. (R. P. Mathisen) [4]

Calculations of Flow Oscillations during Reflood Using RELAP4/MOD6

Y.S. CHEN, S.R. FISCHER, and L. H. SULLIVAN
EG&G Idaho, Inc.
Idaho Falls, Idaho 83401, USA

ABSTRACT

RELAP4/MOD6 is an analytical computer code which can be used for best-estimate analysis of LWR reactor system blowdown and reflood response to a postulated LOCA. In this study, flow oscillations in the PKL reflood test K5A were investigated using RELAP4/MOD6. Both calculated and measured oscillations exhibited transient characteristics of density-wave and pressure drop-oscillations. The calculated average core mixture level rising rate agrees closely with the test data. Several mechanisms which appear to be responsible for initiation and continuation of calculated or experimental reflood flow oscillations are (a) the coupling between the vapor generation in the core channel and the U-tube geometrical arrangement of a downcomer and a heated core; (b) the inherent low core inlet resistance and high system outlet resistance; (c) the dependence of heat transfer rate on mass flow rate especially in the dispersed flow regime; (d) the amount of the liquid entrainment fraction of the heated core channel.

INTRODUCTION

In the event of a postulated loss-of-coolant accident (LOCA) in a pressurized water reactor (PWR), emergency core coolant (ECC) would be injected into the reactor system to reduce the fuel rod cladding temperature and prevent fuel rod rupture. After the blowdown phase of the LOCA transient, ECC water would begin to refill the downcomer and lower plenum and reflood the reactor core. During the core reflood phase experimental evidence suggests that flow oscillations occur with constant or damped amplitude. These oscillations could improve the core heat transfer and hence lower the predicted peak cladding surface temperature. Because of this potential effect on peak cladding surface temperature, the prediction of flow oscillations by LOCA codes is important. In order to demonstrate the ability of RELAP4 to predict flow oscillations during reflood relevant experimental data were examined. Recent experimental reflood tests, such as those conducted in Semiscale (EG&G Idaho, Inc.)[1] and FLECHT-SET (Westinghouse Electric Corporation[2,3] test facilities, exhibited flow oscillations between the downcomer and the reactor core. During RELAP4/MOD6 code simulations of these reflood experimental tests, similar flow oscillations were calculated to occur.

The purpose of the current investigation was to examine the primary mechanisms responsible for the initiation and continuation of reflood flow oscillations when subcooled ECC is injected into the reactor system during a LOCA. This investigation was accomplished by first assessing

the capability of RELAP4/MOD6 to calculate simple U-tube manometer type
oscillations. Second a flow oscillation study was conducted on the
German three-loop Primary Kreislauf (PKL) Reflood Experimental System[4,5]
which simulates a typical PWR plant.

U-TUBE MANOMETER FLOW OSCILLATION STUDY

An isothermal liquid oscillation in a U-tube (Figure 1) is a simple
and well understood problem. The analytical solution of this problem
can be obtained and the derivation can be found in most texts on fluid
mechanics[6].

The capability of the RELAP4 code to calculate manometer type flow
oscillations was examined by comparing code calculations with analytical
results.

The U-tube manometer was simulated with two RELAP4 models which are
identified as the three-volume and four-volume models as shown in Figure
2. The purpose of using two models was to investigate the effect of
nodalization on the calculated results. In addition, the four-volume
case was designed to simulate the typical RELAP4 nodalization used in
modeling a PWR, which consists of a downcomer (Volume 1), lower plenum
(Volume 4) and vessel core (Volume 2). Results from the RELAP4 calculation were compared with the exact solution for frictionless U-tube
manometers (Tables I and II). For all of the cases studied, the RELAP4
calculations resulted in an oscillation frequency within 1% of that
obtained from the analytical solution.

Results of the RELAP4 calculation for U-tubes with wall friction were
also compared with the analytical results. Again RELAP4 accurately predicted the damping effect of wall friction on the flow oscillation. In
addition, as was expected, the wall friction and form loss were found to
have negligible effect on the frequency of flow oscillations.

RELAP4/MOD6 CALCULATION FOR THE GERMAN PKL TEST K5A

In a recent RELAP4/MOD6 reflood simulation of Semiscale reflood experiments, the calculated frequency of the flow oscillation was within 10%
of the experimentally measured value[7]. However, since Semiscale is a
highly scaled-down simulation system representation of a typical PWR,
to improve confidence in the predictive ability of RELAP4, additional
reflood studies on systems larger than Semiscale were conducted using
RELAP4/MOD6. One of these large systems is the Kraftwerk Union (KWU)
PKL experimental facility (Figure 3) in Erlangen, West Germany.

Facility Description and Test Conditions

The PKL facility is a three-loop simulation of a West German pressurized
water reactor, fabricated in a reduced scale that maintains prototype
volume-to-power ratio. It was designed specifically for system experiments simulating the reflood phase of hypothesized LOCA accidents.

The full length electrically heated 340-rod core is divided into hot, average, and cool zones and has an overall power capacity of 1.45 MW and a peak power of 1.5 kW/m. Test K5A was a 200% cold-leg break experiment with an initial system pressure of 0.42 MPa. The emergency core coolant was injected into the intact loop cold legs, and into the upper annulus. The coolant was subcooled 100 K. The average injection rate for the first 35 seconds was about 15.5 kg/s. Thereafter, the rate was suddenly reduced to between 10.5 and 6.8 kg/s. The initial cladding temperature at the 2-m elevation was 833 K.

RELAP4 Model of the System

To model the PKL facility for Test K5A, RELAP4/MOD6 standard modeling procedures and guidelines[a] for input parametric values were employed. The RELAP4 PKL model consists of 37 control volumes, 30 nodes, and 50 heat conductors as shown in Figure 4. Thirty-six heat conductors were used in the core volume to simulate the experimental electrical heater rods. Fourteen heat conductors were also used to model steam generators, the upper annulus, and downcomer walls. One volume, representing the containment system with its suppression tank and phase separators, was assigned pressure time dependency. One junction was assigned as a fill junction for injection of ECC water.

The system model has three loops, one broken and two intact (one of which is of double size), to represent a four-loop PWR. Three steam generators and three simulated pump volumes are used. The break was modeled in the cold leg, between the simulated pump and the upper annulus vessel. The downcomer and upper annulus were represented by a U-tube concept incorporating a steam bypass pipe between the lower plenum and the upper annulus. The RELAP4/MOD6 models for liquid entrainment, vapor superheating, reflood heat transfer, and the moving heat conduction mesh model for tracking the quench front (moving mesh) were implemented in the three core channels for calculating reflood phenomena.

Calculation of system behavior was initiated with the experimental system filled with saturated steam and with representative rods in each of the three electrically isolated core sections at prescribed surface temperatures. ECC injection was initiated in this environment at time equals zero seconds.

RESULTS OF THE PKL TEST K5A STUDY

The RELAP4 calculations of core-downcomer flow oscillations and core mixture level rising rate for the PKL Test K5A compared well with the experimental data. Figure 5 indicates that both calculated and measured oscillations exhibited transient characteristics of density-wave and

---

[a] RELAP4/MOD6 User's Manual can be obtained from the National Energy Software Center, 9700 So. Cass Avenue, Argonne, Illinois 60439, U.S.A.

pressure-drop oscillations in the core channel. The dynamic features of density-wave oscillations in the PKL system are very similar to those observed in the Semiscale and FLECHT-SET reflood experiments.

The RELAP4 calculation of the onset of pressure-drop oscillations occurs about 50 seconds too early when compared with the test data. The calculated density-wave oscillation period is about 2.9 seconds, which is about 14% less than the experimental value of 3.3 seconds. The calculated maximum pressure-drop oscillation period is 7.1 seconds which is also 14% less than the experimental value of 8.3 seconds. This 14% discrepancy is insignificant when instrumentation error of more than 10% is taken into account. Figure 6 shows that the pressure fluctuations are 180 degrees out of phase with mass flow rate at the hot channel inlet, a key feature of density-wave oscillations[8,9]. Figure 7 shows that the pressure drop across the hot channel decreases whereas the channel flow rate increases, an instability criterion for Ledinegg pressure-drop oscillation[10,11,12]. The differential pressure spikes shown in Figure 7 also illustrate the superposition of the calculated density-wave oscillation on the pressure-drop oscillation. Figure 8 shows the relationship between the measured core mixture level and core inlet pressure fluctuations. However, the key feature of the density-wave oscillations (that is, core inlet flow oscillations and pressure fluctuations are 180 degrees out of phase) can still be discerned from Figure 8 by considering the maximum mixture level rising rate as the maximum mass flow rate. Figure 8 also shows that during the subcooled depressurization, the system pressure dropped from 0.42 MPa to as low as 0.26 MPa. Experiments which were carried out by Meyer[13] on water at low pressure (less than 0.42 MPa) indicated that flow oscillations would persist no matter how large the inlet pressure drop was, when the inlet flow is below a certain flow rate. Dr. A. S. Foust has also found, in experiments in the Chemical Engineering Department at Lehigh University, that low pressure water systems are highly unstable when generating vapor.

The relationship between the measured pressure drop across the upper annulus and the upper plenum and the liquid velocity in the downcomer volume is shown in Figure 9. Since the mass flow rate is directly proportional to liquid velocity, Figure 9 clearly satisfies the instability criterion for pressure-drop oscillations.

The effect of increasing core inlet resistance on flow oscillations is shown in Figure 10. Increasing the inlet resistance twentyfold did not completely dampen out oscillations, but the oscillation amplitude did decrease slightly. A similar damping effect on the flow oscillations could be achieved by decreasing the outlet orifice-resistance in each loop. Figure 11 shows that increasing the dependence of heat transfer rate on mass flow rate in the dispersed flow regime tends to decrease the oscillation amplitude and stabilize the system. Figure 12 shows that increasing the liquid entrainment fraction, thereby lowering the core channel exit void fraction and two-phase frictional pressure drops, tends to decrease the oscillation amplitude, eliminate pressure-drop oscillations, and stabilize the system.

CONCLUSIONS

RELAP4/MOD6 is a computer code developed specifically to calculate the transient thermal-hydraulic behavior of a PWR. In this study, flow oscillations during reflood were investigated using RELAP4/MOD6. In a simple U-tube oscillation study, RELAP4 was used successfully to calculate the oscillation frequency within 1% of that obtained from the analytical solution. In the PKL Reflood Test K5A study, both calculated and measured oscillations exhibited transient characteristics of density-wave and pressure-drop oscillations. The RELAP4 predicted average core mixture level rising rate agrees closely with the test data. Several mechanisms which appear to be responsible for initiation and continuation of reflood flow oscillations were identified as follows:

(1) The coupling between the vapor generation in the core channel and the U-tube geometrical arrangement of a downcomer and a heated core tends to initiate flow oscillations. When subcooled ECC water was injected into the cold legs and the upper annulus, a rapid system depressurization (Figures 6 and 8) occurred especially in the upper annulus and the downcomer. Consequently an excessive ECC water accumulation in the upper annulus and the downcomer established more than enough hydrostatic head to accelerate ECC water into the heated core channel. This liquid flow, in turn, provided sufficient two-phase liquid flow to the heated channel and the rest of the system to generate density-wave oscillations, resulting in flow oscillations.

(2) The PKL reflood test facility is a low pressure (0.42 MPa) system. Vapor generation in such low system tends to induce flow oscillations.

(3) The inherent low core inlet resistance and high system outlet resistance are also responsible for flow oscillations. The PKL Test K5A was conducted with three high resistance orifice-type measuring devices. They were installed downstream of three steam generator outlet pipe lines in order to measure the vapor flow in each loop.

(4) A superposition of the calculated density-wave oscillation on the pressure-drop oscillation was observed over a portion of the reflood transient.

(5) Other factors affecting flow oscillations in the calculation were also observed. These are (a) the dependence of heat transfer rate on mass flow rate especially in the dispersed flow regime, and (b) the amount of liquid entrainment fraction in the heated core channel.

The boiling two-phase flow oscillations are a complex problem because of the coupling effect with thermal-hydrodynamic interactions. Its existence in a experimental system during the reflood phase of a LOCA transient has been observed in the Semiscale, FLECHT-SET and PKL test facilities. During a postulated LOCA in a PWR, the calculation of peak rod cladding surface temperature for fuel rods is of primary interest for all LOCA related computer codes. However, in this study, flow oscillations were found to affect liquid-drop entrainment and heat transfer in the heated core channel and, hence, affected the peak rod cladding surface temperature of fuel rods. Therefore, additional work needs to be done to further understand two-phase flow oscillations and its effect on core heat transfer and fuel rod temperature. The current RELAP4 computer code has demonstrated that it may be a powerful thermal-hydraulic calculation tool for analyzing either LOCA or two-phase flow instability.

REFERENCES

1. James M. Couzzuol, Thermal-Hydraulic Analysis of Semiscale Mod-1 Integral Blowdown-Reflood Tests (Baseline ECC Test Series), TREE-NUREG-1077 (1977).

2. J. A. Blaisdell, L. E. Hochreiter and J. P. Waring, PWR-FLECHT-SET Phase A Report, WCAP-8238 (1973).

3. J. P. Waring and L. E. Hochreiter, PWR FLECHT-SET Phase B1 Evaluation Report, WCAP-8583 (1975).

4. R. Mandl, Reflood Tests with a Consideration of the Primary Loops and Instrumentation of the Test Facility, KWU Progress Report No. 343/75 (October 1975).

5. H. Schweikert, Refilling Tests with Consideration of the Primary Loops, PKL, KWU Report No. RS 36/2 (March 1975).

6. V. L. Streeter and E. B. Wylie, Fluid Mechanics, New York: McGraw-Hill Book Company, USA (1975).

7. C. J. Bliem and S. R. Fischer, "Thermal-Hydraulic Analysis of Semiscale Mod-1 Reflood Test S-03-2 and S-03-6 Using RELAP4/MOD6," Proceedings of Topical Meeting on Thermal Reactor Safety, Sun Valley, Idaho, 1977.

8. A. H. Stenning and T. N. Veziroglu, "Flow Oscillation Modes in Forced-Convection Boiling," Proceedings of the 1965 Heat Transfer and Fluid Mechanics Institute, University of California, Los Angeles, California, 1965.

9. L. G. Neal, S. M. Zivi and R. W. Wright, "The Mechanisms of Hydro-dynamic Instabilities in Boiling Channel," EURATOM Report, Proceedings of Symposium on Two-Phase Flow Dynamics, Eindhoven, 1967.

10. J. A. Boure, A. E. Bergles and L. S. Tong, "Review of Two-Phase Flow Instability," ASME Publication No. 71-HT-42 (1975), pp 1-17.

11. D. H. Weiss, Pressure Drop in Two-Phase Flow, ANL-4916 (October 1952).

12. W. H. Jens and P. A. Lottes, Analysis of Heat Transfer, Burnout, Pressure Drop, and Density Data for High Pressure Water, ANL-4627 (May 1, 1951).

13. D. Meyer, "Instabilities in Boiling Water Flow," M. S. Thesis, Department of Mechanical Engineering, University of Miami, Coral Gables, Florida (October 1966).

ACKNOWLEDGMENT

The knowledge of Dr. A. S. Foust's experimental work reported in this paper was obtained from Dr. A. H. Stenning's unpublished notes, "Density-Wave Oscillation".

TABLE I

U-TUBE FLOW OSCILLATION STUDIES WITH THREE VOLUME MODEL (FRICTIONLESS) SHOWN IN FIGURE 2.

Test conditions $(ML_1/ML_2) \times D$	Oscillation period (s)	
	Analytical solution	RELAP4 calculation
(8/5) × 1	2.82	2.8
(9/8) × 1	3.23	3.2
(30/20) × 1	5.54	5.5

INEL-A-11 752

TABLE II

U-TUBE FLOW OSCILLATION STUDIES WITH FOUR VOLUME MODEL (FRICTIONLESS) SHOWN IN FIGURE 2.

Test conditions $ML_1/(ML_2+ML_4)$	Oscillation period (s)	
	Analytical solution	RELAP4 calculation
30/20	5.54	5.5
20/12	4.43	4.4
38/30	6.45	6.4
38/5	5.13	5.1

INEL-A-11 753

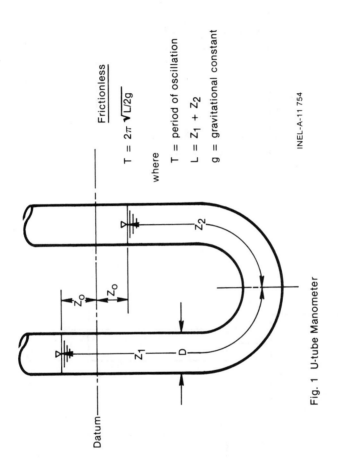

Frictionless

$$T = 2\pi \sqrt{L/2g}$$

where

T = period of oscillation

L = $Z_1 + Z_2$

g = gravitational constant

INEL-A-11 754

Fig. 1 U-tube Manometer

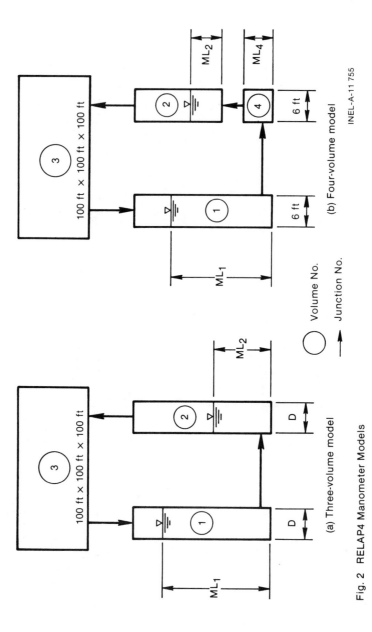

Fig. 2 RELAP4 Manometer Models

INEL-A-11 755

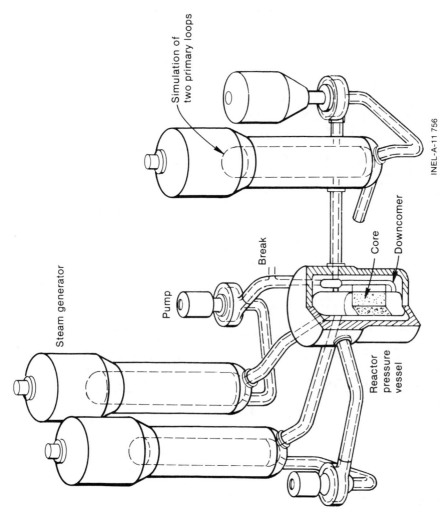

Fig. 3   The West German PKL Reflood Test Facility

INEL-A-11 756

1383

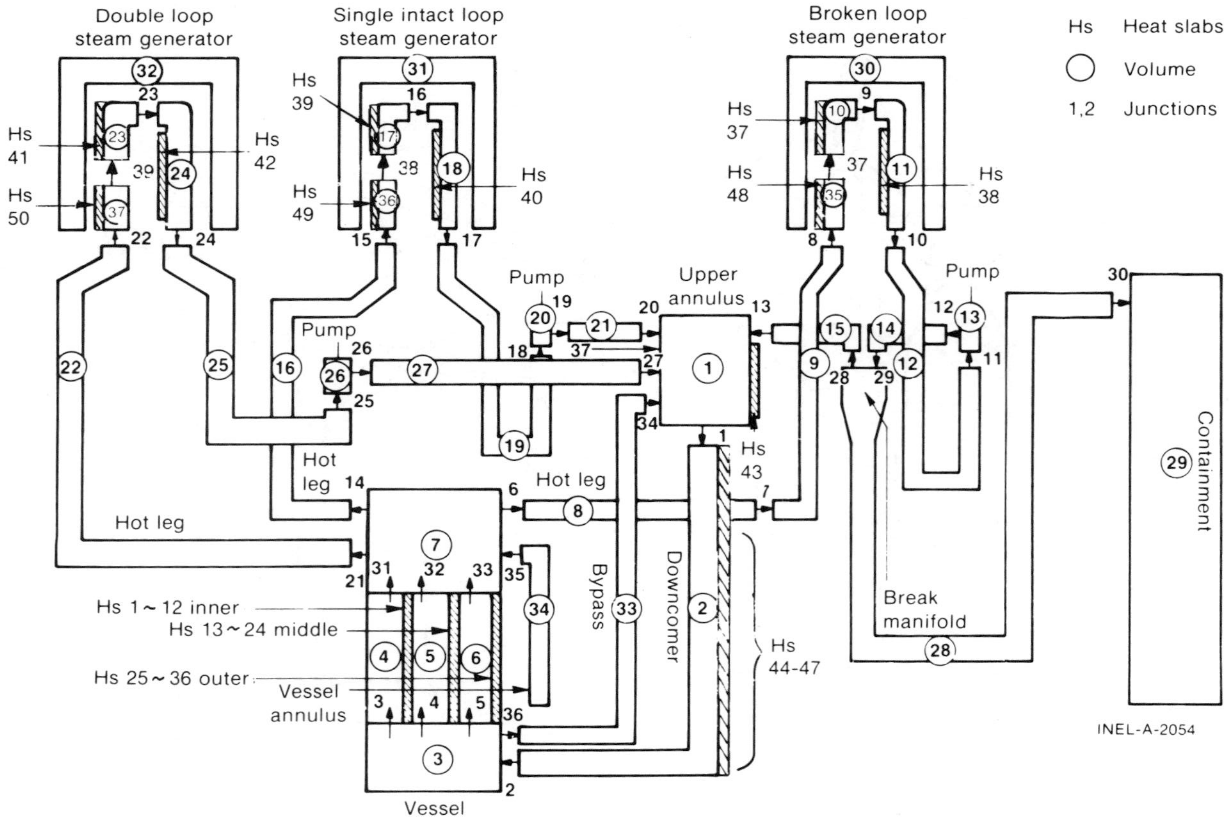

Fig. 4 PKL Three-loop RELAP4/MOD6 Nodalization

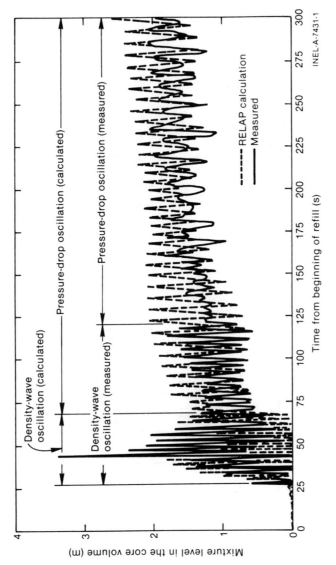

Fig. 5 Comparison of Calculated and Measured Flow Oscillations in the Core Volume for PKL Reflood Test K5A

INEL-A-7431-1

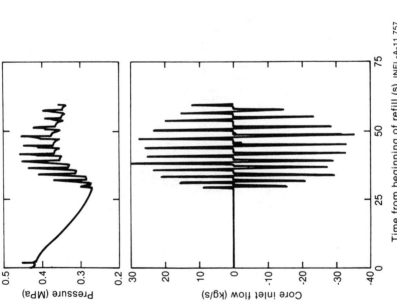

Fig. 6 Comparison of the Calculated Lower Plenum Pressure Fluctuations and Mass Flow Rate at the Core Hot Channel Inlet

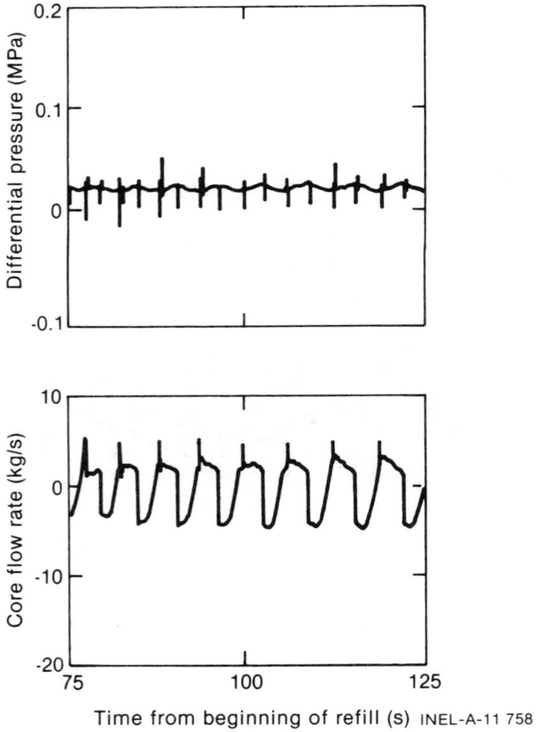

Fig. 7 Relationship Between the Calculated Pressure Drop Across the Core Hot Channel and the Net Core Mass Flow Rate

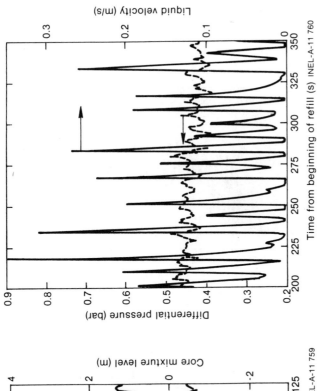

Fig. 9 Comparison of the Measured Pressure Drop Across the Upper Annulus and the Upper Plenum, and the Liquid Velocity in the Downcomer

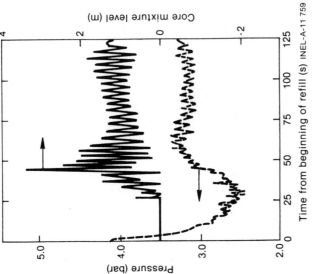

Fig. 8 Comparison of the Measured Core Mixture Level with Measured Core Inlet Pressure Fluctuations

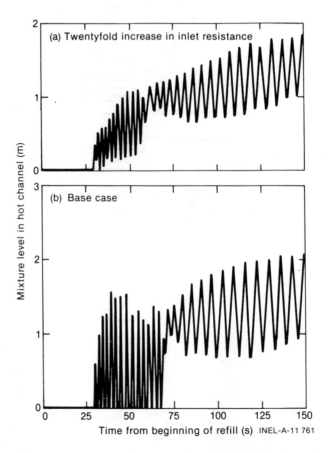

Fig. 10 The Effect of Increasing Core Channel Inlet
Resistance on Calculated Mixture Level Oscillations

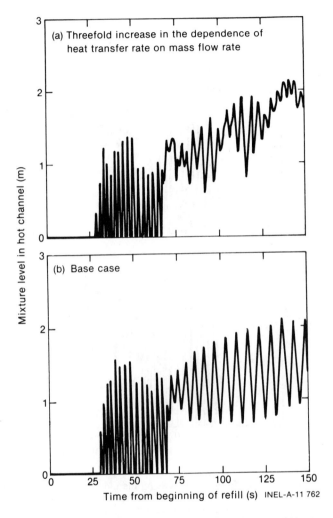

Fig. 11 The Effect of Increasing the Dependence of Heat
Transfer Rate on Mass Flow Rate on Calculated
Mixture Level Oscillations

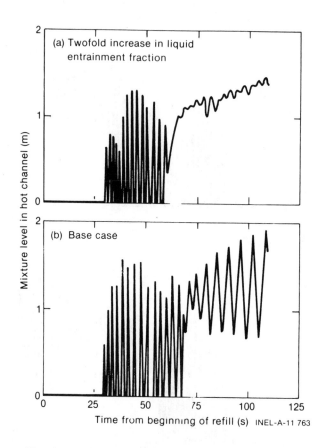

Fig. 12 The Effect of Increasing the Liquid Entrainment
Fraction in the Core Channel on Calculated
Mixture Level Oscillations.

A System Mean Void Fraction Model for Predicting Transient Pressure Drop in Two-Phase Evaporating Flows

B.T. BECK
Kansas State University
Manhattan, Kansas 66506, USA

G.L. WEDEKIND
Oakland University
Rochester, Michigan 48063, USA

ABSTRACT

A variety of models have been proposed for the analysis of transient two-phase flows. This paper represents an additional application of the system mean void fraction model. A solution to an integral formulation of the momentum principle is presented for the class of transient evaporating flow problems involving complete vaporization, and where the system mean void fraction can be considered to be time-invariant. The result is an explicit analytical prediction of the transient pressure drop, expressed in terms of the transient response of the effective point of complete vaporization and the outlet mass flux of superheated vapor. The capability of the proposed model is demonstrated by comparison with experimental measurements of the transient pressure drop in a horizontal tube evaporator, following a step decrease in the inlet mass flowrate. Good agreement is shown between the predicted and experimental results.

INTRODUCTION

The system mean void fraction model [1] is an integral model which converts the two-phase evaporating flow system into a type of lumped parameter system. The principle virtue of this model is simplicity. Its capability to predict the transient response of various important boundary phenomena has previously been demonstrated for the class of transient evaporating flow problems involving complete vaporization, and where the system mean void fraction could be considered to be time-invariant [1]. Furthermore, existing applications of the model have included not only transient evaporating flows, but transient condensing flows as well [1, 2, 3].

The assumed time-invariance of the system mean void fraction is key to the simplicity of the model, and has the effect of uncoupling the conservation of mass and energy principles from the transient form of the momentum principle. This represents an analytical simplification of considerable magnitude. Prior to this current investigation, however, no attempt had been made to establish the significance of this particular uncoupling on the transient momentum principle itself.

The favorable consequences of a similar type of uncoupling had, however, been recognized earlier [4, 5]. Inayatullah and Nicoll [4, 5] have noted the apparent weak coupling between the conservation of mass and energy principles and the transient form of the momentum principle, under the assumption of a spatially-invariant system pressure. They interpreted this to mean that the phenomena involved are largely thermally governed. They then suggested a procedure [4] whereby the solutions based on the above simplification could be fed back into the momentum principle to yield a prediction of the corresponding transient system pressure drop. Recent numerical predictions using this procedure are given by Hemphill, et al [6], and indicates good agreement with the experimental blowdown data of Premoli [7], for subcooled inlet conditions.

Some additional, but more sophisticated, methods for calculation of transient system pressure drop are discussed by Weisman and Choe [8]. These approaches employ numerical procedures of additional complexity to solve various forms of the more general coupled partial differential equations. Furthermore, although some experimental pressure drop measurements in response to oscillatory inlet mass flowrate and inlet flow shut down have been made [9, 10], there appear to be no closed-form analytical solutions for the transient pressure drop in the published literature. In general, the transient pressure drop appears to have received relatively little attention in comparison to void fraction response and other related phenomena.

The purpose of this paper is to further exploit the particular uncoupling which has been observed in connection with the system mean void fraction model. The result will be an explicit analytical prediction of the transient pressure drop for the class of transient evaporating flow problems involving complete vaporization.

THEORETICAL MODEL FOR TRANSIENT PRESSURE DROP

The approach taken here will be similar, in principle, to that proposed by Inayatullah and Nicoll [4] and utilized by Hemphill, et al [6], in conjunction with the drift-flux model; that is, the solutions to the conservation of mass and energy equations, uncoupled from the transient momentum equation, and essentially unaffected by the spatial pressure variation, will be fed into the momentum principle yielding the desired prediction of transient pressure drop. The present method differs from the above approaches [4,6], in that the solutions to the system mean void fraction model will be utilized, rather than those of the drift-flux model. Furthermore, an integral formulation of the momentum principle will be employed, and the numerical iteration procedure discussed by Hemphill, et al [6] will not be necessary for convergence of solutions.

Concept of a System Mean Void Fraction Model

A detailed development of the system mean void fraction model, as applied to transients within an evaporating flow system undergoing complete vaporization, has been presented in Reference [1]. The purpose here is merely to summarize the important concepts as a prerequisite to the development of a model for transient pressure drop.

Previous applications of the system mean void fraction model to transient evaporating flows [1] have been based primarily on the following simplifications:

1. Negligible effects of entrainment.
2. Random fluctuations due to the inherent stochastic nature of the two-phase flow process exhibit negligible influence on deterministic transients.
3. Contributions due to kinetic and gravitational potential energies, viscous dissipation, and longitudinal heat conduction are negligible.
4. Properties of the liquid and vapor are saturation properties, evaluated at the system mean pressure.
5. Spatial and temporal variations in system pressure exhibit negligible influence on the conservation of mass and energy principles.
6. System mean void fraction is invariant with time.

The specific transient phenomena investigated include the responses of the non-fluctuating[2] effective point of complete vaporization, $\tilde{n}(t)$, and the corresponding instantaneous outlet mass flowrate of superheated vapor, $m_t(z,t)_{z=L}$. These phenomena are within the class of transient phenomena for which the assumption of a time-invariant system mean void fraction appears to be valid. A schematic of a horizontal-tube evaporator depicting the above physical quantities are shown in Fig 1

The non-fluctuating system mean void fraction, $\bar{\alpha}$, represents the instantaneous spatial average of the non-fluctuating area mean void fraction, $\tilde{\alpha}(z,t)$, over the length of the two-phase region, and may be expressed as

$$\bar{\alpha} \equiv \frac{1}{\tilde{n}(t)} \int_{z=0}^{\tilde{n}(t)} \tilde{\alpha}(z,t)dz \qquad (1)$$

Mathematically, a sufficient condition for the assumed time-invariance of the system mean void fraction is that the area mean void fraction, $\tilde{\alpha}(z,t)$, be expressible as a function of a single dimensionless variable, ξ; that is

$$\tilde{\alpha}(z,t) = \tilde{\alpha}(\xi) , \quad \text{where} \quad \xi \equiv z/\tilde{n}(t) \qquad (2)$$

When the conservation of mass and energy principles are formulated in terms of this system mean void fraction, they are in effect uncoupled from the

---

[2] It is important to note that the term "fluctuation" is in reference to random behavior only, and does not preclude the existence of a deterministic oscillatory behavior such as might arise in response to a sinusoidal-type input. The random fluctuations have been investigated elsewhere [11, 12, 13].

transient form of the momentum principle. All that is required of the momentum principle is sufficient information to evaluate the system mean void fraction. A discussion as to how this can be accomplished through the use of available steady-state relationships is presented in Reference [1].

It is important to emphasize the physical implications of the above uncoupling. It implies that for the specific transient phenomena which have previously been investigated, the transient form of the momentum principle is not important. This suggests that the phenomena under consideration are largely thermally governed, a conclusion consistent with that reached by Inayatullah and Nicoll [4, 5] in reference to the drift-flux model. Furthermore, this simplification has other implications insofar as the transient form of the momentum principles itself is concerned, as will be demonstrated in the ensuing analysis.

Application of Transient Momentum Principle

In addition to the list of assumptions presented above, the following simplifications will be made specifically in reference to an integral formulation of the transient momentum principle:

1. Pressure drop contributions due to gravity and inertia are negligible.
2. Transverse distribution of velocity and pressure within each phase cross-section is uniform.

Application of the momentum principle in integral form to the liquid and vapor within the entire two-phase region, out to the effective point of complete vaporization, as shown in Fig. 1, yields[3]

$$\left\{ \tilde{p}(z,t)_{z=0} - \tilde{p}(z,t)_{z=\tilde{n}(t)} \right\} A_t - \int_{z=0}^{\tilde{n}(t)} \tilde{\tau}_w P dz = \left\{ \left[1 - \left(\frac{\rho' A_t}{\tilde{m}_t} \right) \frac{d\tilde{n}}{dt} \right] \frac{\tilde{m}^2_t}{\rho' A_t} \right\}_{z=\tilde{n}(t)}$$

$$- \left\{ \left[\frac{(1-\tilde{x})^2}{(1-\tilde{\alpha})} + \left(\frac{\rho}{\rho'} \right) \left(\frac{\tilde{x}^2}{\tilde{\alpha}} \right) \right] \frac{\tilde{m}^2_t}{\rho A_t} \right\}_{z=0} \tag{3}$$

Physically, the two terms on the left-hand-side of the equation represent the net pressure force and the total viscous shear force acting on the fluid within the two-phase region, in the axial direction, respectively. The two terms on the right-hand-side combined represent the net instantaneous rate at which momentum is being transported out of the two-phase region, in the axial direction.

---

[3] A more general treatment of the integral formulation in which certain of the underlying assumptions are relaxed is given in Reference [14].

A similar application of the momentum principle, in integral form, to the superheat region, yields

$$\left\{ \tilde{p}(z,t)_{z=\tilde{n}(t)} - \tilde{p}(z,t)_{z=L} \right\} A_t - \int_{z=\tilde{n}(t)}^{L} \tilde{\tau}_w P dz = \left\{ \frac{\tilde{m}^2_t}{\rho' A_t} \right\}_{z=L}$$

$$- \left\{ \left[1 - (\frac{\rho' A_t}{\tilde{m}_t}) \frac{d\tilde{n}}{dt} \right] \frac{\tilde{m}^2_t}{\rho' A_t} \right\}_{z=\tilde{n}(t)} \tag{4}$$

The two terms on the left-hand-side of equation (4) represent the instantaneous net pressure force and the total shear force at the wall, analogous to the corresponding terms for the two-phase region given in equation (3). The last two terms, taken together, represent the net instantaneous rate at which momentum leaves the superheated vapor region.

Combining equations (3) and (4) in such a way as to eliminate the pressure contributions at the position of the moving boundary, $\tilde{n}(t)$, yields the resultant momentum principle for the entire evaporating flow system; thus

$$\left\{ \tilde{p}(z,t)_{z=0} - \tilde{p}(z,t)_{z=L} \right\} A_t - \int_{z=0}^{L} \tilde{\tau}_w P dz = \left\{ \frac{\tilde{G}^2 A_t}{\rho'} \right\}_{z=L}$$

$$- \left\{ \left[\frac{(1-\tilde{x})^2}{(1-\tilde{\alpha})} + (\frac{\rho}{\rho'})(\frac{\tilde{x}^2}{\tilde{\alpha}}) \right] \frac{\tilde{G}^2 A_t}{\rho} \right\}_{z=0} \tag{5}$$

where $\tilde{G}(z,t)$ is the local mass velocity (or cross-sectional average mass flux) defined by

$$\tilde{G}(z,t) \equiv \tilde{m}_t(z,t)/A_t \tag{6}$$

Now, solving equation (5) for the system pressure drop, $\Delta \tilde{p}(t)$, and introducing the definitions of the characteristic component pressure drops for friction and momentum yields

$$\Delta \tilde{p}(t) = \tilde{p}(0,t) - \tilde{p}(L,t) = \Delta \tilde{p}_F(t) + \Delta \tilde{p}_M(t) \tag{7}$$

where $\Delta \tilde{p}_F(t)$ and $\Delta \tilde{p}_M(t)$ represent the contributions to the total pressure drop due to friction and momentum transport, respectively, for the entire evaporating flow system, and are defined as follows:

$$\Delta \tilde{p}_F(t) \equiv \int_{z=0}^{L} \left(\frac{\tilde{\tau}_w P}{A_t}\right) dz \tag{8}$$

$$\Delta \tilde{p}_M(t) \equiv \frac{G^2(L,t)}{\rho'} - \left[\frac{(1-\tilde{x}_i)^2}{(1-\tilde{\alpha}_i)} + \left(\frac{\rho}{\rho'}\right)\left(\frac{\tilde{x}_i^2}{\tilde{\alpha}_i}\right)\right] \frac{\tilde{G}^2(0,t)}{\rho} \tag{9}$$

where $\tilde{\alpha}_i$ and $\tilde{x}_i$ are the inlet void fraction and flow quality, respectively. Note that equation (9) expresses the momentum pressure drop directly in terms of the instantaneous outlet mass flux, $\tilde{G}(L,t)$, which, using the system mean void fraction model [1], may be determined solely through consideration of the transient conservation of mass and energy principles, for a specified inlet flow transient. The friction pressure drop contribution given by equation (8), however, requires further specification of the local wall shear stress, $\tilde{\tau}_w$, in terms of known physical quantities.

Friction Pressure Drop in Two-Phase and Superheat Regions

The total friction pressure drop given in equation (8) can be further resolved into the separate two-phase and single-phase superheated vapor contributions as follows:

$$\Delta \tilde{p}_F(t) = \Delta \tilde{p}_{TF}(t) + \Delta \tilde{p}_{SF}(t) \tag{10}$$

where

$$\Delta \tilde{p}_{TF}(t) \equiv \int_{z=0}^{\tilde{n}(t)} \tilde{\tau}_w P dz \tag{11}$$

and

$$\Delta \tilde{p}_{SF}(t) \equiv \int_{z=\tilde{n}(t)}^{L} \tilde{\tau}_w P dz \tag{12}$$

represent the two-phase and single-phase friction pressure drops, respectively.

Adopting the usual methods employed in the analysis of two-phase friction pressure drop [8, 15, 16], in the two-phase region the local wall shear stress, $\tilde{\tau}_w$, may be expressed in terms of an "equivalent" single-phase shear stress, $\tilde{\tau}_f$, based on the total mass flowrate as liquid, in the following manner:

$$\tilde{\tau}_w = \phi \tilde{\tau}_F \tag{13}$$

where ϕ is a suitably defined two-phase friction multiplier. Furthermore, as is quite common in the literature [8, 17], this multiplier, while established in steady-state,[4] is assumed to be equally valid during a transient, provided that the appropriate local time-dependent physical quantities are utilized. In general, the two-phase friction multiplier is a function of flow quality and mass flux and may be represented by the following functional form:[5]

$$\phi = \phi(\tilde{x}, \tilde{G}) \tag{14}$$

The equivalent shear stress, $\tilde{\tau}_f$, may be expressed in terms of local instaneous mass flux as follows:

$$\tilde{\tau}_f = \frac{f\tilde{G}^2(z,t)}{2\rho} \tag{15}$$

where f is the appropriate Fanning friction factor for single-phase liquid flow. For fully developed turbulent flow in smooth tubes or channels, the single-phase friction factor depends on local mass flux and may be represented by the functional form

$$f = f(\frac{\tilde{G}d}{\mu}) \tag{16}$$

where $\tilde{G}d/\mu$ is an equivalent Reynold's number for single-phase liquid flow. Thus, introducing equation (15) into (13) and the result into equation (11) yields

$$\Delta\tilde{p}_{TF}(t) = \int_{z=0}^{\tilde{n}(t)} \frac{\phi f\tilde{G}^2(z,t)P}{2\rho A_t} dz \tag{17}$$

Note that equations (13) through (17) imply that the time dependence of the two-phase friction pressure drop, $\Delta\tilde{p}_{TF}(t)$, is directly connected to the spatial variation of the local flow quality, $\tilde{x}(z,t)$, and that of the local mass flux, $\tilde{G}(z,t)$. It turns out that these two physical quantities are related as a direct consequence of the assumed time-invariance of the system mean void fraction. Furthermore, the existence of the similarity relationship expressed by equation (2) implies that during a transient the local flow

---

[4] A number of steady-state two-phase friction multiplier relationships have been proposed [15, 16, 22, 23], primarily for steam-water applications.

[5] Actually, some dependence of ϕ on the applied heat flux has also been observed [8, 15], however, this influence is presumed to be quite small, since the majority of existing relationships are of the form given by equation (14).

quality and void fraction may be related directly to the instantaneous effective point of complete vaporization; thus

$$\tilde{\alpha}(z,t) = \tilde{\alpha}(\tilde{x}(z,t)) \tag{18}$$

where

$$\tilde{x}(z,t) = \tilde{x}_i + (1-\tilde{x}_i)z/\tilde{n}(t) \tag{19}$$

Now, it can be shown [14] that the local instantaneous mass flux within the two-phase region may be expressed as

$$\tilde{G}(z,t) = \frac{[1-(\frac{\rho'}{\rho})]\frac{\bar{f}_q Pz}{(h'-h)A_t} + \{1-[1-(\frac{\rho'}{\rho})](1-\tilde{x}_i)\}\ \tilde{G}(0,t)}{\{1-[1-(\frac{\rho'}{\rho})][1-\tilde{x}(z,t)]\}} \tag{20}$$

Introducing equation (19) into (20) then yields after considerable rearrangement

$$\tilde{G}(z,t) = \tilde{G}(L,t) + \frac{[(\frac{\rho'}{\rho})(1-\tilde{x}_i)+\tilde{x}_i](1-\tilde{x})}{[(\frac{\rho'}{\rho})(1-\tilde{x})+\tilde{x}](1-\tilde{x}_i)}\{\tilde{G}(0,t) - \tilde{G}(L,t)\} \tag{21}$$

where, $\tilde{G}(L,t)$, the instantaneous outlet mass flux, is given from reference [1] in conjunction with the definition given in equation (6); thus

$$\tilde{G}(L,t) = [1-(\rho'/\rho)]\frac{\bar{f}_q P\tilde{n}(t)}{(h'-h)A_t} + \{1-[1-(\rho'/\rho)](1-\tilde{x}_i)\}\ \tilde{G}(0,t) \tag{22}$$

Equation (21) now represents the instantaneous spatial dependence of the local mass flux solely in terms of the local flow quality, $\tilde{x}$. Therefore, it is convenient to likewise express the spatial integration in equation (17) also in terms of flow quality. Thus, introducing a change of variables into equation (17) by means of the similarity relationship given in equation (19) yields

$$\Delta\tilde{p}_{TF}(t) = \frac{P\ \tilde{n}(t)}{2\rho A_t(1-\tilde{x}_i)} \int\limits_{\tilde{x}=\tilde{x}_i}^{1} \phi f\tilde{G}^2 d\tilde{x} \tag{23}$$

Note that equation (23) now relates the instantaneous two-phase friction pressure drop directly in terms of the response of the effective point of complete vaporization, $\tilde{n}(t)$, through equations (14), (16), (21), and (22).

Lastly, the single-phase friction pressure drop in the superheated vapor region may be expressed in the following form:

$$\Delta\tilde{p}_{SF}(t) = \frac{P[L-\tilde{n}(t)]f'\tilde{G}^2(L,t)}{2\rho'A_t} \tag{24}$$

where f' is the appropriate single-phase friction factor for vapor flow. For simplicity, the properties of superheated vapor are approximated by those of saturated vapor at the system mean pressure.[6]

Predicted Transient Pressure Drop Response

The separate friction and momentum pressure drop contributions, given by equations (9), (23) and (24) can now be determined at each instant of time once the instantaneous effective point of complete vaporization has been evaluated. For the case of an exponential inlet mass flowrate change and a constant spatially-averaged heat flux, f_q, the response of the effective point of complete vaporization may be expressed as follows [1]:

$$\left\{\frac{\tilde{n}(t)-\tilde{n}_f}{\tilde{n}_i-\tilde{n}_f}\right\} = e^{-t/\tau} + \frac{(\tau_m/\tau)}{[1-(\tau_m/\tau)]} [e^{-t/\tau}-e^{-t/\tau_m}] \tag{25}$$

where $\tilde{n}_i$ and $\tilde{n}_f$ are the initial and final steady-state positions of the effective point of complete vaporization, τ_m is the time constant associated with the inlet flow change, and τ is the evaporating flow system time constant given by

$$\tau = \frac{\rho(h'-h)(1-\bar{\alpha})A_t}{\bar{f_q}P} \tag{26}$$

Simplified Model for Two-Phase Friction Pressure Drop

Because of the highly empirical nature of the two-phase friction multiplier, ϕ, evaluation of the two-phase friction pressure drop contribution in general requires numerical evaluation of the integral given in equation (23), at each instant of time during a transient. Considerable simplification in the expression for transient friction pressure drop can be achieved by noting that for a considerable range of the inlet flow quality, $\tilde{x}_i$, the dependence of local mass flux, $G(z,t)$, on flow quality, as given from equation (21), appears to be quite small insofar as evaluation of the integral in equation (23) is concerned. In fact, a very good approximation results from neglecting the dependence of local mass flux on flow quality altogether er. Thus, the two-phase friction pressure drop, $\Delta p_{TF}(t)$, represented by equation (23) may be approximated by

$$\Delta\tilde{p}_{TF}(t)= \frac{P}{2\rho A_t} \frac{\tilde{n}(t)}{(1-\tilde{x}_i)} \int_{\tilde{x}=\tilde{x}_i}^{1} \phi f\tilde{G}^2 d\tilde{x} \approx \frac{\bar{\phi} f\tilde{G}^2(L,t)\tilde{n}(t)}{2\rho A_t} \tag{27}$$

---

[6] If the single-phase friction pressure drop contribution is larger than on the order of 10%, a better approximation would be to represent the vapor properties in terms of some sort of average during the transient [14].

where [7]

$$\bar{\phi} \equiv \frac{1}{(1-\tilde{x}_i)} \int_{\tilde{x}=\tilde{x}_i}^{1} \phi(\tilde{x}) d\tilde{x} \qquad (28)$$

and where the equivalent friction factor, f, based on total mass flowrate as liquid, is likewise expressed entirely in terms of the instantaneous outlet mass flux, G(L,t), during a transient. Note that $\bar{\phi}$, the average two-phase friction multiplier, is thus virtually a constant during a transient and is readily evaluated using any one of a number of existing steady-state relations [15, 16, 21, 22, 23]. The resulting expression for transient pressure drop is thus simplified to a completely closed-form expression, expressed solely in terms of the important physical and system parameters involved. Furthermore, it is nearly identical in form with the corresponding steady-state expression for two-phase pressure drop, but is expressed in terms of the appropriate time-dependent physical quantities.

EXPERIMENTAL OBSERVATIONS

As has been mentioned earlier, transient pressure drop measurements appear to have received very little attention in the published literature, at least in comparison with transient void fraction measurements. In particular, there appears to have been no measurements of system pressure drop response to inlet flowrate transients of an exponential nature, involving saturated inlet conditions with either complete or incomplete vaporization. Since such measurements provide for the most direct evaluation of the proposed pressure drop model, such measurements have been undertaken in this study. The transients to be presented here involve a step change in the inlet mass flowrate, under conditions of a uniform heat flux, for horizontal flow in a circular tube.

Experimental Apparatus

A considerable amount of special purpose equipment and instrumentation was required in obtaining the measurements of transient system pressure drop. The major portion of this equipment has been used in a number of earlier investigations [1, 11, 13], therefore, only the essential details as they pertain to the present experimental work will be discussed here. A schematic of the current experimental apparatus is shown in Fig. 2.

The evaporating flow system consisted of a single horizontal copper tube, 5.49 m in length, with an inside diameter of 0.815 cm and a nominal wall thickness of 0.076 cm. The heat flux was applied electrically by means of a pressure sensitive self-adhering heating tape, helically wound around the outside periphery of the tube. Refrigerant-12 was the working fluid used in all tests.

---

[7] The influence of mass flowrate on the two-phase friction multiplier, ϕ, has also been neglected.

Pressure taps at the inlet and outlet of the system facilitated the measurement of system pressure drop during a transient. The taps were located 5.0 cm from each end of the heated length, giving a total tap to tap distance of 5.59 m. Sight-glass sections, 10 cm in length, provided visual indication of inlet and outlet flow regimes.

Transient pressure drop measurements were obtained using two Validyne DP15 differential pressure transducers in conjunction with associated Validyne CD12 transducer indicators, with a selected output bandwidth of 10 Hz. Diaphram ranges of 345 kN/m^2 were selected and spanned to a sensitivity of .072 volts-m^2/kN. This represented a compromise between sensitivity, linearity and over-range protection. Calibration was periodically checked against a Mid-West Model 110 differential pressure gauge, having a range of 70 $kN/m^2 \pm$ 1% full scale.

For pressure drop measurements, inlet and outlet transducers were connected to a common elevated reference line, which in turn was connected to a reservoir in an effort to minimize reference drift due to the presence of any small leak. Refrigerant-12 vapor was maintained in this reference line at all times. Subtraction of the electrical outputs from each transducer, in conjunction with suitable strip chart recording equipment, then yielded the corresponding transient system pressure drop.

During operation of the system, the room temperature was maintained at least 5-8 °C above the saturation temperature at the system mean pressure, in order to maintain pure superheated vapor on both sides of each transducer diaphram, and in the accompanying reference lines. The reference was in turn maintained at a level slightly below the system pressure. To minimize calibration drift due to temperature gradients set up within the transducer housings, a short length of clear nylon tubing was introduced between the test section pressure taps and each transducer. The reference lines were likewise of the same material. Thus, the temperatures of the transducers were effectively allowed to "float" at the elevated room temperature.

In addition to the pressure drop measurements, inlet and outlet flowrates were also measured during a transient. The initiated inlet mass flowrate transients were measured by means of a Cox Model LF6-1 liquid turbine in conjunction with a Cox Model A1B frequency converter. The outlet mass flowrate of superheated vapor was also measured with a Cox Model GH-8 vapor turbine.

Comparison of Model Prediction with Experimental Data

The results of a typical test, corresponding to an inlet flow quality of about 1%, are shown in Fig. 3, where the system experienced a step decrease in the inlet flowrate of about 20%. The open circles represent actual measured pressure drop, while the broken line represents the predictions of the system mean void fraction model, based on the approximate relationship for two-phase friction pressure drop given in equation (27). For comparison purposes, the result of using the more general friction pressure drop expression given in equation (23) is also shown as a solid line. The sim-

plified model is seen to deviate almost imperceptively from the more general version which required some numerical integration.

The relationship between void fraction and flow quality utilized in the
evaluation of the system pressure drop response was that suggested by
Fujie [18]. This model has been shown [1] to given reasonable agreement
with measurements for Refrigerant-12, and also embodies the correct limiting behavior as $\tilde{x} \to 0$ and $\tilde{x} \to 1$.

The correlation for the two-phase flow multiplier, ϕ, utilized in the evaluation of the friction pressure drop contribution, was that proposed by
Izumi, et al [19]. This empirical correlation was developed specifically
for flow of Refrigerant-12 in a horizontal tube. Furthermore, as shown in
the Appendix, this correlation does a reasonable job of representing .he
steady-state adiabatic pressure drop measurements of Sacks [20] for Re-
frigerant-12 in horizontal flow, under conditions similar to those encountered in the transient pressure drop measurements associated with this
study.

Considering the complexity of the evaporating flow process, the agreement
between predictions and the measured response is quite good. The characteristic shape of the measured pressure drop decay is indeed well represented by the model predictions. The initial and final steady-state predictions are also in reasonable agreement with the measured data, which
provides additional evidence as to the validity of the particular two-phase
friction multiplier correlation which was used.

It is of interest to note that the predicted pressure drop response also
indicates an abrupt surge in pressure drop, immediately following the flowrate change. Although it is difficult to discern this effect in the measured response shown in Fig. 3, it is considerably more pronounced for a
higher inlet flow quality as shown in Fig. 4. This is due to the greater
percentage of vapor flowrate entering the system. When the transient is
initiated, a significant decrease in vapor flowrate is immediately felt
throughout the entire flow system, thus causing the abrupt surge in pressure drop.

SUMMARY AND CONCLUSIONS

The principal purpose of this paper has been to present an extension of the
system mean void fraction model for predicting transient pressure drop in
two-phase evaporating flow systems. Previous applications of the system
mean void fraction model to transient evaporating flows have been directed
primarily at the responses of the effective point of complete vaporization
and the outlet flowrate of superheated vapor. These system responses are a-
mong the class of transient phenomena for which the system mean void fraction is time-invariant, and the transient form of the momentum principle is
not required. In this paper, the underlying concepts of the system mean void
fraction model, including the integral formulation, are further exploited

to include an investigation of its implications on the momentum principle. The result was an analytical model for transient pressure drop, expressed directly in terms of previously developed solutions for the transient response of the effective point of complete vaporization and the corresponding outlet mass flowrate of superheated vapor.

Experimental measurements of the transient pressure drop for Refrigerant-12 flowing in a horizontal tube evaporator subjected to a uniform and constant heat flux have been presented for comparison with the model predictions. The transients were initiated by an approximate step change in the inlet mass flowrate. The theoretical predictions of the proposed model, including the completely closed-form version which was based on a simplified model for the two-phase friction pressure drop, compare favorably with the observed transient pressure drop response. The abrupt pressure drop surge observed during the initial portion of the transients is also predicted quite accurately. These results provide additional experimental evidence as to the range of applicability of the system mean void fraction model in the analysis and prediction of transient two-phase evaporating flow phenomena.

ACKNOWLEDGEMENTS

The authors would like to acknowledge the National Science Foundation, Engineering Division, Mechanical Sciences and Engineering Section, Heat Transfer Program for its part in the support of this research under Grant GK-35884. The Oakland University Research Committee is also acknowledged for its equipment support during the experimental phase of this research.

NOMENCLATURE

A_t total cross-sectional area of flow channel, m^2

d diameter of tube or equivalent diameter of flow channel, m

f single-phase friction factor based on total mass flowrate as saturated liquid

f' single-phase friction factor based on total mass flowrate as saturated vapor

f_q peripherally-averaged applied heat flux, W/m^2

G instantaneous local total mass flux, g/m^2-s

h enthalpy of saturated liquid, J/g

L length of evaporating flow system, m

L_a unheated length of test section, m

m_t local total mass flowrate of fluid (liquid and vapor), g/s

p local pressure of fluid, N/m^2

P inside perimeter of flow channel, m

Δp total pressure drop across evaporating flow system, nt/m^2

Δp_F frictional pressure drop contribution, N/m^2

Δp_M momentum pressure drop contribution, N/m^2

Δp_{SF} single-phase friction pressure drop in superheated vapor region, N/m^2

Δp_{TF} two-phase frictional pressure drop contribution, N/m^2

Re Reynold's number for single-phase flow

t   time, s

x   local instantaneous flow quality

x_i flow quality at inlet

z   axial position in evaporating flow system measured from inlet, m

Greek Symbols

α instantaneous area mean void fraction

α_i void fraction at inlet

η instantaneous effective point of complete vaporization, m

μ viscosity of saturated liquid, $N-s/m^2$

ξ dimensionless similarity variable

ρ density of saturated liquid, g/m^3

τ evaporating flow system time constant, s

τ_f equivalent single-phase wall shear stress based on total mass flow-rate flowing as liquid, N/m^2

τ_m time constant of exponential inlet mass flowrate change, s

τ_w peripherally-averaged wall shear stress, N/m^2

ϕ two-phase friction multiplier based on total mass flowrate flowing as liquid

$\bar{\phi}$ system mean two-phase friction multiplier

Subscripts and Superscripts

Unless otherwise indicated above, subscripts generally have the following representations:

     i   initial steady-state value

     f   final steady-state value

Primed (') symbols generally refer to properties of saturated vapor.

Physical quantities which possess a tilda ($\sim$) are generally considered to be non-fluctuating (or time-averaged), where "fluctuating" is in reference to the inherent stochastic nature of the two-phase flow process. The tilda is omitted, for simplicity, in reference to fluid properties other than pressure.

Barred ($^-$) quantities are generally considered to be non-fluctuating and spatially-averaged, where the averaging is presumed to take place over the entire two-phase region.

APPENDIX

In this appendix various steady-state correlations for the two-phase friction multiplier are compared with the experimental data of Sacks [20] for adiabatic flow of Refrigerant-12 in a horizontal tube. This experimental data was obtained under operating conditions which closely approximate those encountered in the measurements of transient pressure drop presented in this paper. In addition, measurements of the associated single-phase friction factor are compared with the predicted characteristics based on fully-developed turbulent flow in a smooth tube.

Two-Phase Friction Multiplier

A variety of correlations for the steady-state two-phase flow multiplier have been proposed, the majority of which were developed principally for steam-water flows. The Martinelli-Nelson correlation [21] and the various forms of the homogeneous two-phase flow multiplier [22] are among the most well established relationships for evaporating steam-water flows. Izumi, et al [19] recently proposed an empirical two-phase friction multiplier specifically for Refrigerant-12 evaporating in a horizontal tube. The above two-phase friction multiplier relationships are compared in Fig. 5 with the measurements of Sacks [20] as a function of flow quality. A more detailed discussion of these relationships in connection with their use in the proposed model is given in Reference [14].

It would appear from Fig. 5 that, at least for Refrigerant-12, the correlation proposed by Izumi, et al [19] is superior to the other correlations discussed above. It represents the experimental measurements quite well over the entire range of flow quality. Therefore, this correlation was selected for use in evaluating the predictions of the proposed model for transient pressure drop. In terms of flow quality, the two-phase friction multiplier is thus given by the following empirical relationship:

$$\phi = 1.515(1-\tilde{x})^{.18} \left\{ 1 + [(\rho/\rho')^{2/3} - 1]\tilde{x} \right\}^{1.57} \tag{29}$$

Single-Phase Friction Factor

Measurements of the friction factor for the horizontal evaporating flow system depicted schematically in Fig. 2 are shown in Fig. 6. These measurements were obtained using air and Refrigerant-12 vapor. As is apparent from Fig. 6, the data are well represented by the Blasius equation for turbulent flow in a smooth tube

$$f = .0791 \, Re^{-1/4} \tag{30}$$

Furthermore, the range of Reynold's number spanned in Fig. 6 is sufficient to include both single-phase liquid and single-phase vapor refrigerant flow for the operating conditions encountered in the pressure drop transient tests presented in this paper.

REFERENCES

1. Wedekind, G.L., Bhatt, B.L. and Beck, B.T., "A System Mean Void Frac-
    tion Model for Predicting Various Transient Phenomena Associated with
    Two-Phase Evaporating and Condensing Flows," Proceedings of the NATO
    Advanced Study Institute on Two-Phase Flows and Heat Transfer, Istanbul,
    Turkey, August 1976, and published in the International Journal of Mul-
    tiphase Flow, Vol. 4, 1978, pp. 97-114.

2. Wedekind, G.L. and Bhatt, B.L., "An Experimental and Theoretical Inves-
    tigation into Thermally Governed Transient Flow-Surges in Two-Phase
    Condensing Flow," Two-Phase Transport and Reactor Safety, Vol. II, Hem-
    isphere Publishing Corporation, Proceedings of the Two-Phase Flow and
    Heat Transfer Symposium-Workshop, Fort Lauderdale, Florida, Oct. 1976,
    pp. 691-711; also Journal of Heat Transfer, Vol. 99, No. 4, Nov. 1977,
    pp. 561-567.

3. Bhatt, B.L., "An Experimental and Theoretical Study of Various Tran-
    sient and Oscillatory Flow Phenomena in Two-Phase Condensing Flow Sys-
    tems," Ph.D. Thesis, Oakland University, Rochester, Michigan, 1978.

4. Inayatullah, G. and Nicoll, W.B., "A Suggestion Concerning a Possible
    Fast Solution Procedure for Transient Two-Phase Flows," Letters in
    Heat and Mass Transfer, Vol. 2, 1975, pp. 325-328.

5. Inayatullah, G. and Nicoll, W.B., "Prediction of Flashing Diabatic
    Steam-Water Flows," Waterloo Research Institute, Sept. 1976, Report
    No. 16.

6. Hemphill, F., Khater, H., Inayatullah, F., Raithby, G., Strong, A.B.
    and Nicoll, W.B., "A Finite-Interval Analytic Solution Technique for
    Transient Two-Phase Flows," Two-Phase Transport and Reactor Safety,
    Vol. II, Hemisphere Publishing Corporation, Proceedings of the Two-
    Phase Flow and Heat Transfer Symposium-Workshop, Fort Lauderdale,
    Florida, Oct. 1976, pp. 815-837.

7. Premoli, A., "An Experimental Investigation on Voiding of Power Chan-
    nels Cooled by Steam-Water Mixtures," Energia Nucleare, Vol. 16, No. 10
    1969, p. 625.

8. Weisman, J. and Choe, W.G., "Methods for Calculation of Pressure Drop
    in Cocurrent Gas-Liquid Flow," Two-Phase Transport and Reactor Safety,
    Vol. I, Hemisphere Publishing Corporation, Proceedings of the Two-Phase
    Flow and Heat Transfer Symposium-Workshop, Fort Lauderdale, Florida,
    Oct. 1976, pp. 193-224.

9. Paul, F.W. and Riedle, K.J., "Experimental Frequency Response Character-
    istics for Diabatic Two-Phase Flow in a Vertical Monotube Vapor Gener-
    ator," Journal of Heat Transfer, Nov. 1974, p. 504.

10. Gaspari, G.P., Riccardo, G., Premoli, A., and Sandri, C., "Mass Holdup,
    Pressure and Time-to-Dryout Predictions under LOCA Conditions. Compar-
    isons with Scaled-Down Experimental Results," ASME Paper 74-WA/HT-43,
    Nov. 1974.

11. Wedekind, G.L., "An Experimental Investigation into the Oscillatory Motion of the Mixture-Vapor Transition Point in Horizontal Evaporating Flow," Journal of Heat Transfer, Vol. 93, 1971, pp. 47-54.

12. Wedekind, G.L. and Beck, B.T., "Theoretical Model of the Mixture-Vapor Transition Point Oscillations Associated with Two-Phase Evaporating Flow Instabilities," Journal of Heat Transfer, Vol. 96, 1974, p. 138.

13. Wedekind, G.L. and Beck, B.T., "Correlation Between Outlet Flowrate and Mixture-Vapor Transition Point Oscillations in Two-Phase Evaporating Flow," Proceedings of the Fifth International Heat Transfer Conference, Tokyo, Japan, Vol. IV, September 1974, p. 220.

14. Beck, B.T., "A Generalization of the System Mean Void Fraction Model with Applications to Transient Two-Phase Evaporating Flows," Ph.D. Thesis, Oakland University, Rochester, Michigan, August 1978.

15. Collier, J.G., Convective Boiling and Condensation, McGraw-Hill, 1972.

16. Wallis, G.B., One-Dimensional Two-Phase Flow, McGraw-Hill, 1969.

17. Inayatullah, G. and Nicoll, W.B., "A General Implicit Eulerian Numerical Prediction Method for Transient Two-Phase Flows," Proceedings of the NATO Advanced Study Institute on Two-Phase Flows and Heat Transfer Istanbul, Turkey, August 1976.

18. Fujie, H., "A Relation Between Steam Quality and Void Fraction in Two-Phase Flow," AIChE Journal, Vol. 10, 1964, p. 227.

19. Izumi, R., Ishimaru, T. and Matsuzaki, K., "Heat Transfer and Pressure Drop for Refrigerant R-12 Evaporating in a Horizontal Tube," HEAT TRANSFER-Japanese Research, Vol. 4, No. 2, 1975, pp. 82-91, Translation of original paper published in Kagaku Kogaku, Vol. 38, No. 12, 1974, pp. 884-889.

20. Sacks, P.S., "Measured Characteristics of Adiabatic and Condensing Single-Component Two-Phase Flow of Refrigerant in a 0.377-in. Diameter Horizontal Tube," ASME Paper 75-WA/HT-24, August 1976.

21. Martinelli, R.C. and Nelson, D.B.,"Prediction of Pressure Drop During Forced Circulation Boiling of Water," ASME Transactions, Vol. 70, August 1948, pp. 695-702.

22. Idsinga, W., Todreas, N. and Bowring, R., "An Assessment of Two-Phase Pressure Drop Correlations for Steam-Water Systems," International Journal of Multiphase Flow, Vol. 3, 1977, pp. 401-413.

23. Hancox, W.T. and Nicoll, W.B., "A Wall Shear Stress Formula for Adiabatic Two-Phase Flow," CWAPD-210, Westinghouse Canada Limited, November 1972.

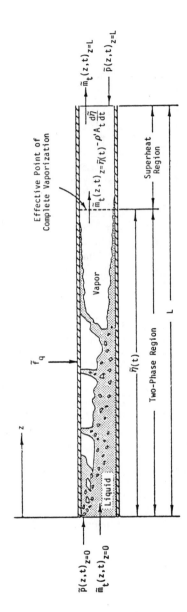

Fig. 1 Schematic of Evaporating Flow System Undergoing Complete Vaporization

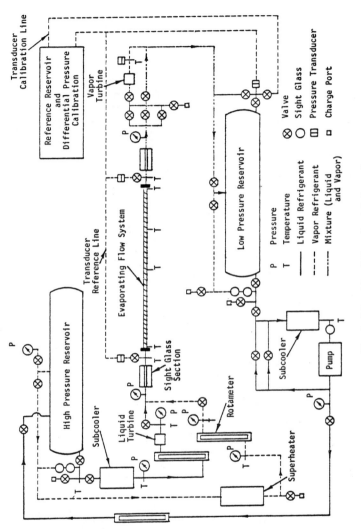

Fig. 2 Schematic of Experimental Apparatus

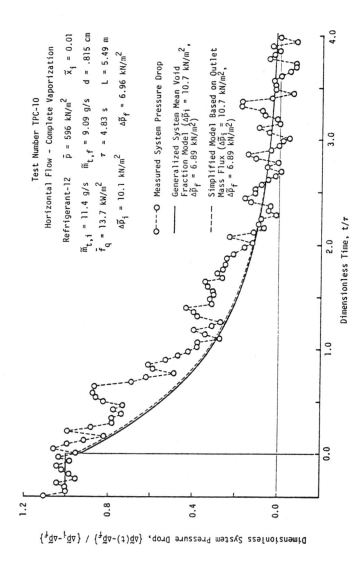

Fig. 3 System Pressure Drop Response to Step Decrease in Inlet Flowrate

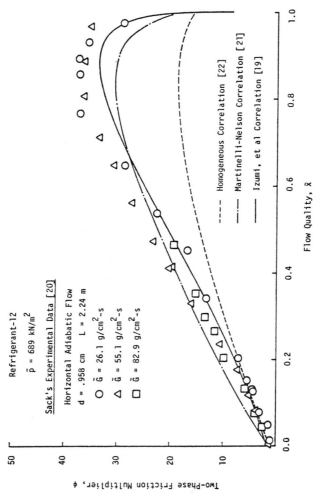

Fig. 5 Comparison of Several Correlations for Two-Phase Friction Multiplier

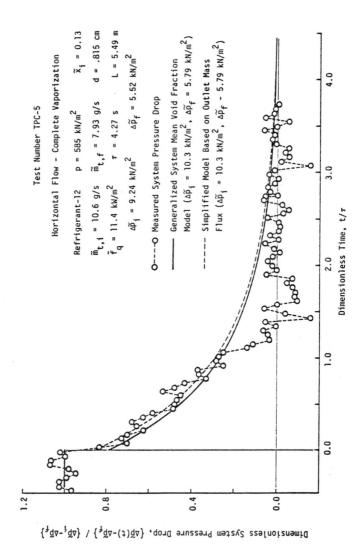

Fig. 4 System Pressure Drop Response to Step Decrease in Inlet Flowrate

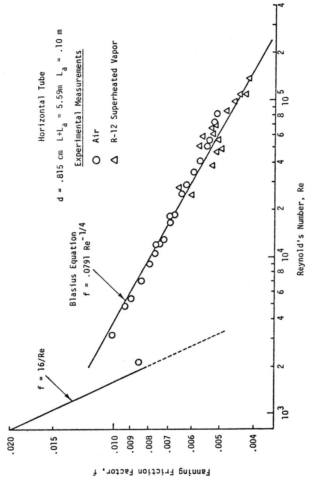

Fig. 6 Comparison of Measured Single-Phase Friction Factor with Smooth Tube Relationships

REACTOR SAFETY
AND APPLICATIONS

A Multidimensional Analysis Based on a Two-Fluid Model of Fluid Flow in a Component of the Loft System during a Loss of Coolant Experiment

P.N. DEMMIE
EG&G Idaho, Inc.
Idaho Falls, Idaho 83401, USA

ABSTRACT

A computer analysis of fluid flow in the Loss-of-Fluid Test (LOFT) cold leg blowdown pipe during a Loss-of-Coolant Experiment (LOCE) was performed using the computer program K-FIX/MOD1. This analysis constitutes the first application of a two-fluid model to fluid flow in a component of the LOFT system. The purpose of this analysis was to evaluate the capability of K-FIX/MOD1 to calculate theoretical fluid quantity distributions in the blowdown pipe during a LOCE for possible application to the analysis of LOFT experimental data, the determination of mass flow, or the development of data reduction models. A rectangular section of a portion of the blowdown pipe containing measurement Station BL-1 was modeled with fluid inflow from the upper annulus and fluid outflow from this portion of the blowdown pipe represented by time-dependent boundary conditions. Fluid quantities were calculated during a simulation of the first 26 seconds of LOCE L1-4.

I. INTRODUCTION

A computer analysis of fluid flow in the Loss-of-Fluid Test (LOFT) cold leg blowdown pipe during a Loss-of-Coolant Experiment (LOCE) was performed using the computer program K-FIX/MOD1. This analysis constitutes the first application of a two-fluid model to fluid flow in a component of the LOFT system.

The purpose of this analysis was to evaluate the capability of K-FIX/MOD1 [1] to calculate theoretical fluid quantity distributions in the blow-down pipe during a LOCE for possible application to the analysis of LOFT experimental data, the determination of mass flow, or the development of data reduction models.

The LOFT Program is an indispensable part of the international effort to provide the data required to evaluate the adequacy of and to improve the analytic methods used to predict the behavior of a large pressurized water reactor during a postulated loss-of-coolant accident (LOCA). This program, performed by EG&G Idaho, Inc., is part of the Water Reactor Safety Research Program sponsored by the Nuclear Regulatory Commission and is administered by the Department of Energy.

Complementing the analytic methods presently used in LOCA analysis with multidimensional analytic methods based on two-fluid models is a meaningful approach to analyzing experimental data and developing data reduction models to more reliably interpret instrument measurements. The methodology used in this analysis represents an initial, successful effort to obtain fluid quantity distributions fundamental to such analytic methods. The results of this analysis support the viability of this methodology and also provide information that is applicable to the analysis of LOFT experimental data, the determination of mass flow, and the development of data reduction models to more reliably interpret density (gamma densitometer), momentum flux (drag disk), and volumetric flow (turbine flowmeter) measurements.

The computer program K-FIX/MOD1 used in this analysis is discussed in Section II.

The simulation of fluid flow in the LOFT cold leg blowdown pipe during the first 26 seconds of LOCE L1-4 was used to evaluate the capability of K-FIX/MOD1 to calculate fluid quantity distributions within the blowdown pipe during a LOCE. This simulation is discussed in Section III. The representation of the LOFT cold leg blowdown pipe for this simulation is given in Section III-1, and the initial conditions and boundary conditions for this simulation are given in Section III-2. Section III concludes with discussion of this simulation in Section III-3.

Confidence in the fluid quantity distributions calculated by K-FIX/MOD1 is established by an examination of the pressure, void fraction, and gas and liquid velocity and temperature histories given in Section IV.

With this confidence established the void fraction distributions are applied in Section V to the identification of flow regimes at Location BL-1.

In Section VI these flow regimes are portrayed graphically by void fraction profiles. Also in this section the dynamic development of gas and liquid velocity profiles and phase slip at Location BL-1 is illustrated by velocity profiles.

The conclusions obtained from this computer analysis of fluid flow in the LOFT cold leg blowdown pipe during a LOCE are given in Section VII.

II. THE COMPUTER PROGRAM K-FIX/MOD1

The computer program K-FIX/MOD1 was used in this analysis of fluid flow in the LOFT cold leg blowdown pipe during a LOCE. K-FIX/MOD1 is the result of extensive modifications to the computer program K-FIX [2]

developed at the Los Alamos scientific Laboratory. In this section K-FIX
and the modifications to K-FIX, which resulted in K-FIX/MOD1, are summarized.

K-FIX uses a two-fluid model to simulate two-dimensional, unequal velocity, unequal temperature, single- or two-phase fluid flows. The set of
field equations that constitutes this two-fluid model consists of a continuity, momentum, and energy equation for each phase, gas and liquid,
coupled through mass, momentum, and energy exchange, and the assumption
of pressure equilibrium. Using constitutive relations to close this
equation set and imposing appropriate boundary conditions, this general
equation set determines the pressure, void fraction gas and liquid
velocities, and gas and liquid specific internal energies as functions of
time and position. Numerical solutions to this set of equations are
obtained in K-FIX through use of a point relaxation technique to solve a
set of finite difference equations that approximates this set of field
equations.

Although the computer program K-FIX has been applied to several problems [2,3] , extensive modifications to this program were required
before it could be used to simulate fluid flow in LOFT system piping.
These modifications, which resulted in the creation of the computer
program K-FIX/MOD1, are:

(1) Models for interphase surface area per unit volume, mass
     transfer, interphase friction, and interphase heat transfer
     were inserted to represent interphase quantities more
     realistically.

(2) Equations of state based on the steam tables from the
     RELAP4/MOD5 computer program [4] were incorporated to
     model the thermodynamic quantities more realistically.

(3) Thermal conductivities from the RELAP4/MOD5 computer program
     and microscopic viscosities from the KACHINA computer pro-
     gram [5] were inserted to model transport quantities.

(4) The basic two-fluid model was made more physically realistic by
     incorporating models for turbulent viscosity and turbulent
     thermal diffusivity to represent the effects of turbulence.

(5) Numerical stability in the treatment of boundary conditions was
     achieved by calculating the inflow velocities and using this
     velocities and the inflow data to compute consistent inter-
     phase, thermodynamic, and transport quantities.

(6) Calculation efficiency was enhanced by altering the solution
     technique of the specific internal energy equations and employ-
     ing an implicit solution technique to obtain the void fraction
     using the gas continuity equation.

(7)   Versatility in applications to complex systems was enhanced by incorporating the capability to impose time-dependent inflow and outflow boundary conditions to permit the simulation of fluid flow into and out of the computational region.

(8)   New restart and graphics capabilities were implemented to enable calculations to continue beyond a single computer run and to present the results of a calculation graphically. These modifications were required because of the different computer operating systems at the Idaho National Engineering Laboratory and the Los Alamos Scientific Laboratory.

The modifications given in Items (1) through (8) constitute the major changes made in the computer program K-FIX that resulted in the computer program K-FIX/MOD1. A detailed description of K-FIX/MOD1 is provided in Reference 1.

III. THE SIMULATION OF FLUID FLOW IN THE LOFT COLD LEG BLOWDOWN PIPE DURING LOCE L1-4

The simulation of fluid flow in the LOFT cold leg blowdown pipe during the first 26 seconds of LOCE L1-4 was used to evaluate the capability of K-FIX/MOD1 to calculate fluid quantity distributions within the blowdown pipe during a LOCE.

LOCE L1-4 was the fifth experiment in the L1 series of six nonnuclear isothermal blowdown experiments conducted by the LOFT Program. This experiment simulated a complete double-ended offset shear break as a cold leg of a four-loop pressurized water reactor. A more detailed description of LOCE L1-4 can be found in Reference 6.

A section of the blowdown pipe was modeled for this simulation as a rectangle with fluid inflow from the downcomer specified by time-dependent inflow boundary conditions and fluid outflow from this section of the blowdown pipe specified by time-dependent outflow pressure boundary conditions. The representation of this section of the blowdown pipe and the time-dependent boundary conditions governing fluid flow into and out of it are discussed in Sections 1 and 2, respectively. Also discussed in Section 2 are the remaining boundary conditions and the initial conditions for the simulation.

In Section 3 the simulation is discussed. This discussion includes information concerning computing time and output during this simulation.

1. Representation of the LOFT Cold Leg Blowdown Pipe for the Simulation

The LOFT cold leg blowdown pipe was represented for the simulation of LOCE L1-4 by a rectangle of length 2.2352 m and width 0.284 m. This rectangle represented a vertical section of the 0.284-m diameter section of the pipe extending from its left end at the downcomer to a vertical line 2.2352 m from the downcomer. This line is located between measurement Station BL-1 and a smaller diameter section of the pipe. This geometrically simplified representation of the blowdown pipe was used because K-FIX/MOD1 can only simulate two-dimensional fluid flows and because the region represented contains both the end of the blowdown pipe at the downcomer and measurement Station BL-1. The representation of any larger region would result in the use of excessive computer time.

The computing mesh of fluid cells is obtained by partitioning this rectangle into 110 cells, each with dimensions δx = 0.1016 m and δy = 0.568 m. This partitioning was used because it provides good spatial resolution without using an excessive number of computational cells. The computing mesh of 22 cells in the x-direction and 5 cells in the y-direction was surrounded by a perimeter of fictitious boundary cells as required in K-FIX/MOD1. This computing mesh and its boundary cell perimeter are depicted in Figure 1.

In Figure 1, Cells (1,2), (1,3), (1,4), (1,5), and (1,6) are the inflow boundary cells representing fluid inflow from the downcomer; Cells (24,2), (24,3), (24,4), (24,5), and (24,6) are outflow boundary cells representing fluid outflow from the region of the simulation; Cells (1,1), (1,2), (1,3),...,(1,24) and Cells (7,1), (7,2), (7,3),...,(7,24) are adiabatic rigid cells representing the wall of the pipe. The remaining cells in Figure 1 are fluid cells within the computing mesh. The locations of Cells (22,2), (22,4), and (22,6) are nearly identical with Locations BL-1A, BL-1B, and BL-1C, respectively. Each of these locations - BL-1A, BL-1B, and BL-1C - corresponds to the location of a pod containing a drag disk (measuring momentum flux), turbine flowmeter (measuring fluid velocity), and thermocouple (measuring fluid temperature). Therefore, the values of quantities in these three cells can be used for comparisons with experimental data.

2. Initial Conditions and Boundary Conditions for the Simulation

The initial conditions needed to begin the simulation of LOCE L1-4, the time-dependent inflow boundary conditions needed to model fluid inflow into the LOFT cold leg blowdown pipe from the downcomer, and the time-dependent outflow boundary conditions needed to specify the pressure at the end of the region represented in the simulation were obtained from the RELAP4/MOD5 posttest analysis of LOCE L1-4[7]. The results of this posttest analysis provided the pressure, void fraction, and temperature data required for the inflow cells and the pressure data required for the outflow cells. Experimental data could only provide the pressure and

temperature data required for the inflow cells. The inflow pressure and
temperature data calculated by RELAP4/MOD5 for the first 26 seconds after
blowdown initiation agreed quite well with the experimental data[7].
No direct comparison, however, was possible between the remaining boundary condition data and the experimental data. Indeed, the lack of knowledge of the inflow void fraction data proved to be the greatest source of
uncertainty in this simulation of LOCE L1-4.

An initial pressure of 15.8 MPa was specified in Cell (1,2) and the
initial pressures for the remaining cells in this opening were adjusted
to account for hydrostatic pressure differences. The initial gas and
liquid temperature of 554.8 K was specified in all the inflow boundary
cells. Since initially the fluid is single-phase liquid and initially
there is no significant steady state flow in the blowdown pipe, initial
void fraction and velocity components of zero were specified in all the
inflow boundary cells.

An initial pressure of 15.8 MPa was specified in each fluid cell in the
computing mesh. The initial values of void fraction, velocity components, and temperature for each fluid cell were specified to be the same
values of these quantities as specified for the inflow boundary cells.
These initial data are consistent with the initially single-phase liquid
and no significant steady state flow nature of the fluid in the blowdown
pipe.

The values of the time-dependent inflow pressure, void fraction, and gas
and liquid temperatures were obtained from quantities calculated in the
posttest analysis. Figures 2 through 5 show these time-dependent boundary conditions. Figure 2 shows the inflow pressure in Cell (1,2) as a
function of time; Figure 3 shows the inflow void fraction as a function
of time; Figure 4 shows the inflow temperature as a function of time; and
Figure 5 shows the outflow pressure in Cell (24,2) as a function of time.

The final boundary conditions specified for the simulation of LOCE L1-4
are no-slip boundary conditions for the adiabatic rigid boundary cells
representing the wall of the blowdown pipe. These boundary conditions
model friction between the flowing fluid and the pipe wall.

3. Discussion of the Simulation

The simulation of fluid flow in the LOFT cold leg blowdown pipe during
LOCE L1-4 was implemented by specifying appropriate K-FIX/MOD1 input
data, and was made for the first 26 seconds of this experiment using the
CDC Cyber 76 computer at the Idaho National Engineering Laboratory. A
total of 24433.9 s (6.79 hr) central processing unit (CPU) time was required to complete the simulation. The time step used in a given computer run was determined after an examination of the number of iterations
required for covergence in each cycle of the previous run. On the basis
of this examination the time step was changed for this run only if the
number of iterations required for convergence did not typically fall in

the range of 5 to 10. During the simulation, values of fluid quantities including pressure, void fraction, gas and liquid velocities, specific internal energies, and temperatures, and saturation temperature were printed and written on a tape from which plots were later made.

IV. PRESSURE, VOID FRACTION, GAS AND LIQUID VELOCITY AND TEMPERATURE HISTORIES DURING THE SIMULATION

In this section pressure, void fraction, and gas and liquid velocity and temperature histories are given and discussed. These histories are used to establish confidence in the fluid quantity distributions calculated by K-FIX/MOD1 during the simulation of LOCE L1-4.

Pressure, void fraction, x-component of the gas and liquid velocity, and gas and liquid temperature histories are given in Figures 6 through 12. The pressures calculated in Cell (22,4) during the simulation are shown in Figure 6. These pressures correspond to the pressures measured by the pressure transducer at Station BL-1. Figures 7 through 9 show the void fractions calculated in Cells (22,2), (22,4), and (22,6) during the time intervals 0 to 4.0 s, 0 to 10.0 s, and 0 to 26.0 s respectively. Cells (22,2), (22,4) and (22,6) correspond very closely to Locations BL-1A, BL-1B, and BL-1C, respectively. Figures 10 and 11 show the x-components of the gas and liquid velocities, respectively, calculated in these cells during the simulation. The gas, liquid, and saturation temperatures calculated in Cell (22,4) during the simulation are shown in Figure 12.

The calculated pressures shown in Figure 6 and the pressures measured at Location BL-1 agree well [8]. The pressures shown in Figure 6 exhibit a rapid drop from the initial value at blowdown initiation to a value slightly greater than 6.0 MPa at a relative minimum occurring at approximately 0.2 s after blowdown initiation. After a slight increase to a relative maximum occurring at approximately 0.45 s, they decrease to a value slightly greater than 3.0 MPa at 25.0 s.

The void fractions shown in Figure 7 imply that flashing first occurs in Cell (22,4) at approximately 0.45 s, in Cell (22,6) at approximately 0.5 s, and in Cell (22,2) at approximately 0.9 s. After this initial flashing the void fraction rapidly increases to a relative maximum followed by a decrease to a relative minimum. This general behavior is most pronounced in Cell (22,4) for which this relative maximum of about 0.05 occurs at approximately 1.18 s and this relative minimum of about 0.005 occurs at approximately 1.63 s. For Cell (22,6) these relative extrem a of about 0.014 and 0.007 occur at approximately 1.54 s and 1.58 s, respectively, and for Cell (22,2) these relative extrem a of about 0.012 and 0.006 occur at approximately 2.28 and 2.47 s, respectively. Generally increasing void fractions in each of these cells is observed in Figures 7, 8, and 9 during the remainder of the simulation.

Arithmetic averages of the void fractions in the i = 22 cells were
obtained for comparison with the average experimentally determined void
fractions. Both of these void fractions are plotted in Figure 13 along
with the BL-1 void fractions predicted by RELAP4/MOD5 for LOCE L1-4 at
Location BL-1[9].

Figure 13 shows that relatively good agreement exists between the average
void fractions calculated from the K-FIX/MOD1 simulation and those calculated by RELAP4/MOD5 although both of these average void fractions are
lower than those obtained from the experimental data. That the RELAP4/
MOD5 predicted values are lower than the experimental values suggests
that the values of the inflow void fractions obtained from the RELAP4/
MOD5 posttest analysis and used as inflow boundary conditions for the
simulation are possibly lower than the actual void fractions of the fluid
entering the blowdown pipe or that the reduction of gamma densitometer
measurements to void fractions is incorrect. That the K-FIX/MOD1 calculated values are lower than the experimental values is attributed to the
too low values of the inflow void fractions used as inflow boundary conditions and to the lack of wall heat transfer in K-FIX/MOD1. Early in
the simulation the addition of energy from the walls would increase the
void fraction considerably and the cumulative effect of this increase
would be propagated throughout the simulation. With the inclusion of
wall heat transfer in K-FIX/MOD1, it is expected that a K-FIX/MOD1 simulation would yield average void fractions that agree with the experimental values at least as well as those obtained using RELAP4/MOD5.

The effect of the lack of wall heat transfer on the average void fractions for the i = 22 cells is illustrated in Figure 14. This figure
shows the inflow void fractions and the average i = 22 void fractions
during the simulation. Only from blowdown initiation to 1.4 s and after
21.5 s, approximately, are the average i = 22 void fractions larger than
the inflow void fractions. There is a considerable difference in these
void fractions from approximately 1.4 to 21.5 s after blowdown
initiation.

Since the inflow and Location BL-1 pressures are in excellent agreement
with the measured pressures at these locations and since dissipative
friction effects are included in K-FIX/MOD1, this downstream decrease in
void fraction is consistent only with a lack of transfer of energy from
the wall to the fluid early in the simulation.

The x-components of the gas and liquid velocities calculated during the
simulation shown in Figures 10 and 11 are in very good agreement with the
velocities obtained using the turbine flowmeter during LOCE L1-4[8].
Although the calculated velocities are somewhat higher than the experimental velocities, they fall well within the error bands for the experimental velocities[6].

The calculated gas and liquid velocities exhibit the same general
behavior. From their initial values of zero, they increase rapidly to a
relative maximum occurring at approximately 0.1 s. This is followed by

their decreasing to a relative minimum occurring at approximately 2.3 s. After this relative minimum they increase to a relative maximum occurring between 21.0 and 23.0 s. Then they decrease as shown in the figures.

The gas and liquid temperatures shown in Figure 12 and the TE-BL-1 measured temperatures agree well [8]. The temperatures drop rapidly from the value at blowdown initiation to a relative minimum of about 545 K occurring at approximately 0.2 s. After an increase to a relative maximum of about about 550.8 K occurring at approximately 0.45 s, they gradually decrease to a value of about 510 K.

A comparison of the calculated saturation temperatures with the calculated gas and liquid temperatures shown in these figures indicates the times at which significant evaporation or condensation occurs in Cell (22,4). In particular, the initial flashing occurring at approximately 0.45 s, as shown in Figure 7, coincides with the liquid first reaching the saturation temperature, as shown in Figure 12.

V. APPLICATION TO FLOW REGIME IDENTIFICATION

A significant application of the results of this simulation is the identification of the flow regime present at a given time. The flow regime present in the ith column of cells at time t is determined from the values of the void fractions $\theta_{i,2}$ (t), $\theta_{i,4}$ (t), and $\theta_{i,6}$ (t) as specified by the criteria given in Table I.

Table I gives the conditions on $\theta_{i,2}$ (t), $\theta_{i,4}$ (t), and $\theta_{i,6}$ (t) that specify the presence of homogeneous, annular, inverted annular, or stratified flow in the ith column of cells at time t. An additional examination of the void fraction distribution of a row of cells can detect the presence of slugs of gas or liquid.

The flow regime history for the i=22 cells during the simulation are readily obtained from the criteria specified in Table I and Figures 7, 8, and 9. This history is given in Table II.

VI. VOID FRACTION AND VELOCITY PROFILES

Void fraction profiles for the i = 22 cells, which correspond to Location BL-1, are shown in Figures 15 through 22 every half second from 0.5 to 4.0 s and in Figures 23 through 34 every two seconds from 4.0 to 26.0 s. These void fraction profiles show flow regimes consistent with those given in Table II and graphically portray the dynamical development of void fraction during the simulation.

Distributions of the x-components of the gas and liquid velocities for the i = 22 cells are shown in Figures 35 through 50. Figures 35 through 37 show these velocity profiles at 0.2, 0.5, and 1.0 s, and Figures 38 through 50 show them every two seconds from 2.0 to 26.0 s. In these figures the presence of wall friction as modelled by no-slip boundary conditions, the dynamical development of slip, and the evolution away for initially symmetric velocity profiles are evident.

VII. CONCLUSIONS

A multidimensional computer analysis of fluid flow in the LOFT cold leg blowdown pipe during a LOCE was performed using the computer program K-FIX/MOD1. The main conclusion obtained from this analysis is that K-FIX/MOD1 is a viable tool for calculating theoretical fluid quantity distributions in the LOFT cold leg blowdown pipe during a LOCE. These theoretical fluid quantity distributions have the potential to be useful for the analysis of LOFT experimental data, the determination of mass flow, and the development of data reduction models to more reliably interpret density, momentum flux, and volumetric flow measurements. Some discretion must be excercised, however, in applying K-FIX/MOD1 to similar analyses in other components of the LOFT system since the present analysis indicates that the computer costs of these analyses will be high and since the two-dimensional nature of K-FIX/MOD1 requires that the component of interest in any analysis be represented in a geometrically simplified manner.

K-FIX/MOD1 was used to simulate fluid flow in the LOFT cold leg blowdown pipe during the first 26 seconds of LOCE L1-4. From the results of this simulation the conclusion reached is that with the use of time-dependent boundary conditions obtained from the RELAP4/MOD5 posttest analysis of LOCE L1-4, K-FIX/MOD1 is capable of calculating fluid quantities as functions of position and time within the blowdown pipe during LOCE L1-4. Confidence in the calculated results exists since there is relatively good agreement between the fluid quantities calculated during this simulation and the experimental data, and since there is extremely good agreement between these quantities and those calculated using RELAP4/MOD5.

The significance of this capability of K-FIX/MOD1 is that the spatial distributions of fluid quantities calculated during this simulation made possible the identification of flow regimes and the visualization of the development of velocity and void fraction profiles and the development of phase slip. It is this theoretical predictive capability beyond the analytic methods presently used in LOCA analysis and its aid in understanding fluid flow in LOFT system piping that provided the purpose for the development and application of K-FIX/MOD1.

VIII. REFERENCES

1. P. N. Demmie and K. R. Hofmann, The Computer Program K-FIX/MOD1: A Modification of the Computer Program K-FIX for Applications to Fluid Flow Simulation in LOFT System Piping, NUREG/CR-0646, TREE-1324 (March 1979).

2. W. C. Rivard and M. D. Torrey, K-FIX: A Computer Program for Transient, Two-Dimensional, Two-Fluid Flow, LA-NUREG-6623 (April 1977).

3. Private communication with W. C. Rivard.

4. K. R. Katsma et al, RELAP4/MOD5 - A Computer Program for Transient Thermal-Hydraulic Analysis of Nuclear Reactors and Related System - User's Manual, ed. C. G. Bruch, ANCR-NUREG-1335 (September 1976).

5. W. C. Rivard and M. D. Torrey, Numerical Calculation of Flashing From Long Pipes Using a Two-Field Model, LA-NUREG-6330-MS (May 1976).

6. D. Batt, Experimental Data Report for LOFT Nonnuclear Test L1-4, TREE-NUREG-1084 (July 1977).

7. W. H. Grush and H. L. O. Holmstrom, Posttest RELAP4 Analysis of LOFT Experiment L1-4, TREE-NUREG-1183 (November 1977).

8. P. N. Demmie and K. R. Hofmann, Multidimensional Analysis of Fluid Flow in the LOFT Cold Leg Blowdown Pipe During a Loss-of-Coolant Experiment, NUREG/CR-0645, TREE-1323 (March 1979).

9. J. R. White, et al, Experimental Prediction for LOFT Nonnuclear Experiment L1-4, TREE-NUREG-1086 (April 1977).

TABLE I

FLOW REGIME CRITERIA FOR THE ith COLUMN OF CELLS AT TIME t

Flow Regime	Conditions Satisfied
Homogeneous	$\theta_{i,2}(t) = \theta_{i,4}(t) = \theta_{i,6}(t)$
Annular	$\theta_{i,4}(t) > \theta_{i,2}(t)$ and $\theta_{i,4}(t) > \theta_{i,6}(t)$
Inverted annular	$\theta_{i,4}(t) < \theta_{i,2}(t)$ and $\theta_{i,4}(T) < \theta_{i,6}(t)$
Stratified	$\theta_{i,2}(t) < \theta_{i,4}(t) < \theta_{i,6}(t)$ or $\theta_{i,2}(t) > \theta_{i,4}(t) > \theta_{i,6}(t)$

TABLE II

FLOW REGIME HISTORY FOR THE i - 22 CELLS DURING THE SIMULATION

Time Interval (s)	Flow Regime
0 to 0.42	Homogeneous
0.42 to 1.56	Annular
1.56 to 1.86	Stratified
1.86 to 5.38	Annular
5.38 to 6.00	Stratified
6.00 to 7.82	Annular
7.82 to 26.0	Stratified

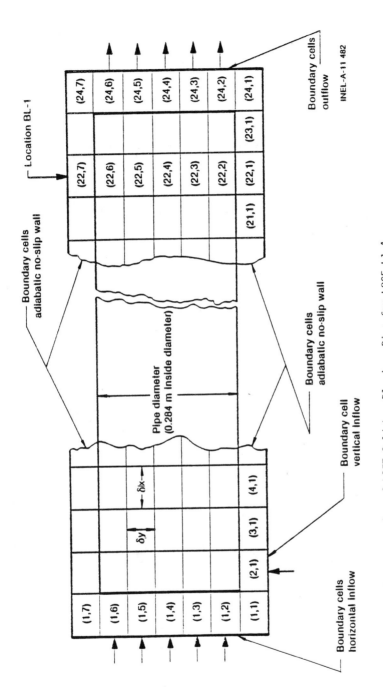

Fig. 1 Representation of LOFT Cold Leg Blowdown Pipe for LOCE L1-4

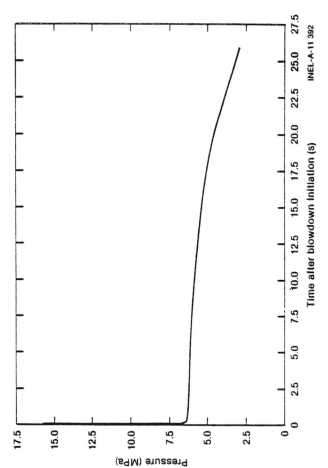

Fig. 2 Specified Inflow Pressure Boundary Conditions in Cell (1,2) from RELAP4/MOD5 Posttest Analysis of LOCE L1-4.

INEL-A-11 392

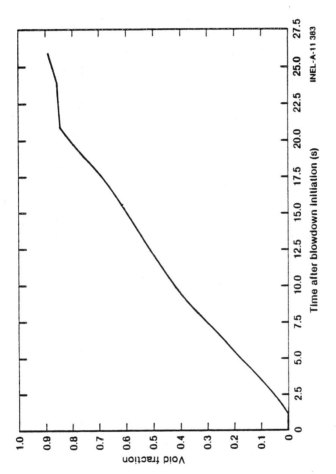

Fig. 3 Specified Inflow Void Fraction Boundary Conditions in Cell (1,2) from RELAP4/MOD5 Posttest Analysis of LOCE L1-4

INEL-A-11 383

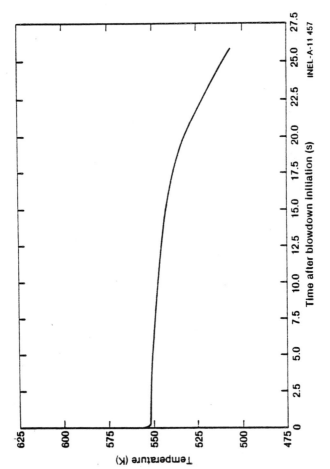

Fig. 4 Specified Inflow Temperature Boundary Conditions for Liquid and Vapor in Cell (1,2) from RELAP4/MOD5 Posttest Analysis of LOCE L1-4

INEL-A-11 457

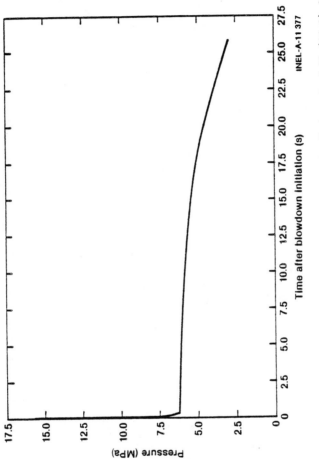

Fig. 5 Specified Outflow Pressure Boundary Conditions in Cell (24,2) from RELAP4/MOD5 Posttest Analysis of LOCE L1-4

INEL-A-11 377

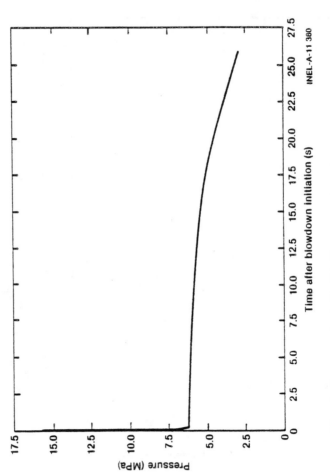

Fig. 6 Pressure in Cell (22,4) at Location B1-1 From 0 to 26 s After Blowdown Initiation

INEL-A-11 380

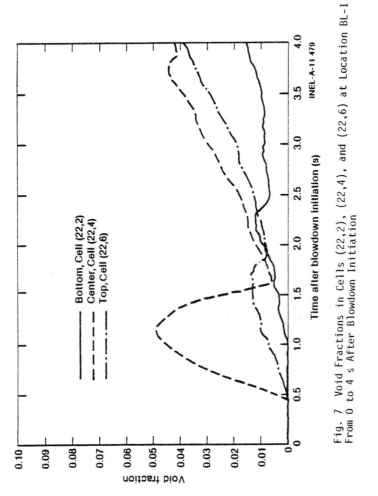

Fig. 7 Void Fractions in Cells (22,2), (22,4), and (22,6) at Location BL-1 From 0 to 4 s After Blowdown Initiation

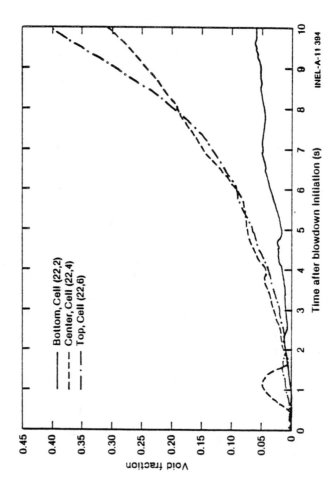

Fig. 8 Void Fractions in Cells (22,2), (22,4) and (22,6) at Location BL-1 from 0 to 10 s After Blowdown Initiation

INEL-A-11 394

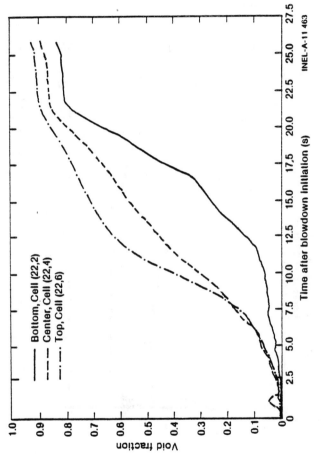

Fig. 9 Void Fractions in Cells (22,2), (22,4), and (22,6) at Location BL-1 from 0 to 26 s After Blowdown Initiation

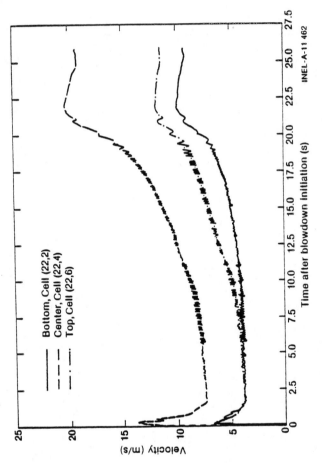

Fig. 10 The x-Components of Gas Velocity in Cells (22,2), (22,4), and (22,6) at Location BL-1 from 0 to 26 s After Blowdown Initiation

INEL-A-11 462

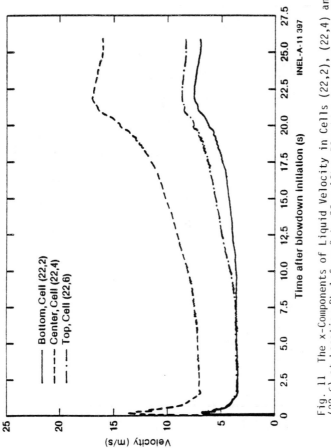

Fig. 11 The x-Components of Liquid Velocity in Cells (22,2), (22,4) and (22,6) at Location BL-1 from 0 to 26 s After Blowdown Initiation

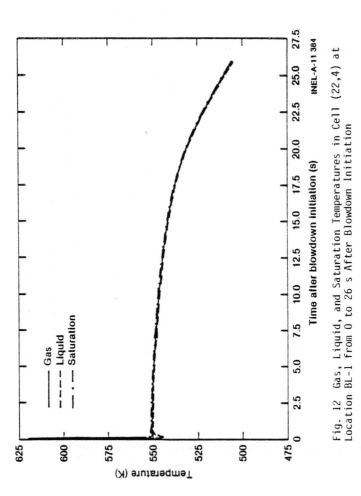

Fig. 12 Gas, Liquid, and Saturation Temperatures in Cell (22,4) at Location BL-1 from 0 to 26 s After Blowdown Initiation

INEL-A-11 384

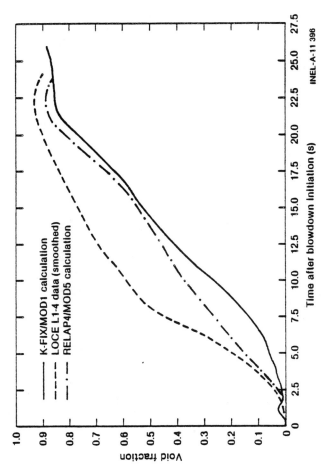

Fig. 13 Comparison of Average Void Fractions at Location BL-1 Among K-FIX/MOD1 and RELAP4/MOD5 Calculations and LOCE L1-4 Data

INEL-A-11 396

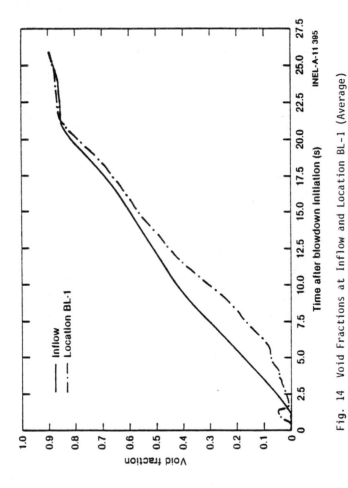

Fig. 14 Void Fractions at Inflow and Location BL-1 (Average)

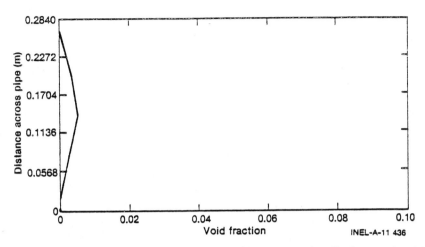

Fig. 15 Radial Void Fraction Distribution at Location BL-1 at 0.5 s After Blowdown Initiation

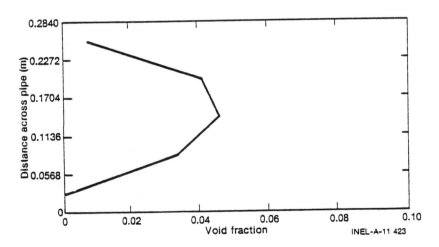

Fig. 16 Radial Void Fraction Distribution at Location BL-1 at 1 s After Blowdown Initiation

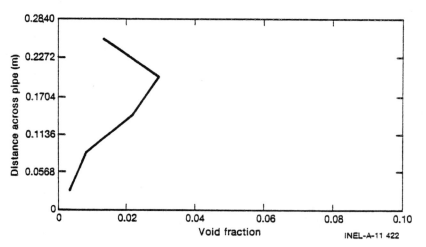

Fig. 17 Radial Void Fraction Distribution at Location BL-1 at 1.5 s After Blowdown Initiation

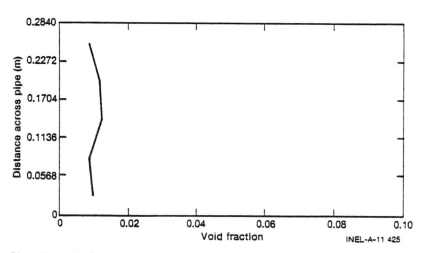

Fig. 18 Radial Void Fraction Distribution at Location BL-1 at 2 s After Blowdown Initiation

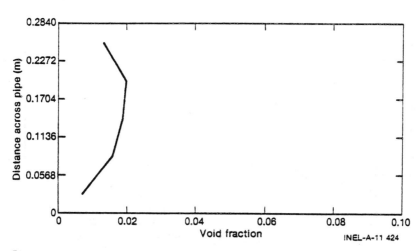

Fig. 19 Radial Void Fraction Distribution at Location BL-1 at 2.5 s After
Blowdown Initiation

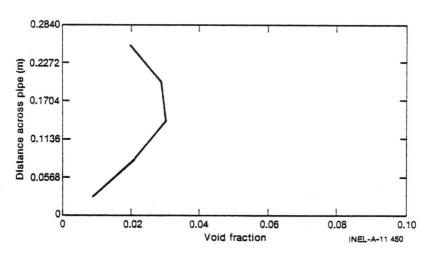

Fig. 20 Radial Void Fraction Distribution at Location BL-1 at 3 s After
Blowdown Initiation

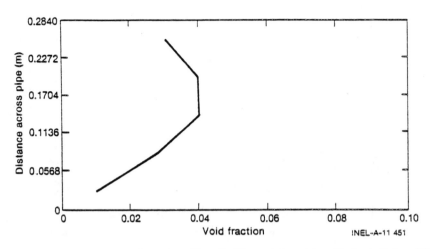

Fig. 21   Radial Void Fraction Distribution at Location BL-1 at 3.5 s After
Blowdown Initiation

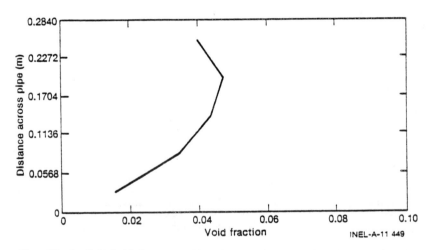

Fig. 22   Radial Void Fraction Distribution at Location BL-1 at 4 s
After Blowdown Initiation

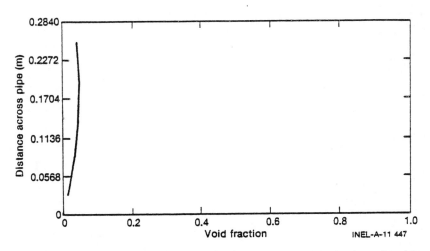

Fig. 23   Radial Void Fraction Distribution at Location BL-1 at 4 s After Blowdown Initiation

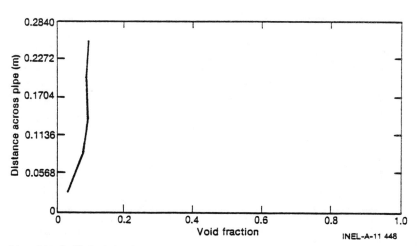

Fig. 24   Radial Void Fraction Distribution at Location BL-1 at 6 s After Blowdown Initiation

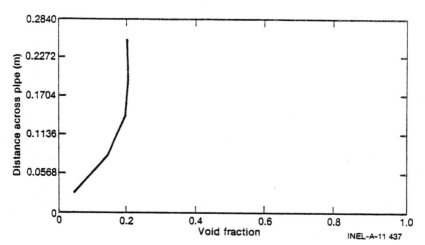

Fig. 25   Radial Void Fraction Distribution at Location BL-1 at 8 s After Blowdown Initiation

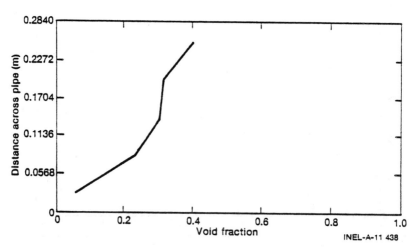

Fig. 26   Radial Void Fraction Distribution at Location BL-1 at 10 s After Blowdown Initiation

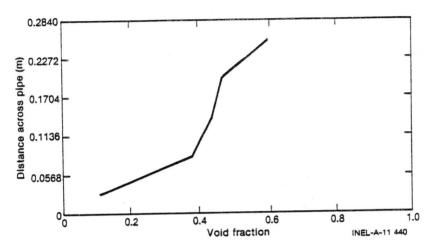

Fig. 27 Radial Void Fraction Distribution at Location BL-1 at 12 s After
Blowdown Initiation

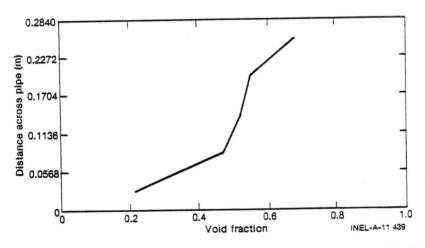

Fig. 28 Radial Void Fraction Distribution at Location BL-1 at 14 s After
Blowdown Initiation

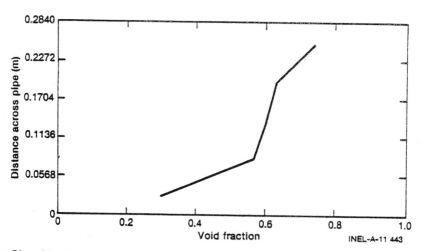

Fig. 29   Radial Void Fraction Distribution at Location BL-1 at 16 s After
Blowdown Initiation

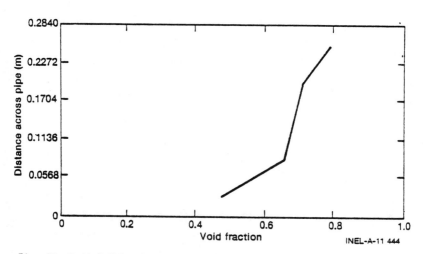

Fig. 30   Radial Void Fraction Distribution at Location BL-1 at 18 s After
Blowdown Initiation

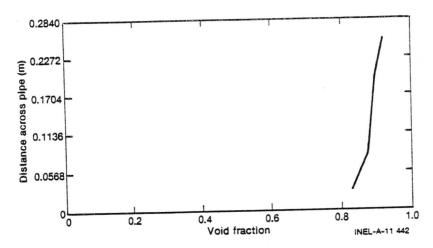

Fig. 31   Radial Void Fraction Distribution at Location BL-1 at 20 s After
Blowdown Initiation

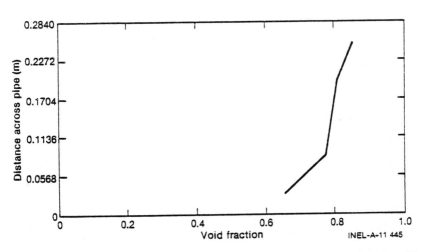

Fig. 32   Radial Void Fraction Distribution at Location BL-1 at 22 s After
Blowdown Initiation

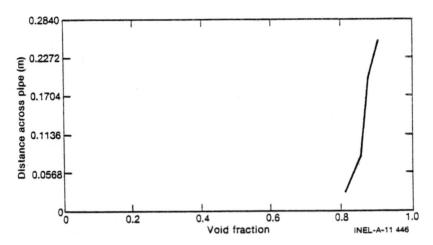

Fig. 33 Radial Void Fraction Distribution at Location BL-1 at 24 s After Blowdown Initiation

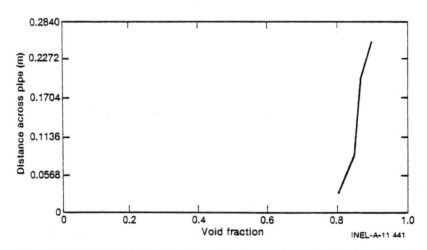

Fig. 34 Radial Void Fraction Distribution at Location BL-1 at 26 s After Blowdown Initiation

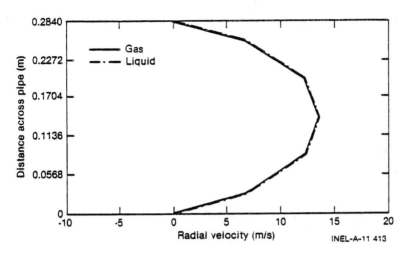

Fig. 35 Radial x-Component of Velocity Distribution at Location BL-1
0.2 s After Blowdown Initiation

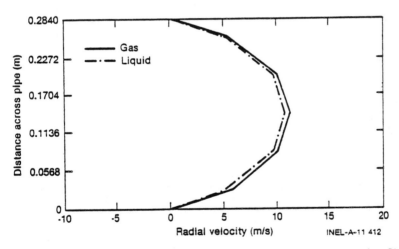

Fig. 36 Radial x-Component of Velocity Distribution at Location BL-1
0.5 s After Blowdown Initiation

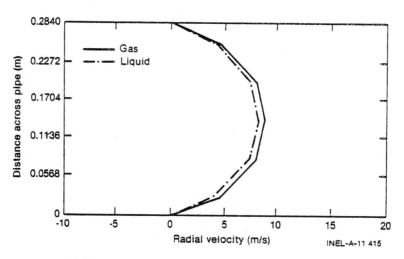

Fig. 37 Radial x-Component of Velocity Distribution at Location BL-1
1 s After Blowdown Initiation

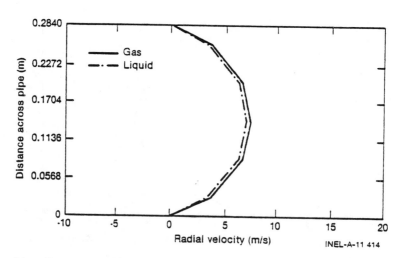

Fig. 38 Radial x-Component of Velocity Distribution at Location BL-1
2 s After Blowdown Initiation

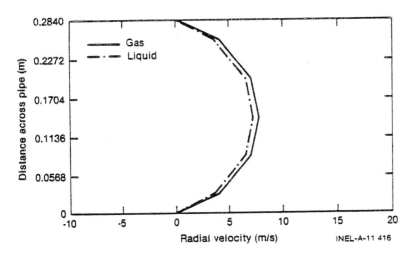

Fig. 39   Radial x-Component of Velocity Distribution at Location BL-1
4 s After Blowdown Initiation

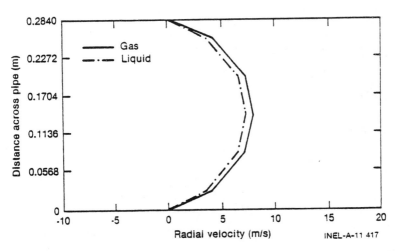

Fig. 40   Radial x-Component of Velocity Distribution at Location BL-1
6 s After Blowdown Initiation

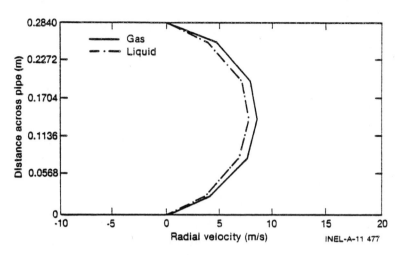

Fig. 41 Radial x-Component of Velocity Distribution at Location BL-1
8 s After Blowdown Initiation

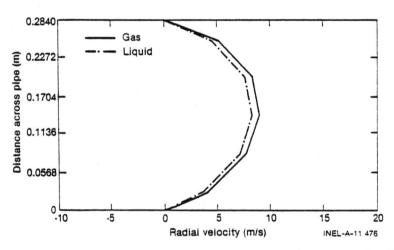

Fig. 42 Radial x-Component of Velocity Distribution at Location BL-1
10 s After Blowdown Initiation

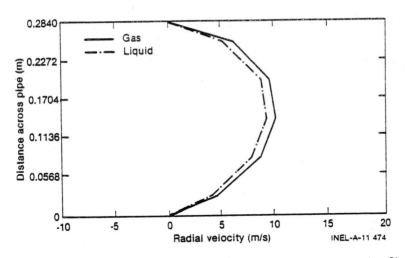

INEL-A-11 474

Fig. 43 Radial x-Component of Velocity Distribution at Location BL-1
12 s After Blowdown Initiation

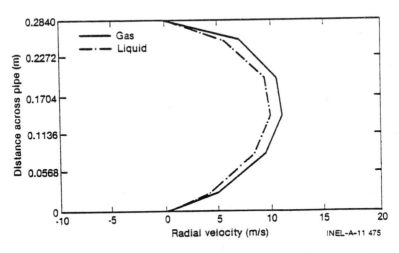

INEL-A-11 475

Fig. 44 Radial x-Component of Velocity Distribution at Location BL-1
14 s After Blowdown Initiation

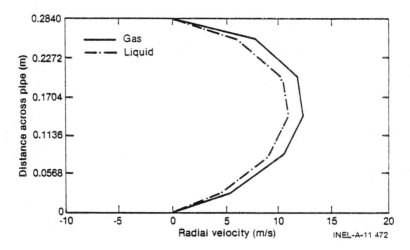

Fig. 45 Radial x-Component of Velocity Distribution at Location BL-1
16 s After Blowdown Initiation

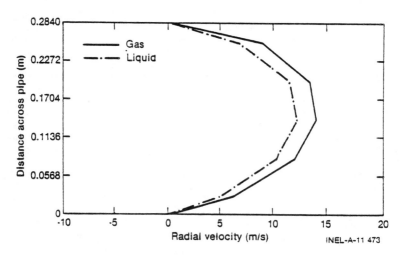

Fig. 46 Radial x-Component of Velocity Distribution at Location BL-1
18 s After Blowdown Initiation

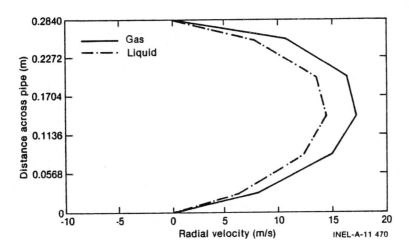

Fig. 47   Radial x-Component of Velocity Distribution at Location BL-1
20 s After Blowdown Initiation

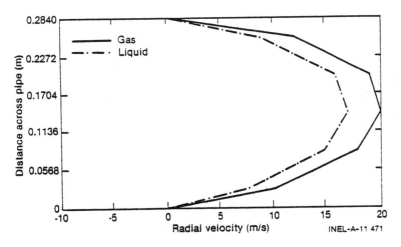

Fig. 48   Radial x-Component of Velocity Distribution at Location BL-1
22 s After Blowdown Initiation

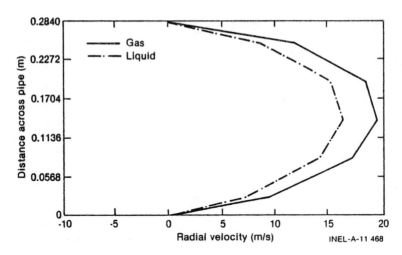

Fig. 49 Radial x-Component of Velocity Distribution at Location BL-1
24 s After Blowdown Initiation

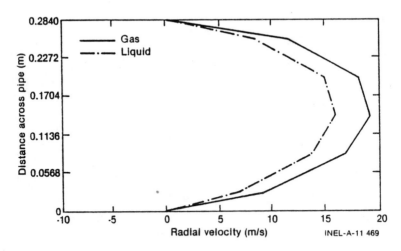

Fig. 50 Radial x-Component of Velocity Distribution at Location BL-1
26 s After Blowdown Initiation

Entrainment of Droplets during the Reflood Phase of a LOCA and the Influence of the Channel Geometry

S.B. van der MOLEN and F.W.B.M. GALJEE
Netherlands Energy Research Foundation E.C.N.,
Petten (N.H.), The Netherlands

ABSTRACT

The entrainment of droplets is an important phenomenon in the reflood process. In calculation models and computerprograms for reflood the onset of entrainment is based on the balance between the drag force and gravity force on liquid droplets of a maximum size, given by a critical Weber number.

From the literature we know that for a good agreement between the calculations and the experimental results the set of chosen thermal hydraulic parameters such as drift velocity below the entrainment level, the critical velocity at the onset of entrainment and the dispersed flow slip ratio, for bundle experiments is different from the set appropriate for a good agreement of tube experiments with calculations. This points to geometry effects.
Recently Jones and Zuber |1| developed a criterion for the slug to annular flow transition, for an adiabatic two-phase flow. They showed geometry effects which can be also important in case of the entrainment phenomena of a reflood process. Therefore experiments have been carried out in tubes, annuli and four-rod bundles in order to investigate geometry effects in simple these configurations.

INTRODUCTION

In recent years several computer codes have been developed for the analysis of the reflood phenomena of a loss-of-coolant accident (LOCA) |2, 3, 4, 5, 6, 7, 8 |. Most computer codes contain coupled heater rod conduction, channel hydraulic and surface heat transfer models. On the hydraulic side it turns out that the most important parameters are the drift velocity in the region below the entrainment level, the critical vapour velocity for the onset of entrainment and the dispersed flow slip ratio.
Comparing the P.W.R.-Flecht, the B.W.R. Flecht and Semiscale bundle experiments with K.W.U. single tube experiments, Holderness |3| mentioned that due to basic differences in fluid flow character, slightly different values for each above mentioned parameter should be used in order to get good agreement between the bundle experiments and calculations on the one hand and the single tube experiments and the calculations on the other hand. He considered this as a geometry effect resulting from differences in fluid flow over exterior and interior surfaces. However, in handling this problem, in nearly all computer codes the coolant subchannels of a bundle are replaced by the hydraulic equivalent tube adjusting the most important thermal-hydraulic parameters.

As mentioned above, one of the most important thermal-hydraulic parameters
is the critical vapour velocity for the onset of entrainment, which is
based on the balance between the gravity force and drag force on the
liquid drops with the maximum stable diameter given by the critical Weber
number for drops. There are no obvious physical reasons why this criterion
for the onset of entrainment should be changed going from bundles to tubes.
We tried to find a criterion where the geometry influences the onset of
entrainment.
The onset of entrainment is first of all based on the way of the production of the droplets, for instance by the fragmentation of liquid jets
following large escaping vapour bubbles or by the transition between slug
or churn flow and a dispersed flow as will be described in the next section. In the second place the height where droplets can be found is dependent on the escape velocity of the liquid and on the balance between the
drag force and the gravity force on droplets and the stability of liquid
droplets in a vapour flow.

We first describe the different reflood phenomena and the most relevant
appearing two phase flow patterns such as the inverted annular, the
annular and dispersed flow regimes and the transitions between the different regimes.
One has to distinguish between the two main types of quench modes of a
heated wall, the liquid column-type with the inverted annular flow which
appears under liquid subcooled conditions at the quench front and the
dryout type where the liquid at the quench front is about saturated.
From high speed films it is clear that the onset of entrainment in case
of the liquid column type quench mode occurs simultaneously with the
transition of churn flow to a dispersed flow whereas in case of the
dryout type quench mode with an annular flow at the quench front, the
onset of entrainment is caused by the interaction of the vapour flow on
the liquid film flow.

ENTRAINMENT AND CHANNEL GEOMETRY.

Before we describe the entrainment phenomena and the criterion for entrainment, we first start with the description of the two phase flow
patterns which occur during a r flood process, because the type of the
two phase flow patterns determines the transition phenomena and the
entrainment mechanisms.
We have to distinguish between the two-phase flow pattern occuring for
topflooding and these occuring in case of bottom flooding. The flow
patterns in case of top flooding are the liquid film flow regime and the
dispersed flow regime. The dispersed flow is created by the entrainment
of droplets from the liquid film. In case of bottom flooding the flow
patterns along a high temperature channel, are less simple than in the
top flooding case. Experiments showed that a number of flow patterns
exist along the channel. Which type exists depends on the subcooling
or quality and on the flooding rate of the coolant.
The main flow patterns in case of bottom flooding are shown in Fig. 1.
We distinguish between the so called liquid column type reflood (A) and

the dryout type (B). These two reflood types are the two extreem cases.
Starting with bottom flooding, a liquid column type reflood in the
lower part of the channel exists. With increasing time the flow pattern
around the quench front changes, dependent on the local void fraction,
to the dryout type as a normal flow pattern transition. On the basis
of these two types we also distinguish between the way of entrainment
coupled to the   various   flow regimes. In case of the dryout type
reflood, droplets forming a dispersed flow are formed from a liquid film.
In case of the liquid column type, the liquid droplets are formed directly from the churn flow.

Upstream of the quench front the two important flow regimes are the nucleate boiling and the transition boiling regime with high void production
regime. Downstream the quenchfront in pattern A, we observe first the
liquid column, known as the inverted annular flow regime, followed by
a slug or churn flow type two phase flow changing at a certain height
into a dispersed or mist flow. (fig. 2.) In case of a flow pattern B
the annular flow at the quench front is directly followed by the dispersed flow regime.

Downstream of the dispersed flow the heat transfer is caused by steam
convection only.

The heat transfer, caused by the dispersed flow, is important in terminating the wall temperature increase during a loss of coolant accident. The
droplet concentration and the amount of liquid is dependent on the
entrainment and carry-over of droplets. The literature gives a number
of entrainment mechanisms |9, 10|. In case of a reflood process the
most important mechanisms are (fig. 3)

- the roll wave and wave undercut mechanism in case of the entrainment
  from a liquid film
- the bubble burst mechanism atomizing a liquid film in small droplets
- the bubble escape followed by the formation of a liquid jet and the
  fragmentation of this jet
- the desintegration of a liquid jet formed by the inverted annular
  flow in small tubes
- the desintegration of liquid bridges in a slug or churn flow by the
  high velocity vapour volumes.

The first mentioned mechanism is important when the quench type model
B is present. The bubble burst mechanism gives only very small liquid
droplets and can be neglected in determining the carry-over of liquid.
The last three mechanisms are not really different, they are all familiar
to the slug-churn to annular flow transition.

In most reflood calculation models the subchannel is replaced by a tubu-
lar channel with an equivalent hydraulic diameter. In the following we
will describe the influence of the geometry on the entrainment mechanisms.
Very recently Saito et al|11| have published an extensive analytical in-
vestigation of the annular two phase flows of both adiabatic and boiling

flows. The developed model can be applied to flows in simple and complex
geometries. Saito et al showed that the entrainment from the liquid films
is related to the geometry of the channels and the subchannels in a bundle because of the difference in liquid film thickness on the various
surfaces in the channel.

The film flows in different geometries are shown in Fig. 4. and are compared to the heat transfer and void production in an inverted annular
flow situation. In case of equilibrium the heat transferred from the
high temperature walls to the two-phase flow gives a mean void fraction
dependent on the total mass flow and therefore on the cross section area
of the channel. However, in case of a non-equilibrium situation, the
heat is received by only a small part of the cross section area. In the
first case, comparing the phenomena in different geometries, one can use
the hydraulic diameter concept because the ratio between the cross section
area and the heated surface area determines the mean void fraction and
the other coupled properties. In the non-equilibrium situation the ratio
of the liquid volume in a part of the cross section and the heated surface
area is important. Therefore in a non-equilibrium process like the reflood process, one cannot replace symply the subchannel of a bundle by
a tube of the same hydraulic diameter.

Besides the difference in heat transfer there exists a difference in
the drift velocity of vapour slugs or large bubbles in various channel
geometries. Griffith |12| showed in a bundle there is a channeling of
vapour which influences the rise velocity of the bubble in a bundle.
Comparing to the symmetrical flow in a tube, the bubble flow in annuli
and bundles can be non symmetrical. Recently Jones and Zuber |1| showed
that in case of the transition from a slug flow to the annular flow this
difference in bubble behaviour is also important. They found that the
drift velocity at the transition can be written as

$$V_{vd} = K \sqrt{gD\Delta\rho/\rho_\ell} \tag{1}$$

The K en D values for different geometries are taken from ref. |1| and
are shown in TABLE I.
With this relation we can write the difference between the vapour and
liquid phase velocity as

$$V_v - V_\ell = \frac{K}{1-\alpha} \sqrt{gD\Delta\rho/\rho_\ell} \tag{2}$$

We assume that in case of the liquid column type reflood process, with
heat addition to the two phase flow, the criterion for a transition is
of the same form. However a transition to annular flow is impossible
because of the high wall temperatures. We therefore assume a direct
transition from the slug or churn flow to the dispersed flow regime but
at higher void fraction than the α at the slug to annular transition.
The velocity difference determined by (2) can be taken as the criterion
for the production of droplets necessary for entrainment. This criterion
should be added to the criterion used in a number of computer programs
which is based on the balance between the drag force and gravity force

on a bubble with a maximum diameter given by the stability criterion
for liquid droplets in a vapour flow.

$$V_v - V_\ell = \left[\frac{4}{3}\frac{W_e}{C_D}\right]^{\frac{1}{4}} \left[\frac{\sigma(\rho_\ell - \rho_v)g}{\rho_v^2}\right]^{\frac{1}{4}} \qquad (3)$$

The criterion of formula (3) does not involve geometry effects. As men-
tioned in the introduction, Holderness |3| showed that in order to get
good agreement between calculations and experiments the criterion for
the onset of entrainment for bundle experiments should be slightly
different from that for tube experiments. From formula (3) it is not
clear what type of physical mechanism is changed going from bundles to
tubes. With the formulation (2) as the start of droplet production a
geometry effect is introduced.

EXPERIMENTS

We carried out three categories of experiments. First simple reflood experiments in glass tubes studying the wetting of glass tubes by liquid
nitrogen and the wetting of heated glass tubes by water of room temperature. The second category is a set of reflood experiments in annuli and
the third category is a number of experiments in four-rod bundles.
In order to get an idea about the two phase flow pattern in simple geometries like tubes, reflood experiments in glass tubes of about 1 meter
length have been carried out with liquid nitrogen, starting with a glass
wall temperature around 20ºC. We did the experiments for various tube
diameters in the range of 4 - 14 mm and flooding rates in the range of
1 - 2 cm/sec.

With the glass tube of 14 mm diameter we carried out also a reflood
experiment with water for a glass wall temperature around 600° C.
From these experiments in simple geometries we determine the flow
pattern and the entrainment during the reflood process by means of
filming the process with a high speed HYCAM camera.

The second set of reflood experiments have been carried out with annuli
consisting of an heater element with a diameter of 11,4 mm surrounded
by a glass tube of around 25 mm. First for annuli with short heater
elements of 0,3 meter heated length and secondly for annuli with heater
elements with a heated length of 1,5 meter. The hydraulic diameters
of the annular channels are around 14 mm, the same as that of the largest glass tube diameter for the nitrogen and water reflood experiments
described above. The wall temperatures are measured in both cases by
5 thermocouples along the heated length. The initial wall temperatures
are chosen in the range of 500°C to 900°C and the flooding rate in the
range of 3 - 10 cm/sec.

We planned a number of four-rod bundle experiments, three bundles surrounded by a circular glass tube and three bundles with a rectangular
housing. As shown in Fig. 5, each bundle consists of four heater elements
of around 12 mm diameter and 1 meter heated length. The bundles differ
from each other with respect to the distance between the heater elements

(Pitch 17; 15,6 and 14 mm). The diameters of the surrounding glass tubes are chosen in such a way that the distance between the glass tube and a heater pin is equal to the distance between two heater rods. The bundles surrounded with quartz glass tubes differ therefore in crosssection area. The area are 11,6 cm^2; 8,7 cm^2 and 5,6 cm^2 respectively. The wall temperature along the bundles is measured by 24 thermocouples devided along the heated length of the four heater elements over 5 planes as illustrated by Fig. 5. For the bundle with pitch 17 mm and a glass tube as housing, 20 thermocouples are devided over the inner subchannel and gaps between the heater elements and 4 thermocouples are positioned in the outer subchannels on a distance of 75 cm from the onset of the heated length.

For the bundle with the pitch of 15,6 mm the arrangement of thermocouples is somewhat different from that of the first bundle, described above. We made an arrangement of 16 thermocouples over the planes along the heater elements on the inner channel and gap locations of the heaters. The other 8 thermocouples are devided over the two planes IV and V on the heaters in the outer subchannels.

Up to now we carried out a number of experiments with bundle I (17 mm pitch) and bundle II (15,6 mm pitch). For bundle I and II we carried out reflood experiments with 2 cm/sec. flooding rate and initial wall temperatures of 500°C, 600°C and 700°C, with a flooding rate of 4,5 cm/sec. for 500°C and 600°C and 700°C and with 6,5 cm/sec. flooding rate also for the initial wall temperatures 500°C, 600°C and 700°C.

RESULTS AND DISCUSSION

Before we describe and discuss the experimental results we first repeat two phenomena which are important in case of the reflood process. The rewetting of a nuclear fuel element is influenced by the boiling mechanism in the wetted part of the rods and by the cooling capacity of the two phase flow downstream the quenchfront. The boiling just upstream of the quenchfront is very explosive. One can say that all nuclei on the heated surface can be activated. The coalescence of the growing bubbles and the departure of the coalesced bubbles and the rising to the continuous liquid level is dependent on the distance between the heated surfaces. Important for entrainment is the forming by coalescence of large vapour bubbles rising with high velocity to the continuous liquid level.

Tube Experiments.

We started the experimental investigations determining the influence of the geometry on entrainment with reflood experiments in small tube diameters, followed by experiments with larger diameters.
The experiments showed that the rewetting of small diameter glass tubes (4 and 6 mm) is of the dryout quench type whereas at the end of the process also impinging droplets are able to contact the wall providing for a second wetted region. The quench front velocity is very fast and the process looks more or less like a cocurrent flooding process with droplet entrainment from the liquid film on the tube surface. We try to

answer the question whether or not there is a similar flooding process
in the gaps between the fuel pins in a bundle.
In case of the small diameter tubes we did not observe an inverted annular flow along the tube. The stability of a liquid column is dependent
on the length diameter ratio. Bailey |13| determined the maximum stable
length L max of a vertical column with a diameter D_ℓ.

$$L_{max} = D_\ell\ \pi/0,484 \tag{4}$$

For small diameter tubes this means that the stable length of the inverted annular flow becomes very small and therefore the flow patterns
changes easily to a dispersed flow.

The reflood of a glass tube of 14 mm is of the liquid column type as
well as for wetting with liquid nitrogen as for the wetting of the heated
glass tube by water of room temperature. The reflood starts with an inverted annular flow type. Downstream the inverted annular flow short
after the start a slug and churn flow regime is formed, due to a high bubble
growth and the coalescense of bubbles in the wetted region.
From the tube experiments is is clear that the transition to a dispersed
flow is reached earlier for the smaller diameters. An earlier transition
to the dispersed flow or entrainment causes a lower quench front velocity.
There are two reasons for the earlier transition. First the ratio between
the heated surface and the available heat receiving liquid changes proportional to 4/D which means that the quality and void fraction at a certain
position reach the critical values earlier. For large diameter values however
this relation with D will be less dominant because non-equilibrium effects will
play an important role. The second reason for an earlier transition is based
on formula (2). The critical velocity difference for a transition between
churn and dispersed flow is related to the root of the diameter.

Annuli Experiments.

Using annuli we have to introduce "cold" wall effects if there exists a
temperature difference between the heater element surface and the temperature
of the surrounding glass tube. The "colder" wall will be wetted first
and provide for a vapour production and therefore for an early entrainment. Comparing to tubes of the same hydraulic diameter this early entrainment should influence the quench front velocity. However on the
basis of formula (1) the drift velocity for transition in flow patterns
is different. The ratio of the critical drift velocity in a tube and
that in annulus is according to (1) and Table I equal to

$$\frac{V_{vd}\ (tube)}{V_{vd}\ (annulus)} = \frac{0,35\ \sqrt{g}\ \ D_{tube}}{(0,35 + 0,058\ D_i/D_o)\ \sqrt{gD_o}} = \frac{0,35}{0,38}\ \sqrt{\frac{D_{tube}}{D_o}} \tag{5}$$

This means that the drift velocity for transition is lower for tubes than
that for annuli of the same hydraulic diameter. This effect will compensate partly the early entrainment by the "cold" wall effect. In future,
experiments with a heated "cold" wall will show the real effect of the
annular geometry on the entrainment and quench front velocity.

Bundle experiments

The "cold" wall effects we described in case of the experiments in annuli
are also present in case of the bundle experiments. That means that at
a certain position of the heated length the void production will start
at the glass surface. In order to investigate the influence of the bundle
geometry on the reflood process and especially on the entrainment and in
order to determine the influence of the gap distance between fuel pins
on the entrainment, one can use the "cold" wall as a heat producing and
therefore void producing surface. Taking the same gap distance between
the glass surface and heater element the effect of gap distance, if there
is any, occurs in a non symmetrical way but will demonstrate the type of
phenomena within the gap.
The entrainment phenomena and the dispersed two phase flow just above the
entrainment level at the position between 20 and 25 cm from the beginning of
the heated length, have been filmed by a high speed film camera with a
speed of 2500 pictures per second. This means that we observe the phenomena
in case of the liquid column type quench front mode. The films showed
similar pictures as we found in case of the reflood process in the annuli.
However there is a difference in the trajectories passed along by the
liquid droplets. The liquid droplets in the bundle are formed in one of
the subchannels of the bundle and are carried away by the vapour coming
down in other subchannels of the bundle. We found also from the pictures
a steep droplet concentration gradient along the channel and a distribution
of droplets with a maximum for droplets of 1 mm diameter.
The steep gradient in droplet concentration for droplets with the same
diameter can occur when the start velocities of the droplets are different.
This velocity difference is dependent on the jet velocity or liquid bridge
velocity caused by escaping vapour. The vapour escape velocity will not
be the same for all vapour bubbles and slugs. Therefore the droplets start
with different velocities. The steep axial concentration gradient along
the channels means a small difference in void fraction. From

$$N = \frac{6}{\pi} \frac{(1 - \alpha)}{D_d^3}$$

we learn that a steep droplet concentration change, for droplets of 1 mm
diameter for instance, from 40 per cm^3 to 0 per cm^3, the α changes from
$\alpha = 0,98$ to $\alpha = 1,00$. This change in α means only a small change in vapour
velocity in the dispersed flow region. The droplet diameter distribution
being present will not change dramatically the conclusion.
From the temperature decrease plots of the thermocouple signals appear
that the temperature decrease at a certain position above the quench front
is nearly constant during a long time of the reflood process. Neglecting
the heat diffusion effect in the heater elements one can say that a
constant temperature decrease corresponds to a continuous increasing
heat transfer coëfficient and that the heat transfer coëfficient in the
region before the quench front is more or less a linear function of the
temperature up to temperatures near the quench temperature. The quench
temperatures we found were in the range of $350 - 420^\circ$ C.

The quench front velocities in the two bundles are shown in Fig. 7, 8,
9 and 10. Comparing these velocities no remarkable difference between

The short annulus experiments (30 cm heated length) have been used to study the development of the flow pattern during the reflood process and to study the way of entrainment. Like in case of the rewetting of a tube of the same hydraulic diameter (14 mm), in case of subcooled liquid, the two phase flow pattern is built up as shown in Fig. 2 with the inverted annular flow and the slug-churn flow regime downstream this annular flow. The transition to the dispersed flow is shown in Fig. 6.
The entrainment is caused by the fragmentation of liquid jets and fragmentation of liquid bridges or elongated liquid formations. Analyzing the films and photographs made of the dispersed flow just around the entrainment level we obtained a droplet start velocity of 1,0 - 1,5 m/sec. Dependent on the vapour velocity the droplets are accelerated to velocities of 3 m/sec. The films show a spectrum of bubble diameters with maximum values between 3 and 4 mm and a maximum concentration in the range of 0,5 - 1,0 mm. Based on our observations the number of droplets just above the entrainment level is of the order of 20 - 40 per cm³. For droplets of 1 mm this means a void fraction of 0,99 - 0,98. Based on formula (6)

$$V_v - V_\ell = (0,35 + 0,058 \frac{D_i}{D_o}) \; \frac{\sqrt{g \, D_o \, \Delta\rho/\rho_\ell}}{1 - \alpha}$$

(6)

The velocity difference between the vapour and liquid phase at the transition is in the range of 9,5 - 19 m/sec.
Based on a critical Weber number of 6,5 for a maximum droplet diameter of 3 mm, we find for the velocity difference between the vapour phase and the liquid droplet velocity a value of

$$V_v - V_{\bar{v}} = (\frac{6,5 \; \sigma}{\rho_v \, D_{dr}})^{\frac{1}{2}} \approx 14,5 \; m/sec.$$

(7)

For a liquid droplet velocity of 3 m/sec this means a vapour velocity of 17,5 m/sec., which is in the range of the velocity calculated from the transition criterion.

The experiments with the longer length annuli (1,5 meter heated length) showed a similar flow pattern at the start of the reflood process, with an inverted annular flow regime, churn flow regime and dispersed flow regime. However dependent on the initial temperature and on the heat production, after the rewetting of a certain length the existence of an inverted annular flow regime could not firmly recorded and we only observed the slug-churn flow type flow pattern.

The quench front velocity showed a small decrease special in the case of high heat flux and high wall temperatures. This change in quenchfront velocity along the length is also found for the tube experiments described by Wahba |7|. Kaminaga et al |14| showed that this change in quench front velocity along the length can be described by introducing a heat transfer coëfficient in the film boiling region of the form

$$\alpha = C \left[\frac{\lambda^3_v \, \rho_v \, (\rho_\ell - \rho_v) \, g \, h_{fg}}{\mu_v \, \ell_x \, (T_w - T_s)} \right]^{\frac{1}{4}}$$

(8)

with $C = 0,023 \, U^{1,6} + 0,8$

the two quench front velocities have been found for corresponding wall temperatures and corresponding flooding rates, whereas the crossection area is changed from 11,6 cm^2 to 8,7 cm^2. At the same time the heat producing surface was changed from 296 cm^2 to 279 cm^2 which is a change of 6% whereas the change in cross section about 25%. Comparing the equivalent hydraulic diameter of bundle I (D_H = 15,6) with that of II (D_H = 12,4) one supposes on the basis of the results of K.W.U. tube experiments [3] a larger increase in quench times.

Using the criterion for entrainment based on the flow pattern transition as given in formula (1) and (2) and assuming the same α for transition, one obtains for two tubes of diameter D_H = 15,6 mm and D_H = 12,4

$$\frac{(V_v - V_\ell)_I}{(V_v - V_\ell)_{II}} = \sqrt{\frac{15,6}{12,4}} = 1,12 \tag{10}$$

and for the bundles I and II

$$\frac{(V_v - V_\ell)_I}{(V_v - V_\ell)_{II}} = \frac{\left[0,35 + 0,8 \ (1 - D_H/D_o)^3 \right]_I}{\left[0,35 + 0,8 \ (1 - D_H/D_o)^3 \right]_{II}} . \sqrt{\frac{15,6}{12,4}} = 1,04 \tag{11}$$

On the basis of the calculated ratio one can explain why the difference in quench front velocity in case of tubes is larger than in case of the bundle configuration.

For annuli this change in hydraulic diameter should give the ratio

$$\frac{(V_v - V_\ell)_I}{(V_v - V_\ell)_{II}} = \frac{\left[0,35 + 0,058 \ D_i/D_o \right]_I}{\left[0,35 + 0,058 \ D_i/D_o \right]_{II}} . \sqrt{\frac{45,5}{41,0}} = 1,05 \tag{12}$$

CONCLUSION

On the basis of computer calculations, Holderness [3] concludes that in order to get good agreement between experiments and the calculations, one should use different criteria for slip, drift velocity and onset of entrainment. The entrainment criterion based on the Weber number for the maximum stable diameter and the drag coëfficient for spherical droplets does not involve geometry effects. The experiments showed that there are reasons to introduce a second entrainment criterium concerning the creation of liquid droplets. We assume a start of creating droplets when the slug-churn flow to dispersed flow transition occurs. Using the same type of geometry influence on the transition as proposed by Griffith [12] and Jones and Zuber [1] one can explain why the difference in quench front velocity for changing tube diameters is larger than in case of the same change in bundle hydraulic diameter.

ACKNOWLEDGEMENTS

The authors wish to thank Mrs. P.A. Bozelie and A. Warmenhoven for their extensive assistance during the experiments and Mr. H. Hoogland for the

discussions concerning the influence of different parameters on the reflood process.

REFERENCES

1 Jones, O.C. and Zuber, J.R., Slug - Annular transition with parti-
   cular reference to narrow rectangular ducts.
   Int. Sem. Momentum Heat and Mass Transfer in Two - Phase Energy and
   Chemical Systems.

3 Holderness, J.H., THERM: A Thermal Hydraulic Emergency Reflood
   Model, Combustion Engineering, Inc. report CENPD 228, 1977.

2 Kirchner, W.L., Reflood Heat Transfer in a Light Water Reactor,
   Ph. D. Thesis, M.I.T. Nuclear Engineering Department. Jan. 1976.

4 Peterson, A.C., Loomis, G.G. and Chen, L.L.,
   Thermal and Hydraulic Response of the Semiscale Mod - 1 Core. during
   Forced Feed Reflood Tests. TREE NUREG -1001 Jan. 1977.

5 Andersen, J.G.M.,"CORECOOL: A Model for the Temperature Distribution
   and Two - Phase flow in a Fuel Element Under LOCA Conditions",
   General Electric Co, Report NEDO - 21325 1976.

6 Seidelberger, E. and Weiss, P., Models of Reflood Heat Transfer
   and Hydraulics in a Heated Rod Bundle.
   Paper presented at the European Two - Phase Flow Group Meeting 1978,
   Stockholm, May 29 - June 1, 1978.

7 Wahba, A.B. Heat Transfer to Two - Phase Flow During a Rewetting
   Process.
   Paper presented at the European Two-Phase Flow Group Meeting
   Stockholm May 29 - June 1, 1978.

8 Murao Y., An Analytical Study of the Thermo-Hydrodynamic Behaviour
   of the Reflood - Phase during a LOCA. KFK 2545.

9 Ishi, M. and Grolmes, M.A., Inception Criteria for Droplet Entrainment
   in Two - Phase Concurrent Film Flow.
   AICHE Journal vol. 21, no. 2, page 308 (1975).

10 Mayinger, F. and Viecenz, H.J., Vapour Separation from the Horizontal
   Surface of a Boiling Two - Phase Mixture Pool with Special Regard to
   the Liquid Carry-over.
   Paper present at the European Two - Phase Flow Group Meeting.
   Stockholm, May 29 - June 1, 1978.

11 Saito, T., Hughes, E.D. and Carbon, M.W.,
   Multi - Fluid Modeling of Annular Two - Phase Flow,
   Nuclear Engineering and Design 50 (1978) 225 - 271.

12 Griffith, P., The Prediction of Low Quality Boiling Voids,
   ASME Paper No. 63 - HT - 20 National Heat Transfer Conf.
   Boston, Mass. 1963.

13 Bailey, N.A., Film Boiling on Submerged Vertical Cylinders
    AEEW - M 1051 (1971)

14 Kaminaga, F., Uchida, H. and Saito, T.,
    Heat Transfer Model of Quenching in the Reflooding Phase.
    Presented at Ad Hoc Working Group on ECC, CSNI, NEA, OECD,
    August 5 - 6 (1976).

NOMENCLATURE

C	, constant used in formula 8
C_D	, drag coëfficient
D	, diameter; characteristic dimension
D_H	, hydraulic diameter
D_i	, inner diameter annulus
D_ℓ	, diameter liquid jet
D_o	, outer diameter annulus
g	, gravitational acceleration
L	, heat transfer coëfficient
h_{fg}	, heat of vaporization
K	, constant formula (1) and (2)
ℓ_x	, vapour film length from quench front
L_{max}	, maximum stable jet legth
N	, number of droplets per unit volume
q	, heat flux
T_w	, wall temperature
T_s	, saturation temperature
T_{sub}	, liquid subcooling
U	, flooding rate
V_ℓ	, velocity of the liquid phase
V_v	, velocity of the vapour phase
V_{vd}	, drift velocity of the vapour phase
W_e	, droplet Weber number
α	, void fraction
λ_v	, thermal conductivity
ρ_ℓ	, density of the liquid phase
ρ_v	, density of the vapour phase
$\Delta\rho$	, density difference between liquid and vapour
σ	, surface tension
μ_v	, viscosity

Table I: Drift coëfficients for slug to annular transition Ref. [1].

Geometry	Drift Coëfficient	Characteristic Dimension
Tube	$0,35$	D
Annulus	$0,35 + 0,058\ D_i/D_o$	D_o
Rod Bundle	$0,35 + 0,8\ (1-D_H/D_o)^3$	D_H

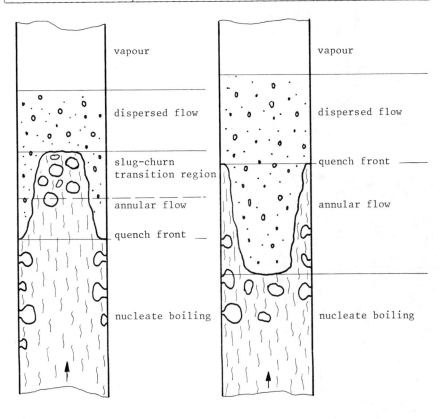

Flow pattern A
Liquid colum type quench

Flow pattern B
Dryout type quench

Fig. 1. Flow patterns in case of a reflood process.

Fig. 2. Photograph of the inverted annular and slug-churn flow in an annulus.

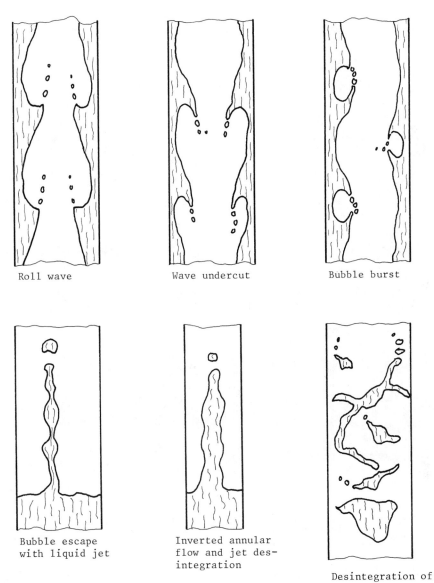

Roll wave   Wave undercut   Bubble burst

Bubble escape   Inverted annular
with liquid jet   flow and jet des-
         integration

Desintegration of
liquid bridges and
the transition from slug or churn flow to dispersed flow.

Fig. 3. Mechanisms of entrainment.

A   B

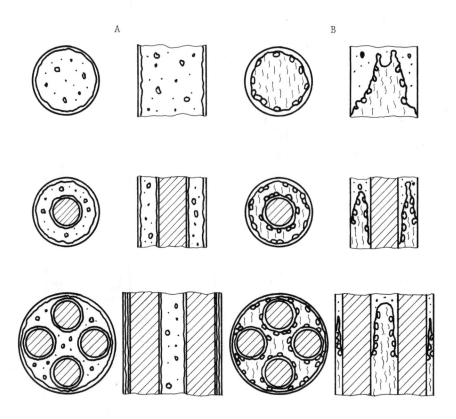

Fig. 4. Geometry effects on film flow entrainment and non-equilibrium heat
transfer (A) and entrainment from two-phase-flows with lower void
fractions (B).

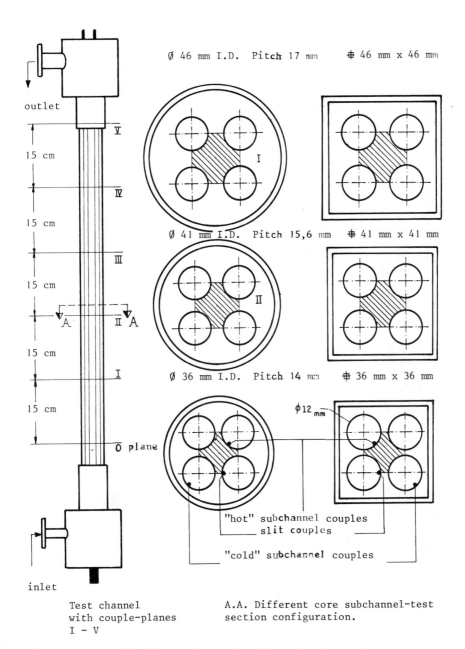

Ø 46 mm I.D. Pitch 17 mm   ⊞ 46 mm x 46 mm

Ø 41 mm I.D. Pitch 15,6 mm   ⊞ 41 mm x 41 mm

Ø 36 mm I.D. Pitch 14 mm   ⊞ 36 mm x 36 mm

φ 12 mm

"hot" subchannel couples
slit couples
"cold" subchannel couples

outlet

15 cm

15 cm

15 cm

15 cm

15 cm

Ⅴ

Ⅳ

Ⅲ

Ⅱ

Ⅰ

Ⅱ

0 plane

inlet

Test channel   A.A. Different core subchannel-test
with couple-planes   section configuration.
I - V

Fig. 5. Four-rod bundle configurations for reflood experiments.

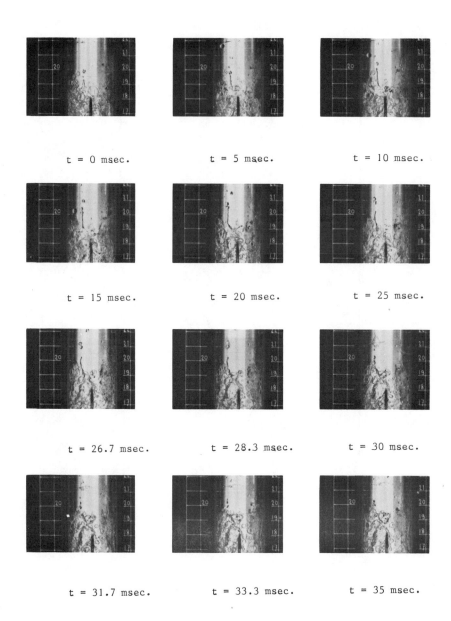

t = 0 msec.   t = 5 msec.   t = 10 msec.

t = 15 msec.   t = 20 msec.   t = 25 msec.

t = 26.7 msec.   t = 28.3 msec.   t = 30 msec.

t = 31.7 msec.   t = 33.3 msec.   t = 35 msec.

Fig. 6. Droplet formation by the fragmentation of liquid jets.

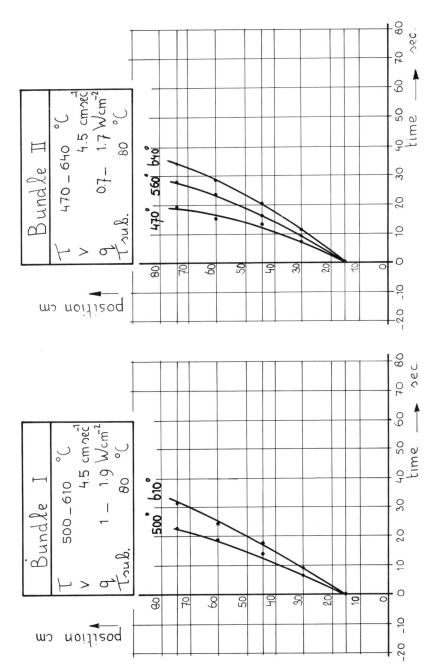

FIG. 7   Experimental values of the quenchfront position as a function of time for the flooding rate 4,5 cm/sec.

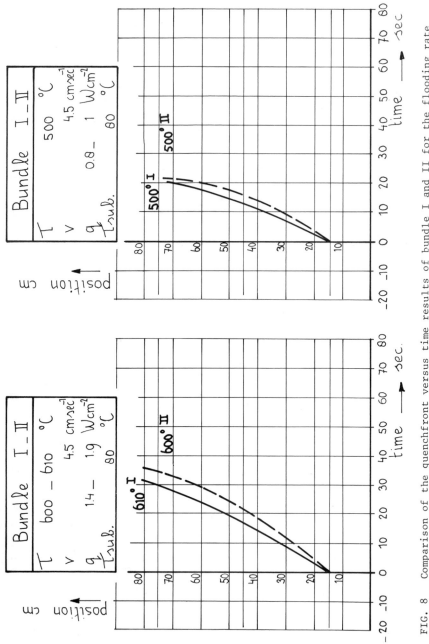

FIG. 8   Comparison of the quenchfront versus time results of bundle I and II for the flooding rate 4,5 cm/sec.

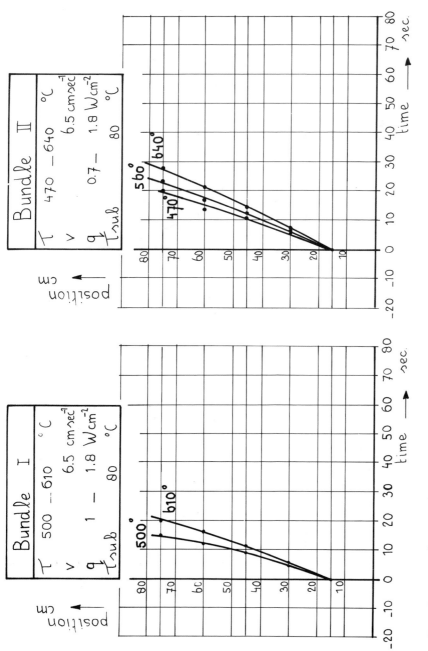

FIG. 9   Experimental values of the quenchfront position as a function of time for the flooding rate of 6,5 cm/sec.

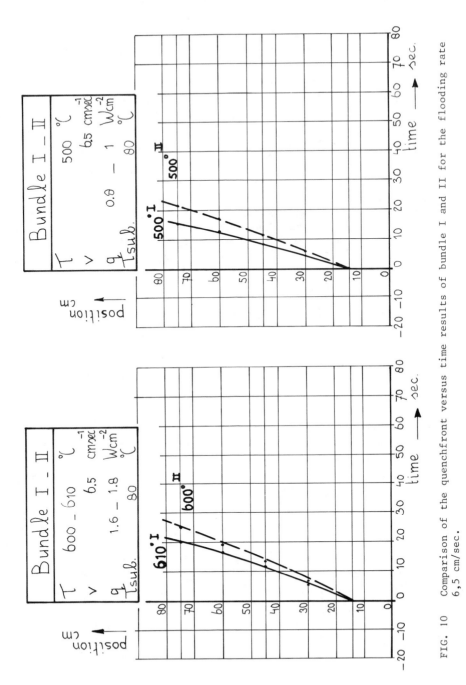

FIG. 10   Comparison of the quenchfront versus time results of bundle I and II for the flooding rate 6,5 cm/sec.

1482

Inlet Geometry Effects upon Liquid Phase Entrainment in Unsteady Duct Flows

N.E. WIJEYSUNDERA and C.W. SAVERY
Drexel University
Philadelphia, Pennsylvania 19104, USA

ABSTRACT

A series of bench experiments have been conducted to study the entrainment of liquid phase in exiting vent flows from nuclear containment subcompartments subjected to hypothetical pipe ruptures. Measured rates of air and water flow are introduced through an inlet nozzle into a transparent test section containing a square cross section and fitted with an outlet orifice. Entrainment tests were conducted with four different inlet nozzle arrangements, three inlet nozzle axis elevations, three nozzle axis angles with the horizontal and three duct geometries. Flow observation and entrainment measurements have shown the existence of three distinct phases of the process, each associated with different entrainment mechanisms.

INTRODUCTION

In the design of nuclear power plants the effects of pipeline ruptures in the containment buildings are considered. Current subcompartment licensing problems include primary coolant, feed water and steam line breaks. In these hypothetical accidents high energy fluid is vented into a subcompartment and the resulting transient two-phase flow among the interconnected subcompartment is analyzed. The calculated absolute pressure, differential compartmental pressures and temperature histories are considered in the building structural design and in safeguarding the integrity of building components. The peak pressures calculated during the transient depend upon the extent of droplet phase entrained in the intercompartmental vent flow [1]. Significant reductions in peak pressures result from entrainment fractions reduced from the current conservative practice of assuming complete entrainment. In this study, the entrainment phenomenon is investigated with a bench scale experiment.

A bench scale experiment was built and entrainment data corresponding to a constant coaxial flow of an air-water mixture through a critical flow nozzle into a square horizontal duct were obtained. The variables investigated were air and water flow rates, exit orifice position, shape and size and test section tilt to horizontal. For an axially located, fixed geometry critical flow inlet nozzle the instantaneous entrainment rate data were correlated with duct air flow rate and average separated phase depth. These results were reported in Ref. [2].

In the present study, experiments were conducted in which the effect of inlet nozzle and test section geometry were investigated.

EXPERIMENTAL PROCEDURES

The experimental arrangement is illustrated schematically in the line diagram shown on Fig. 1. The experiment consisted of a rectangular duct into
which a metered mixture of air and water was fed through a nozzle. The
outlet end of the duct contained a replaceable orifice plate. Four different types of inlet nozzles were used. These were: (i) a converging sonic
nozzle, (ii) an air atomizing narrow cone spray, (iii) an air atomizing
flat spray, and (iv) an air atomizing multi-hole spray. The air atomizing
nozzles which have replaceable air and liquid orifices enable the air flow
rate to be varied up to about 25 g/s and the water flow rate to about 10
g/s, while maintaining sonic conditions at the nozzle outlet. These are
commercial atomizing nozzles for which the estimated liquid drop size is in
the range 30-50 µm. The axial position of the inlet nozzle and the inclina-
tion of its axis of spray to the horizontal were varied by using different
end plates. Three different inlet nozzle elevations and nozzle angles were
considered in the present study. The additional important variables of
test section length relative to the pre-attachment distance of the jet and
the aspect ratio of the duct were studied by performing tests with three
different test sections. These had nominal dimensions of 95 mm x 95 mm x
760 mm; 95 mm x 95 mm x 380 mm and 95 mm x 190 x 380 mm. All test sections
were made of plexiglas which facilitated flow observation and the use of
photographic techniques.

The air flow rate was controlled by a pressure regulator and was measured
by a laminar flow element. The pressure drop across the laminar flow element was measured by an inclined manometer. The water flow rate was
varied with a needle valve and was measured by a rotameter. The rate of
liquid entrainment from the duct was determined by measuring the volume
of the separated liquid in the test section at different times in the history. This was done by measuring the depth of liquid using a micrometer
depth gauge. The different processes which contribute to liquid entrainment were studied by flow observation and a number of distinct phases of
the entrainment history were identified. The relative contribution of
some of the entrainment mechanisms were estimated by devising experiments
where each of these mechanisms in turn were suppressed. A short baffle
was fixed to the inner wall of the test section to suppress the entrainment which occurs by film flow along the walls. An outlet orifice mask
was used to suppress the liquid entrainment by film flow along the outlet
end wall.

The static pressure distribution in the test section was measured with air
purged wall pressure taps. Also, some measurements were made of the flow
field in the duct with dry air flow. These were done to confirm flow
observations.

EXPERIMENTAL RESULTS

Phases of Entrainment History

Flow visualization and photographic study of the flow process in the test section have shown the existence of a number of distinct phases in the entrainment history. This was found to be true for all the nozzle types and test sections considered in the present study. The histories shown in Figs. 3 - 8 for conditions in Table 1 can be discussed in terms of these different phases of the entrainment history. The liquid phase undergoes a number of different processes during its passage through the test section. The flow diagram of Fig. 2 shows the various mechanisms, which lead to liquid phase entrainment. These are outlined below:

(i)   The atomized water and air mixture entering the duct strikes the walls and this results in impingement separation of the liquid phase. The separated liquid forms a film on the duct wall as seen on Fig. 9. This film in general flows upstream and collects under the jet as seen in Fig. 11. A comparison of the static pressure profiles shown on Fig. 9 and the separated liquid-surface shape of Fig. 11 shows that initially the separated liquid occupies the low pressure region in the duct between points A and B on Fig. 9. The separated liquid has a rectangular shape with one end at the point where the static pressure in the duct is a minimum. Velocity measurements with dry air only flowing in the duct indicate that at this point the recirculation flow velocity is a maximum. The separated liquid surface is wavy due to the recirculating flow above it. The liquid entrainment during this phase is low due mainly to the unseparated drops in the main flow which reach the exit orifice. The downstream end of the test section has very little separated liquid at this stage.

(ii) As more separated liquid collects under the jet, the height of the liquid surface increases. Also, the height of the waves on the liquid surface becomes large as seen from Fig. 19. At this stage some of the waves are cut by the recirculating flow above it. This results in the generation of large drops, some of which are redeposited in the upstream end and others which are entrained by the expanding jet. This leads to secondary atomization. At this stage the droplet concentration in the downstream end increases with attendent increasing rate of entrainment from the duct. Some of the drops produced by secondary atomization are splashed on the walls of the duct which results in a film flow along the top and side walls of the duct. This film flow is visible on Fig. 13. Also, the drops splashed on the end wall of the duct result in a film flow which contributes to the entrainment. Some of the drops are redeposited on the downstream end of the test section which results in the formation of a liquid pool at the downstream end. As time proceeds, the interaction between the jet and the separated liquid becomes more intense and the height of the downstream liquid pool increases. This is seen on Fig. 14. This period corresponds to the region C – D of curve b of Fig. 3. For high air flow rates the system reaches a steady-state during this phase.

(iii)   For certain test section and nozzle configurations, and mainly for low air flow rates, a third phase of the entrainment history was observed. During this phase, the liquid redeposited in the downstream side of the test section resulted in a high liquid level. At some point in the history this liquid begins to spill over the outlet orifice. This process is enhanced by the surface waves formed due to the jet – liquid interaction which occurs at the upstream end. Fig. 15 shows the onset of this phase. The rate of entrainment during this phase is very large, and consequently, the system usually attains a steady-state.

Effect of Variables

Air Flow Rate

The air flow rate is one of the most important variables which affects the different phases of the entrainment history. This is seen from the entrainment histories shown on Fig. 3. The rate of entrainment during the first phase is not strongly dependent on the air flow rate. However, the onset of the second phase is strongly dependent on this variable. At low air flow rates secondary atomization does not begin until the level of the separated liquid phase has reached its limiting value and even at this stage the extent of droplet formation is low. Also, when droplet entrainment occurs, most droplets are redeposited in the downstream end of the test section. The contribution to entrainment from the top and end wall film flow is very low as seen from the curves of Fig. 4. For very low air flow rates a third entrainment mechanism, that is spilling over the outlet orifice, occurs. For high air flow rates, the level of separated liquid necessary for the onset of secondary atomization is low because the velocity of the recirculating flow, which causes the secondary atomization, increases with increasing air flow rate. This is shown on Fig. 16. Also, there is a substantial contribution to entrainment from the top and end wall film flow for this case as shown on Fig. 4.

It is seen from Fig. 3 that for the low air flow rate of 3.6 g/s the slope of the entrainment rate curve is larger than the slope for 4.77 g/s after about 28 minutes. For the lower air flow rate, the second phase of entrainment begins at about 18 minutes and by this time the downstream end also has a substantial amount of separated liquid. When the jet-separated liquid interaction proceeds, liquid begins to spill over the outlet orifice at about 28 minutes. The additional entrainment by this mechanism changes the slope of the entrainment curve. Thus, the part GH of this curve corresponds to a combined effect of mechanisms one and two.

For a flow rate of 4.77 g/s, secondary atomization starts at about 5 minutes and is the main mechanism of entrainment until about 30 minutes, when there is some spilling over of liquid. It is seen that for the higher air flow rates of 10, 16 and 23 g/s, secondary atomization begins very early in the history and liquid entrainment is governed by this mechanism during the entire history. For these high flow rates, the liquid fraction retained in the test section is relatively small and direct spilling over of liquid does not occur. For these cases, the system usually reaches a steady-state during the second phase of entrainment.

The importance of film flow along the top and end walls are seen from Fig. 4. For the high air flow rate of 10 g/s, these contributions are significant until about 15 minutes. Both the mask around the outlet orifice and the baffle on the top wall drain the liquid to the downstream liquid pool. During the early part of the history, this decreases the rate of entrainment. However, at longer times the entrainment increases because of a more intense jet-separated liquid interaction which results due to the higher separated liquid fraction.

Nozzle Type

The multi-hole nozzle used in the present study has six small orifices, which produce a spray with an overall cone angle of about ninety degrees. In the flat spray, the air-water mixture discharges through a round orifice which then passes through a rectangular slit. This produces a spray which is initially flat in one direction and triangular in the perpendicular direction. The narrow cone spray had a cone angle of about ten degrees. Dry measurements for the nozzle flow showed that the multi-hole spray and the flat spray nozzles have lower momentum in the axial direction due to their larger spread compared to the narrow cone nozzle. The entrainment histories for all the nozzles considered in the present study exhibited the three phases of entrainment described above. It is seen from Fig. 5 that the rate of entrainment for the critical nozzle is lower than for the atomizing nozzles, during the first phase. This is because the flow in the critical nozzle is separated flow and therefore does not produce good atomization as in the case of atomizing nozzles. It is seen from Fig. 5 that for the flat spray and the multihole spray, significant entrainment does not occur until about 25 minutes. It is found that for these nozzles, the extent of secondary atomization is much lower than for the narrow cone spray. During the early part of the history a large fraction of the separated liquid phase is retained in the test section. Also, a large fraction of the drops produced by secondary atomization is redeposited in the test section because of the low axial momentum of the jet. The sharp increase in the rate of entrainment at about 27 minutes is due to the spilling over of liquid through the outlet orifice. For these nozzles, the system usually reaches a steady-state during the third phase of entrainment. This shows that for a given mass flow rate of air, the nozzles which have a high degree of initial atomization and high axial momentum produce larger liquid entrainment rates throughout the history.

Inlet Nozzle Elevation

There is a large difference in the flow pattern in the test section for the
cases of an axial nozzle, a nozzle located above the axis and a nozzle located below the axis. This is evident from Figs. 17 and 18. When the
nozzle is above the axis, the main recirculation eddy region is below the
jet axis and the separated liquid is collected upstream under the jet as
seen from Fig. 17. The separated liquid level necessary for the onset of
the second phase is higher than for the axial nozzle. When secondary atomization occurs there results greater liquid redeposition in the downstream
end.

It is seen from Fig. 6 that for the case of a nozzle located above the axis,
significant secondary atomization does not begin until about 22 minutes.
By this time, there is a large volume of separated liquid in the upstream
end of the test section. After about 30 minutes, the rate of entrainment
increases sharply due to liquid spilling over the outlet orifice. Increasing the air flow rate has the effect of increasing liquid entrainment for
all three inlet nozzle geometries but its effect on the overall flow patterns is small.

When the nozzle is located below the axis, the main eddy is found to be
above the jet axis. The separated liquid film tends to follow the stream
lines of this recirculation region. As the liquid is unable to remain in
the region above the jet due to the gravitational force, it falls back and
is swept by the expanding jet to the downstream end of the test section.
It is seen from Fig. 18 that there is no separated liquid under the jet
as in the previous case. All the liquid collection occurs in the downstream end. There is direct interaction between the expanding jet and this
separated liquid surface. The resulting secondary atomization increases
the rate of entrainment. The rate of liquid entrainment for this nozzle
position is marginally larger than for the axial nozzle as seen from Fig. 6.
The system soon enters the third phase due to the surface wave formation
caused by the jet - separated liquid interaction. For this arrangement,
the entrainment reaches a steady-state due to a combination of these processes.

Inlet Nozzle Axis Angle

The effect of inlet nozzle angle was similar to the effect of elevation.
When the nozzle is directed upwards from the horizontal, the main eddy is
formed under the jet axis and a large amount of liquid has to be collected
under the jet before secondary atomization takes place. This is shown on
Fig. 19. When this occurs, much of the liquid phase is redeposited in the
downstream end of the duct.

It is seen from Fig. 7 that for a nozzle directed upwards from the horizontal, secondary atomization does not begin until about 25 minutes. Also,
during this phase the slope of the entrainment rate curve is smaller than
that for an axial nozzle. This is because for this nozzle geometry there

is very little direct interaction between the jet and the separated liquid
even at high liquid levels. Also, there is very little wave formation on
the surface of the separated liquid at the downstream end and therefore,
the contribution to entrainment from liquid spilling is very small. The
system usually reaches a steady-state during the third phase of the history.

For nozzles directed downwards from the horizontal, the main eddy is formed
above the jet axis. The separated liquid is swept by the expanding jet and
the liquid is collected at the downsteam end of the test section. The main
mechanism of entrainment is atomization due to the jet - liquid interaction
as in the case of a jet located below the axis. As more liquid collects on
the downstream side of the duct the interaction between the expanding jet
and this liquid becomes more intense. This produces large surface waves
on the liquid which in turn leads to the spilling over of liquid at about
20 minutes. The rate of entrainment increases sharply during this period.
The system attained a steady-state due to liquid spilling over the outlet
orifice.

Duct Length and Aspect Ratio

The effect of these variables on entrainment is shown on Fig. 8. The rate
of entrainment during the first phase and the onset of second phase is not
strongly affected by the duct length. However, it is seen that for the
shorter duct the rate of entrainment during the second phase is much larger.
It is observed that there is much less liquid redeposition for this duct as
compared to the longer duct. Also, the contribution to entrainment by film
flow along the top and end walls is much larger.

It is found that for a duct of rectangular cross section, the overall flow
pattern and rate of liquid entrainment is dependent on whether the vertical
side of the duct is longer or shorter. It is observed that for an axial
nozzle arrangement, the flow in the duct had two main eddies on either side
of the jet axis. This is seen from Fig. 20. When the longer side is vertical, the separated liquid collected under the jet, as in the case of a
square duct. Also, the other processes of entrainment described above take
place during the history. When the nozzle is located above or below the
axis, most of the phenomena which take place are similar to those observed
with a square duct. This is also seen from the entrainment histories
shown on Fig. 8. It is seen from these curves that the rate of entrainment is very high for the case of a nozzle located below the axis of the
test section with the longer side vertical. The main recirculating eddy
for this case is above the jet axis and the separated liquid film flows
along the streamlines of this region. Being unable to remain in the upper
part of the test section, the liquid drains down and is swept by the jet.
Much of this liquid is entrained directly because of the short length of
the test section.

It is seen from Fig. 8 that for a nozzle located above the axis, a significant increase in liquid entrainment does not occur until about 40 minutes.
During this period a large fraction of the separated liquid is retained in
the test section. The sharp increase in the rate of entrainment which

occurs at about 40 minutes is due to the spilling over of liquid from the outlet orifice. For a nozzle located at the axial position, secondary atomization does not occur until about 25 minutes. A comparison of these curves show the importance of the location of the nozzle in determining the rate of liquid entrainment, for a duct of rectangular section.

When the longer side of the duct is horizontal, however, the overall flow pattern changes dramatically. The two recirculating eddies are now formed on either side of the jet in a horizontal plane and are visible from the top of the test section. The separated liquid occupies the bottom of the duct and the surface of the separated liquid is broken by the recirculating flow to form secondary atomization. This is shown on Fig. 21 where the three distinct phases of entrainment described above are not evident. There is a jet-separated liquid interaction which produces secondary atomization during the entire entrainment history.

The flow pattern of the air relative to the duct is determined by the geometry of the duct and the nozzle and is not strongly dependent on the orientation of the duct with respect to the vertical because the effect of gravity on air flow is small. However, the gravitational force plays a dominant role in determining the distribution of the separated liquid phase in the duct. This in turn determines the onset and extent of secondary atomization.

CONCLUSIONS

This paper describes the results of a series of experiments to determine the effect of inlet geometry and test section geometry on the liquid phase entrainment during the flow of a ducted two-phase jet. Several conclusions are reached. They are:

1.   The entrainment histories could be described in terms of distinct phases of entrainment history for most of the tests.

2.   For the same mass flow rate of air, the narrow cone nozzle produces larger liquid entrainment than the flat spray nozzles and the multi-hole nozzle.

3.   The onset of high entrainment due to secondary atomization is delayed for nozzles located above the axis and for axial nozzles directed upwards from the horizontal.

4.   For nozzles located below the axis of the duct and for nozzles directed downwards from the horizontal, the phases of entrainment differ from those for (3).

5.   For ducts with square sections and axial nozzles the rate of liquid entrainment increases with decreasing duct length.

6.   For ducts of rectangular cross section, the rates of entrainment

and the mechanisms of entrainment are dependent on whether the vertical side of the duct is longer or shorter.

The improved understanding of the physical mechanisms described in this paper provides the necessary groundwork for developing a rational model of the entrainment processes. In-progress work is focused upon describing the fluid mechanics of two-phase ducted jets and jet-separated phase inter-actions.

ACKNOWLEDGEMENT

This research is sponsored by the Electric Power Research Institute, Palo Alto, California. The EPRI project manager is Dr. G. S. Lellouche. The authors gratefully acknowledge the experimental work performed by Research Assistant Alex Venetsky.

REFERENCES

1.   Savery, C. W., Chou, S. F. and Gay, R., "Effect of Entrained Droplet Phase Upon Predicted Compartmental Pressures in Nuclear Containments," Proceedings of Two-Phase Flow and Heat Transfer Symposium Workshop, Fort Lauderdale, FL, October 18-20, 1976, p. 1153-1173, Hemisphere Publishing Corp., WA, D.C. (1978).

2.   Savery, C. W., et al., "Water Entrainment in Intercompartmental Flow," Report EPRI NP-648, Electric Power Research Institute, Palo Alto, CA, 94304, USA, February 1978.

Table 1.

Test conditions for results presented in Figs. 3-21

Figure number	Variable considered	Test conditions					
		Air flow $\dot{m}_a$ (g/s)	Water flow $\dot{m}_w$ (g/s)	Nozzle type	Nozzle elevation h (cm)	Nozzle angle θ	Duct geometry (height×width ×length (cm))
3	Air flow rate	----	1.33	Narrow cone	4.8	0°	9.6x9.6x76
4	Film flow	----	1.33	Narrow cone	4.8	0°	9.6x9.6x76
5	Nozzle type	4.77	1.33	-----	4.8	0°	9.6x9.6x76
6	Nozzle elevation	4.77	1.33	Narrow cone	---	0°	9.6x9.6x76
7	Nozzle angle	4.77	1.33	Narrow cone	---	--	9.6x9.6x76
8	Duct geometry	4.77	1.33	Narrow cone	---	0°	----
9	Pressure distribution	10.00	1.33	Narrow cone	4.8	0°	9.6x9.6x76
10	Flow pattern, 1 min	4.77	1.33	Narrow cone	4.8	0°	9.6x9.6x76
11	Flow pattern, 5 min	4.77	1.33	Narrow cone	4.8	0°	9.6x9.6x76
12	Flow pattern, 10 min	4.77	1.33	Narrow cone	4.8	0°	9.6x9.6x76
13	Flow pattern, 12 min	4.77	1.33	Narrow cone	4.8	0°	9.6x9.6x76
14	Flow pattern, 20 min	4.77	1.33	Narrow cone	4.8	0°	9.6x9.6x76
15	Flow pattern, 25 min	4.77	1.33	Narrow cone	4.8	0°	9.6x9.6x76
16	Flow pattern, 4 min	10.00	1.33	Narrow cone	4.8	0°	9.6x9.6x76
17	Flow pattern, 5 min	4.77	1.33	Narrow cone	7.97	0°	9.6x9.6x76
18	Flow pattern, 5 min	4.77	1.33	Narrow cone	1.62	0°	9.6x9.6x76
19	Flow pattern, 7 min	4.77	1.33	Narrow cone	4.8	15°	9.6x9.6x76
20	Flow pattern, 5 min	4.77	1.33	Narrow cone	9.6	0°	9.6x9.6x38
21	Flow pattern, 5 min	4.77	1.33	Narrow cone	4.8	0°	9.6x9.6x38

Outlet orifice area 5.07 cm²

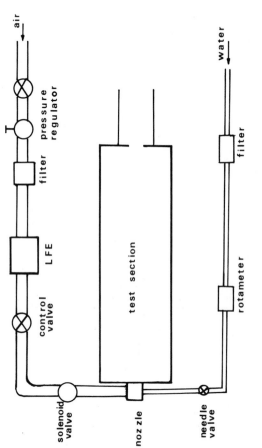

Figure 1   Schematic View of Experimental Arrangement

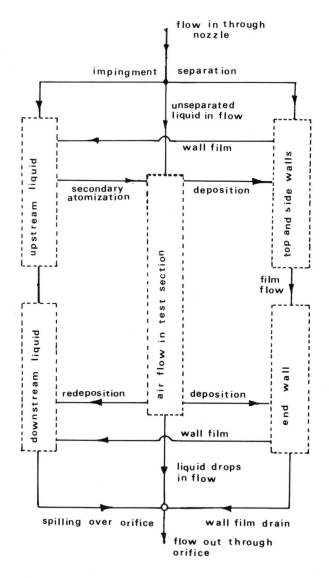

Figure 2 Flow Diagram for Test Section

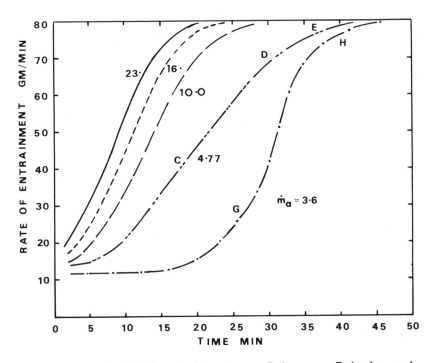

Figure 3   Effect of Air Flow Rate on Entrainment

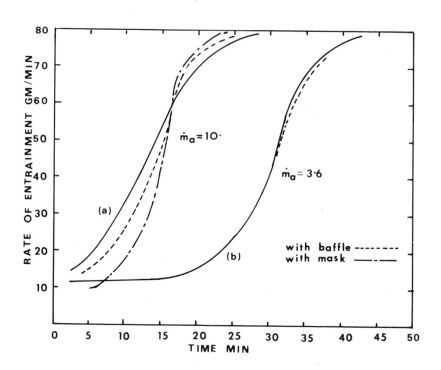

Figure 4 Effect of Baffle and Masked Outlet on Entrainment

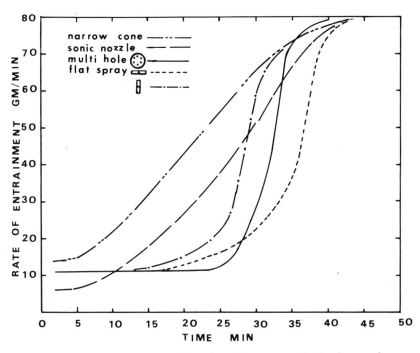

Figure 5 Effect of Nozzle Type on Entrainment

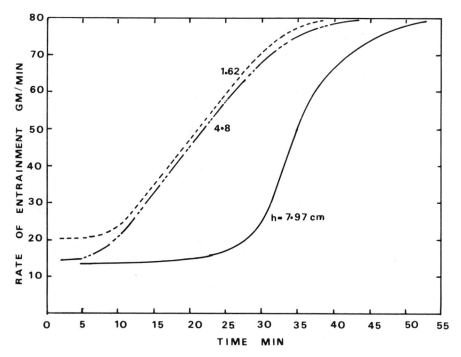

Figure 6 Effect of Nozzle Elevation on Entrainment

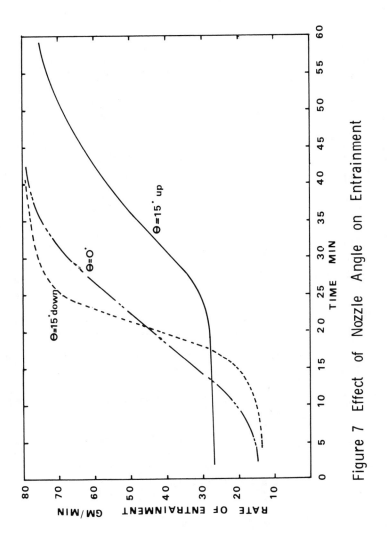

Figure 7 Effect of Nozzle Angle on Entrainment

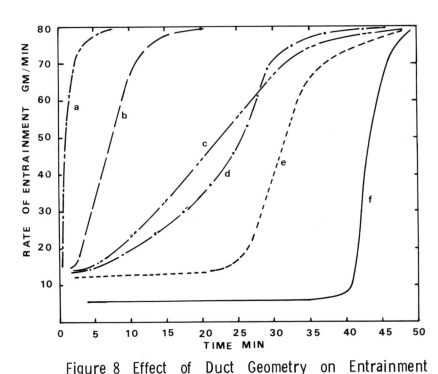

Figure 8 Effect of Duct Geometry on Entrainment

a.	L−38cm	H−19·2cm	W−9.6cm	h−4·8cm
b.	L−38	H−9.6	W−9.6	h−4.8
c.	L−76	H−9.6	W−9.6	h−4.8
d.	L−3 8	H−9.6	W−19·2	h−4·8
e.	L−3 8	H−19.2	W−9.6	h−9.6
f.	L−3 8	H−19·2	W−9.6	h−14.4

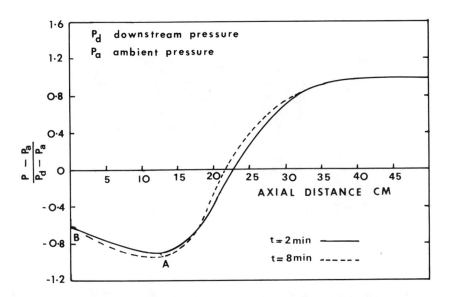

Figure 9 Static Pressure Distribution in Test Section

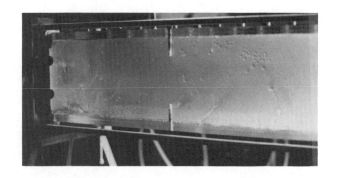

Figure 10   Flow Pattern at t = 1 min.

Figure 11   Flow Pattern at t = 5 min.

Figure 12   Flow Pattern at t = 10 min.

Figure 13 Flow Pattern at t = 12 min.

Figure 14 Flow Pattern at t = 20 min.

Figure 15 Flow Pattern at t = 25 min.

Figure 16 Flow Pattern at t = 4 min.

Figure 17 Flow Pattern at t = 5 min.

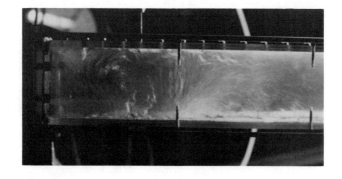

Figure 18 Flow Pattern at t = 5 min.

Figure 19   Flow Pattern at t = 7 min.

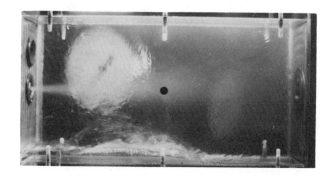

Figure 20   Flow Pattern at t = 5 min.

Figure 21   Flow Pattern at t = 5 min.

Evaluation of the Effect of Break Nozzle Configuration in Loss-of-Coolant Accident Analysis

R.G. HANSON
EG&G Idaho, Inc.
Idaho Falls, Idaho 83401, USA

ABSTRACT

The Semiscale Mod-1 test program has utilized two different break nozzle configurations in a test facility with identical initial and boundary conditions. An evaluation has been made to determine the effect these break nozzle configurations have on system thermal-hydraulic response during a 200% double-ended cold leg break loss-of-coolant accident simulation. The first nozzle had a convergent-divergent design; the second nozzle had a convergent design with an elongated constant area throat followed by a rapid expansion. Analysis of data from tests conducted with the two nozzles shows that the critical flow characteristics at the break plane were affected by the break nozzle geometry. Differences in break flow caused differences in the core inlet flow which in turn affected core heater rod thermal response. The results of this investigation show that the break flow behavior and the resulting core thermal response in the Semiscale experimental facility can be directly correlated.

INTRODUCTION

In loss-of-coolant experiments utilizing small scale integral test facilities, the break flow characteristics during the initial critical flow period can significantly affect the overall system thermal-hydraulic behavior. Since the critical flow characteristics at the break plane can be affected by the break nozzle configuration, a study was undertaken in the Semiscale Mod-1 experimental facility in which two break nozzle configurations were tested using identical throat cross-sectional areas.

The Semiscale Mod-1 experimental facility[1] was a small scale nonnuclear test facility which simulated the principal features of a PWR but was much smaller in volume. The system, shown in Figure 1, was a high pressure system consisting of a pressure vessel with simulated reactor internals (downcomer, lower plenum, core region, and upper plenum); a broken loop with rupture diaphragm assemblies, simulated steam generator, and simulated pump; a pressure suppression system with suppression tank and header; and simulated emergency core coolant (ECC) injection system with accumulators and injection pumps. The system water volume was approximately 0.211 m^3. Detailed descriptions of the system components, including volumes and flow resistances, and of the measurement and data acquisition systems are contained in Reference 2.

The core in the Semiscale Mod-1 system consisted of 40 electrically heated rods having rod diameter and axial power peaking characteristics typical of PWR fuel rods. The measurements taken in the core included rod temperature, fluid temperatures, inlet flow rate, and inlet density. Measurements taken in the Semiscale system other than in the core included volumetric flow rates, fluid temperatures, pressure drops, pressures, and fluid densities.

To investigate each of the nozzle configurations the system was brought to equilibrium at a system pressure of 15.5 MPa and a core flow rate of 9.28 l/s. Once equilibrium was reached throughout the system the test was initiated by breaking the rupture discs in both the inlet and the outlet sides of the broken loop.

The two nozzle configurations tested in the Semiscale Mod-1 facility are shown in Figures 2 and 3. The convergent-divergent nozzle, shown in Figure 2, consisted of a convergent section which extended from the upstream cross-sectional area to the throat area. The constant area throat section was 2.502 cm in length followed by a long divergent region. The convergent-divergent nozzle had four pressure taps designated PB-CN1 through PB-CN4 which were located along the nozzle beginning at the minimum throat area. The pressure tap locations are shown in Figure 2. The elongated throat nozzle shown in Figure 3 had a step reduction in cross-sectional area at the nozzle entrance followed by a short convergent section. The throat area in this nozzle was the same as that for the convergent-divergent design. A 7.303-cm long constant area throat followed the convergent section and in turn was followed by a step increase in cross-sectional flow area. Pressure taps, again designated PB-CN1 through PB-CN4, were located so as to allow comparison of pressure histories in the two nozzle configurations.

DISCUSSION OF RESULTS

Previous work in the area of two-phase critical flow phenomena has shown a strong dependency on nozzle geometry. Sozzi and Sutherland[3] showed that a change in critical mass flux occurred when the nozzle geometry was changed despite identical break areas from test to test. Figure 4 illustrates results from Sozzi and Sutherland showing that a larger subcooled critical mass flux was observed when a convergent-divergent nozzle was used than was observed when an elongated constant-area throat nozzle was used. The higher subcooled flow through the convergent-divergent nozzle in Sozzi and Sutherland's tests was attributed to nonequilibrium fluid conditions whereas in the elongated throat nozzle the fluid reached equilibrium due to a sufficiently long fluid residence time in the nozzle throat section. When equilibrium was reached in the elongated nozzle throat, nucleation began and the effective flow area was reduced.

Testing in the Semiscale Mod-1 system using the nozzle configurations
shown in Figures 2 and 3 produced data that confirmed the results
observed in Reference 3. The Semiscale results were compared to
results for a convergent-divergent configuration obtained by
Zaloudek[4] and, as shown in Figure 5, the data from Zaloudek's test
was in good agreement with Semiscale's elongated throat nozzle test
data. Zaloudek used a nozzle with a throat length-to-diameter ratio
(L/D) of 20. The elongated throat nozzle used in the Semiscale test
had a throat L/D ratio of about 5 which indicates a sufficiently long
residence time such that fluid thermodynamic equilibrium may be
reached prior to leaving the nozzle. However, when Semiscale's
convergent-divergent nozzle (L/D = 1.5) was used in the Semiscale
facility, thermodynamic nonequilibrium existed throughout the nozzle
length resulting in the higher break flow shown in Figure 5.

The effect of the break nozzle geometry on break flow behavior has
been shown to be significant. Therefore it was necessary to
investigate the effect of the varying break flow rate on system
thermal-hydraulic response in the Semiscale test facility.

Evaluation of the Break Behavior

Evaluation of data from the two break nozzle tests performed in the
Semiscale system showed varying thermal-hydraulic response due to
break nozzle configuration changes. The observed break flow rate
shown in Figure 6, was lower during the subcooled portion of blowdown
(0 to 2.4 s) in the elongated throat nozzle than in the
convergent-divergent nozzle. The figure shows that the lower
subcooled break flow rate through the elongated throat nozzle
prolonged the transition from subcooled to saturated flow by 0.5 s.
After the transition from subcooled flow the two nozzles showed the
same break flow rate since from this point in time the upstream fluid
conditions were saturated thereby ensuring equilibrium flow in both
cases.

Evaluation of the Core Response Early in Blowdown

The lower break flow rate demand observed during subcooled and low
quality blowdown through the elongated throat nozzle resulted in lower
core inlet flow reversal as shown in Figure 7. The low resistance
flow path between the core inlet and the break caused the core inlet
flow behavior to be directly influenced by the break flow response.
The difference in core inlet flow behavior, illustrated in Figure 7,
indicates the core hydraulics were also different. To investigate the
effect of core hydraulics on core fluid conditions, calculations were
made using the RELAP4 [5] code utilizing test data from the two break
nozzle configuration experiments as boundary conditions. Figure 8
shows a comparison of calculated core quality at an elevation in the
core just above the axial mid-plane. Different core fluid quality is

shown to have existed which affected the heat transfer from the heater
rod surfaces to the fluid. Figure 8 shows higher quality fluid in the
core earlier in the test using the elongated throat nozzle which
resulted in reducing the surface heat flux.

The core heater rod thermocouples reflected the difference in
surface heat fluxes by exhibiting earlier departure from nucleate
boiling (DNB) in the elongated throat nozzle test. Figure 9 presents
a typical temperature response comparison in the midcore region
showing that DNB occurred at about 600 ms when the elongated throat
nozzle was used and about 3.0 s when the convergent-divergent nozzle
was used. Of the thermocouples that experienced DNB, 75% experienced
early DNB (prior to 1.0 s) in the elongated throat nozzle experiment
whereas only 31% experienced early DNB in the convergent-divergent
nozzle test. As a result of the predominantly early DNB behavior in
the experiment with the elongated throat nozzle, the peak rod cladding
temperature in the core was increased by 28 K. The temperature
measurements presented in Figure 9 are not representative of the peak
clad temperature measurement. A correlation appeared to exist during
the subcooled and low quality blowdown period between the percentage
of rod thermocouples experiencing early DNB response and the core
inlet flow behavior which is affected by the break flow rate. When
the core inlet flow reversal was large, a delayed DNB response was
observed, whereas when the core inlet flow reversal was reduced (when
the elongated throat nozzle was used) earlier DNB response was noted.

Since the core inlet hydraulic behavior is directly influenced by the
break flow response and in turn affects the core thermal-hydraulic
behavior, additional Semiscale experimental data[6,7,8,9] were
considered to determine whether a trend existed between core inlet
flow reversal and the resulting core heater rod DNB response over a
larger range of conditions. The additional data investigated
exhibited a variety of core inlet flow responses due to differences in
experimental conditions other than the break nozzle configuration.
However, each of the tests used the same initial and boundary
conditions as those used in the two nozzle configuration tests.
Figure 10 shows the data follows a trend consistent with results from
the break nozzle configuration experiment illustrating that in the
region of low core inlet flow reversal the percentage of rod
thermocouples experiencing early DNB was large and moderate changes in
the magnitude of the reverse flow rate appear to have only minimal
effect on the DNB response. However, for the higher flow rate cases,
a small change in the core inlet reverse flow rate resulted in a more
significant change in the DNB response. A small variation in core
inlet flow in this region of the curve, caused by differences in break
flow characteristics would be manifested in a substantial change in
core heater rod DNB response.

CONCLUSIONS

The experimental results show that the break nozzle configuration has an effect on the critical flow response at the break nozzle location and, as a result, the core thermal-hydraulic response is affected. The use of the elongated throat nozzle resulted in lower break flow during the subcooled portion of the blowdown than was observed with the convergent-divergent nozzle experiment and resulted in a lower core inlet flow reversal. A calculation was made using data from each test for boundary conditions. The results showed fluid conditions in the core were sufficiently modified to cause a higher percentage of the heater rod thermocouples to experience early DNB in the test using the elongated throat nozzle. Additional Semiscale data was evaluated and showed that a correlation exists between the core inlet flow reversal and the DNB response of the core heater rods as is explicitly shown in Figure 10. The figure shows low core inlet flow reversal is accompanied by a high percentage of heater rod thermocouples exhibiting early DNB response as was the case when the elongated throat nozzle was used. In contrast, Figure 10 shows a stronger core inlet flow reversal corresponding to a low percentage of heater rod thermocouples exhibiting early DNB response which was the case for the convergent-divergent nozzle test. Since the core hydraulic behavior is influenced by the break response, the correlation shown between core thermal response and core hydraulics may be useful in calculating the thermal hydraulic response in LOCA simulation when considering break geometries in small scale experimental facilities.

REFERENCES

1   R. G. Hanson, Evaluation of the Effects of Break Nozzle
    Configuration in the Semiscale Mod-1 System, TREE-NUREG-1118
    (August 1977).

2   E. M. Feldman and D. J. Olson, Semiscale Mod-1 Program and System
    Description for the Blowdown Heat Transfer Tests (Series 2),
    ANCR-1230 (August 1975).

3   G. L. Sozzi and W. A. Sutherland, Critical Flow of Saturated and
    Subcooled Water at High Pressure, NEDO-13418 (July 1975).

4   F. R. Zaloudek, Steam-Water Critical Flow from High Pressure
    Systems (Interim Report), HW-80535 (January 1964).

5   C. G. Bruch (ed.), RELAP4/MOD5, A Computer Program for the
    Transient Thermal-Hydraulic Analysis of Nuclear Reactors and
    Related Systems, Users Manual, ANCR-NUREG-1335 (September 1976).

6   B. L. Collins, M. L. Patton, Jr., and K. E. Sackett, Experiment
    Data Report for Semiscale Mod-1 Test S-05-5 (Alternate ECC
    Injection Test), TREE-NUREG-1054 (April 1977).

7   B. L. Collins, M. L. Patton, Jr., and K. E. Sackett, Experiment
    Data Report for Semiscale Mod-1 Test S-05-4 (Alternate ECC
    Injection Test), TREE-NUREG-1053 (March 1977).

8   H. S. Crapo, B. L. Collins, and K. E. Sackett, Experiment Data
    Report For Semiscale Mod-1 Tests S-04-5 and S-04-6 (Baseline ECC
    Tests), TREE-NUREG-1045 (January 1977).

9   B. L. Collins, C. E. Coppin, and K. E. Sackett, Experiment Data
    Report for Semiscale Mod-1 Test S-28-1 (Steam Generator Tube
    Rupture Tests), TREE-NUREG-1148 (October 1977).

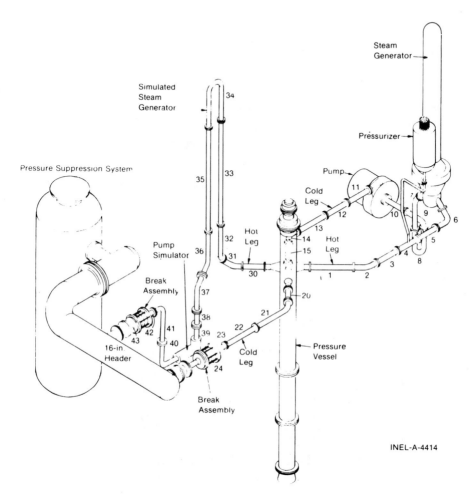

Figure 1   Semiscale Model Facility.

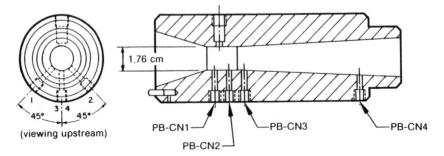

Figure 2   Convergent divergent nozzle configuration.

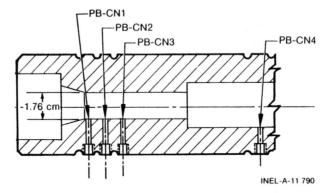

Figure 3   Elongated throat nozzle configuration.

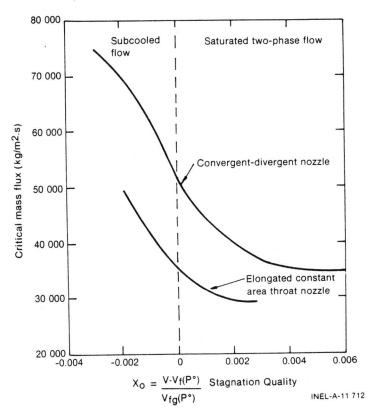

$$X_O = \frac{V - V_f(P^\circ)}{V_{fg}(P^\circ)} \quad \text{Stagnation Quality}$$

INEL-A-11 712

Figure 4   Effect of nozzle geometry (Sozzi and Sutherland[3])
on break flow with critical mass flux shown in
relation to stagnation quality X_o, where V is
the specific volume, $V_f(P^\circ)$ is the saturated
liquid specific volume at stagnation pressure P°,
and $V_{fg}(P^\circ)$ is the specific volume V_f minus V_g
(which is the specific volume of the vapor)
at stagnation pressure P°.

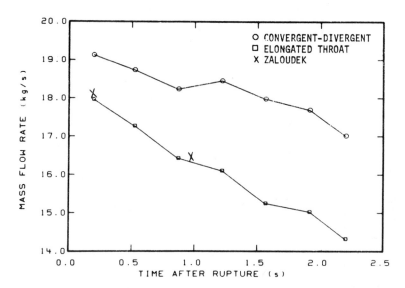

Figure 5   Critical break flow rate drag device-densito-
            meter comgination, FDB-23, GB-23 comparison
            of nozzle test data with Zaloudek's test data.

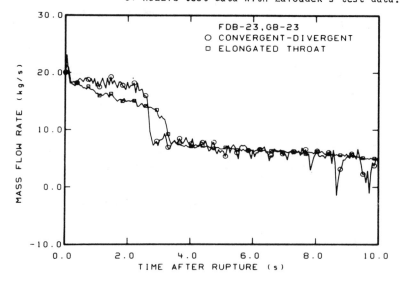

Figure 6   Cold leg break flow during subcooled and low
            quality blowdown as measured from the drag
            device-densitometer combination (FDB-23 and
            GB-23) directly upstream of the break.

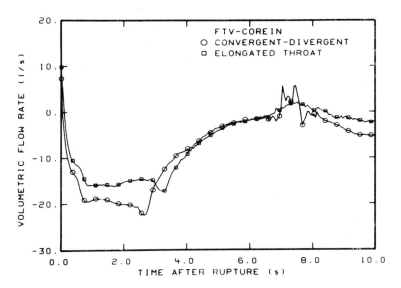

Figure 7   Core inlet flow during early blowdown as
measured by a turbine meter at the core
inlet (FTV-COREIN).

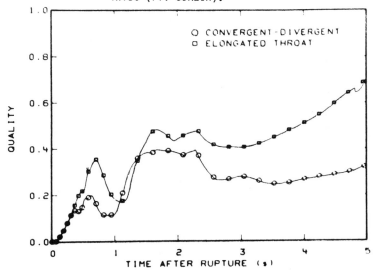

Figure 8   Comparison of calculated quality in the region
above the core high power zone.

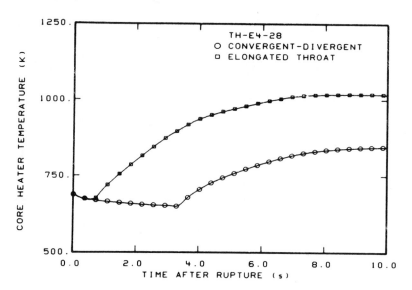

Figure 9   Heater rod thermal response on rod E4 at the
28 inch elevation as measured by thermocouple
TH-E4-28.

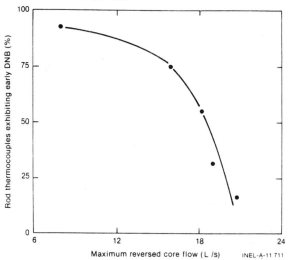

Figure 10   Correlation between the number of rod
thermocouples exhibiting early DNB
behavior and maximum reversed core
flow in the Semiscale Mod-1 system.

Evaluation of Incoherency Effect on Cladding Motion in LMFBR Loss-of-Flow Accident Experiments Based on a Multichannel Model

T.M. KUZAY, W.L. CHEN, and M. ISHII
Reactor Analysis and Safety Division
Argonne National Laboratory
Argonne, Illinois 60439, USA

ABSTRACT

In a hypothetical unprotected loss-of-flow accident in liquid-metal fast breeder reactors, coolant sodium is rapidly heated to boiling. The sodium boiling leads to the dryout and virtual loss of cooling from cladding surfaces. Because of the continuous internal heat generation from the fuel pins, melting of clad and fuel occurs soon after the subassembly voiding. This leads to the motion and relocation of the cladding and fuel materials. The clad motion upon melting is considered to be important in determining the reactivity effect, blockage formation, and its effect on subsequent fuel motion.

It is expected that the initial upward clad motion in the central (hotter) subchannels is severely limited due to the sodium vapor diversion to peripheral (colder) subchannels. This also should have a significant influence on the blockage formation in the central region. On the other hand, molten clad in the outer colder subchannels moves much like that predicted by the conventional one-dimensional clad motion models, since the bypass effect of sodium vapor is non-existing.

The three experiments considered to study incoherency effects in a rod bundle are R4 and R5 series tests of TREAT in-pile experiments and the recently completed P3A test by SLSF (Sodium Loop Safety Facility) Project in the Engineering Test Reactor. A computer code MULCLAD which is based on multi-channel cladding motion model is used for the comparative studies with the experimental data. The agreement between the experimentally established clad motion scenarios and the analytical model predictions is generally satisfactory. It is shown that the motion of molten clad and the subsequent blockage formations can be significantly influenced by the interconnected channel effects and can be successfully predicted by the model.

I.   NOMENCLATURE

A_j total flow area of intact jth channel

D_{wr} shortest distance between fuel pins

ℓ_m subassembly film section length

ℓ_F length of heated section

ℓ_o upper level at the end of fuel pins

L_{ins} total insulator pellet region length

L_{ref} total reflector pellet length

R_c outer radius of the cladding region in a fuel pin

R_F outer radius of the fuel region in a fuel pin

Z axial position

Z_{downm} lowest position among the molten clad films in a subassembly

Z_{downj} lower end of the molten clad film

Z_{moj} position where the film motion initiates

Z_{upm} highest position among the molten clad films in a subassembly

Z_{upj} upper end of the molten clad film

Z_{1j} lower end of the melted cladding section

Z_{2j} upper end of the melted cladding section

Z_p total subassembly pressure drop

Δp_m subassembly film section pressure drop

δ_j thickness of molten clad film

δ_c original cladding thickness

λ_{mj} length of the molten clad film in jth channel

λ_j length of the melted cladding section in jth channel

II. INTRODUCTION

In a hypothetical unprotected loss-of-flow accident in liquid-metal fast
breeder reactors (LMFBR), coolant sodium is rapidly heated to boiling.
Because of a large density ratio between the liquid and vapor sodium and
unstable characteristics of the sodium boiling, the reentry of the liquid
sodium is prevented once a subassembly is voided. Consequently, the
sodium boiling leads to the dryout and virtual loss of cooling from cladding
surfaces. Because of the continuous internal heat generation from the
fuel pins, melting of clad and fuel occurs soon after the subassembly
voiding. This leads to the motion and relocation of the cladding and fuel
materials. The clad motion upon melting is considered to be important in
determining the reactivity effect, blockage formation, and its effect on
subsequent fuel motion [1].

It can be said that sodium boiling and vapor streaming significantly
affect the timing and extent of clad relocation. By knowing the local
dryout time from a thermo-hydraulic analysis of coolant channels [2,3],
the clad melting time can be predicted from a simple thermal transient
model for fuel pins [4]. The time interval between the dryout and clad
melting depends on the rate of heat generation. At the normal power
level, the dryout is followed by clad melting in the order of one second,
then the melting of fuel occurs within several seconds.

Based on these observations, a simple one-dimensional clad motion model
had been developed previously [1]. The model is satisfactory when each
subassembly can be lumped into one channel and the incoherency effects [5]
within a subassembly can be neglected. However, the one-dimensional model
cannot take into account the effects of geometrical differences and thermal
incoherency among the interconnected subchannels.

During an LMFBR undercooling accident without scram, a non-uniform, transverse cladding-melting pattern develops within each subassembly due to
incoherency effects [5]. This is because power skewing and heat losses to
the hexcan wall can generate radial temperature differences of ∿200°C at
boiling inception. Hence the time of cladding-surface dryout and of
cladding-motion initiation can be significantly different among subchannels.

It is expected that the initial upward clad motion in the central (hotter)
subchannels is severely limited due to the sodium vapor diversion to
peripheral (colder) subchannels. This also should have a significant
influence on the blockage formation in the central region. On the other
hand, molten clad in the outer colder subchannels moves much like that
predicted by the conventional one-dimensional models [1], since the bypass
effect of sodium vapor is non-existing.

These incoherency effects on clad melting result in significant differences
in hydraulic resistance among subchannels, because the length of the
molten clad films and subsequent developments of a blockage formation due
to freezing of clad films are not uniform within a subassembly. Since the
subchannels are interconnected, this will lead to sodium vapor diversions

in order to equalize the axial pressure drops. Because the interfacial
shear forces on the molten clad films due to the streaming sodium vapor
are the main upward driving force, the motion of molten clad can be
significantly influenced by this interconnected channel effects.

In the present study we have used a multidimensional cladding-motion model
[6] based on a rough wavy-film flow with upper and bottom plugging mechanisms
due to freezing of the molten clad on cold surfaces. MULCLAD code is an
extension of the one-dimensional cladding-motion model [1] to the case
with interconnected parallel channels. The important aspects included in
the analysis are the subassembly incoherency effects and the interconnected-
channel effects that permit the diversion of sodium vapor. The motion of
molten cladding, which is induced by sodium-vapor shear stress and the
gravitational force, is subjected to complicated sequences of rapid acceleration, slowing down, flow reversal, reflooding, and eventual slumping down
into liquid sodium at the lower end of the heated section.

The results from recent experiments are compared with the predictions by
MULCLAD. The three experiments considered are the R4 and R5 TREAT in-pile
experiments [7] and the recently completed P3A test [8] by SLSF (Sodium
Loop Safety Facility) Project in the Engineering Test Reactor. TREAT R4
and R5 were 7-pin tests whereas the latter is a 37-pin in-pile test. Both
R5 and P3A were early termination loss-of-flow cases where significant
amount of test section information has been preserved in the subassembly
due to prevention of extensive fuel melting. It is shown that the motion
of molten clad and the subsequent blockage formations can be significantly
influenced by the interconnected channel effects and can be successfully
predicted by the model.

III. ANALYTIC MODEL

Current LMFBR core design is based on the arrangement of fuel pins in a
number of hexagonally-shaped subassemblies. A large number of cylindrical
fuel pins are arranged in a triangular array and contained in a subassembly
duct (hexcan). These pins are separated by means of spacer wires which
are spirally wrapped around the pins. Individual triangular elements form
the basic subchannel configuration. In the present analysis, these subchannels are lumped into several computational channels according to their
thermohydraulic characteristics. In the absence of power skewing, sub-
division into ringlike regions brings about great economy. It is estimated
that the subassembly incoherency effects on the clad relocation can be
satisfactorily modeled by using three to five channels.

The Multi-Channel Clad (MULCLAD) relocation model [6] considered in the
present analysis is shown in Figures 1 and 2. It was assumed that the
subassembly was voided prior to the onset of molten clad motion. The
origin of the axial coordinate was taken at the lower end of the fuel.
After the voiding of liquid sodium from the fuel section, the sodium vapor
is generated at the bottom of the heated section by chugging at the lower
liquid level. Reentry of the upper liquid sodium into the hot core will
not take place, because in whole-core loss-of flow accidents the rate of

evaporation generally exceeds the rate of condensation in the channel as long as the power generation is not severely dropped. Reentry is only considered possible after complete blockage formation. In the present model the average lower liquid level was taken at the bottom of the heated section (Z=0) and the upper level at the end of the fuel pins (Z = ℓ_o). The pressure drop imposed on the system ℓ_o may be approximated by the liquid sodium hydrostatic head [6]. This pressure drop roughly corresponds to the vapor velocity of 80 m/s. In veiw of the above facts, it is expected that the molten clad moves as a film rather than as entrained droplets.

A typical subchannel in the computational channel is shown in Figure 1. The length of the heat generating section is denoted by ℓ_F, whereas the upper and lower end of the melted cladding section is Z_{2j} and Z_{1j}, respectively. The total length of the molten clad film is denoted by λ_{mj}, the thickness of the film by δ_j, and the initial solid cladding thickness by δ_c. The location of the upper and lower end of the film is Z_{upj} and Z_{downj}. The radius of the fuel and cladding prior to melting is given by R_F and R_c, and the shortest distance between pins is denoted by D_{wr} which is approximately the diameter of the wire wrap. The total flow area of intact jth channel is denoted by A_j. For the case of the wall channel adjacent to a subassembly hexcan, the subchannel geometries are somewhat different, since one or two of the fuel pins are replaced by the duct wall as a bounding surface, see Figure 1. This will bring considerable thermo-hydraulic differences between the central and wall subchannels.

Figure 2 shows the interconnected parallel channel clad motion model. The highest position of all the molten clad films is denoted by Z_{upm} such that

$$Z_{upm}(t) \equiv \max [Z_{upj}]$$

On the other hand, the lowest film position Z_{downm} is given by

$$Z_{downm}(t) \equiv \min [Z_{downj}]$$

Then the subassembly film section is given by $Z_{downm} \leq Z \leq Z_{upm}$ and its length by

$$\ell_m \equiv Z_{upm} - Z_{downm}$$

Because of the upward driving force due to high sodium vapor velocity, it is possible that the molten steel reaches the unheated region and freezes. Whether this frozen layer of steel forms a partial blockage or a total channel plug depends on the extent of the upward penetration and the thermal inertia and the temperature of the upper section of the fuel pins; that is of the blanket or Inconel reflector section. The partial flow blockage due to frozen steel layer is treated as a flow nozzle with a changing nozzle size.

After clad film flow reversal, the film drains down the channel and eventually it slumps into the cold liquid sodium. The solidification of the molten clad and formation of the flow blockage due to bottom freezing is also included in the subsequent analysis. In order to model the interconnected parallel channel effects, sodium vapor flow in each channel is allowed to divert to other channels according to the hydraulic resistances of the sections of the channels. However, it was assumed that interchannel transfer of molten clad materials does not take place until the formation of the bottom blockage. This assumption is consistent with the film flow model used in the analysis.

In the present analysis, a subassembly is divided into several axial sections, and the equal axial pressure drop condition has been imposed on each of these sections. This assumption implies that the transverse diversions of sodium vapor flows occur according to the changes in the axial hydraulic resistances and that the transverse pressure drop and flow resistance can be considered as a secondary effect.

It is noted that in the present analysis, the motion of the fuel has not been considered. However, for larger reactors under unprotected loss-of-flow accidents, the complete melting through of fuel may occur prior to the clad slumping, since in these reactors the sodium voiding may have significant effects on the reactivity and power. In such cases, it is evident that the molten fuel-steel mixing might occur before clad slumping, as proposed in [9]. If this occurs, the structural integrity of the subassembly is lost completely and the geometry of the flow is quite different from the one considered in the analysis. Therefore, the onset of fuel motion caused by fuel melting is also a practical termination to the clad relocation in a manner considered in the present analysis.

For our present purposes, this brief outline of the analytical model is sufficient. Full detail of the model can be found in references [1], [6].

IV.   EXPERIMENTAL DATA AND DISCUSSION ON PREDICTIONS AND DATA

The three experiments considered are the R4 and R5 TREAT in-pile experiments [7] and the recently completed P3A test by SLSF (Sodium Loop Safety Facility Project in the Engineering Test Reactor [8]. R4 and R5 were 7-pin tests whereas the latter was a 37-pin in-pile test. Both R5 and P3A were early termination loss-of-flow accident simulation with a significant amount of test section information preserved in the subassembly due to lack of extensive fuel melting.

Case 1.   TREAT Reactor Tests:

The first case considered here is the simulation of the R-series 7-pin in-pile tests in the TREAT reactor. The R4 and R5 tests were run under the basically same loss-of-flow conditions with 7-pin test sections. The difference between these two tests was the timing of the power termination. The purpose of the R4 test was to obtain data for an integrated sequence of events up to and including complete meltdown, whereas in the R5 test the power was terminated prior to fuel melting in order to preserve evidence of molten clad relocation.

The dimensions of the fuel pins are identical to those of the Fast Flux Test Reactor (FFTR) and the cross section of the 7-pin test assembly as shown in Figure 3. The test fuel power was kept constant at 29 kW/pin until the power termination. Radially flat power profile was obtained by using different enrichment for the center pin, and the internal spacer wires and small-diameter wire wraps on exterior pins gave same power-to-flow ratio for interior and exterior subchannels.

The key times of important events beyond sodium boiling in these tests [7] are shown in Table 1.

This indicates that it takes about 1.9 s from the inception of boiling to dryout and one second from dryout to clad failure. The posttest radiographs of the test sections are shown in Figure 6, which indicates the extent of the clad relocation in the R4 and 5 tests. The interpretation of the radiographs is that a minimal plug was formed at the exit of the heated zone and the significant amount of clad material drained prior to the fuel melting.

The input data Z_{1i} (t) and Z_{2i} (t) for the present clad motion model have been obtained from the simple thermal transient analysis for fuel pins [4]. The total pressure drop in the voided section was taken as the hydrostatic head of the liquid sodium. The inlet temperature T_i was 327°C and the liquid sodium density was 0.873 g/cm^3. The fuel pin geometry was that of the FFTF. Thus R_F = 0.254 cm, R_c = 0.292 cm, ℓ_o = 214.6 cm, ℓ_F = 91.44 cm, ℓ_{ins} = 2.03 cm, and $\ell_{ref} \doteq$ 14.5 cm were used. The channel dimensions of the 7-pin test are given in Figure 3. The hexagonal duct which encased the seven fuel pins had the dimension of 2.13 cm across the flats with 0.05 cm wall thickness. In the present calculation the cross section was divided into two ring-wise channels. Thus by denoting the central channel and the wall channel by a subscript 1 and 2, respectively, the standard hydraulic diameter was D_{o1} = 0.324 cm and D_{o2} = 0.217 cm. The area fraction of the intact clad in the flow area with stripped fuel pins, $1 - \alpha_{oi}$, was 0.2726 and 0.2079, respectively. The sodium saturation temperature T_{sat} was 899°C and the clad melting temperature T_{cp} was 1427°C.

During the molten clad motion, the steel properties corresponding to the liquid state at melting were used; μ_c = 0.065 g/cm s and ρ_c = 7.36 g/cm^3. On the other hand, the sodium vapor properties were calculated at the saturation temperature, hence ρ_g = 3.12 x 10^{-4} g/cm^3 and μ_g = 1.98 x 10^{-4} g/cm sec.

The results of the sample calculation under the above condition is shown in Figures 4 and 5. The input data were the ones for the R5 test case; however, the conditions for the R4 test case were considerably similar to those used in the calculation. The thermohydraulics of sodium flows in a multi-channel geometry were analyzed by using a forced flow diversion model [2] up to the time of boiling initiation.

The sodium boiling and occurrences of dryout in a multi-channel geometry are quite complicated phenomena and a method to predict these phenomena is not well established. However, in the present multi-channel clad motion model, the extent of the dryout region as a function of time for each channel should be supplied to the fuel pins melting model in order to calculate the clad melting boundaries, Z_{1i} and Z_{2i}. Therefore, as a first estimate a simple calculation procedure has been adopted in the absence of a more complete model. It is basically an extension of the heat capacity model [3] with the assumption of the complete liquid sodium bypassing of boiling subchannels. This assumption is based on the observation that for a forced convection system with a high heat flux and with a very large liquid to vapor density ratio, the pressure drop increases considerably by going from a subcooled liquid flow condition to a two-phase flow condition. Therefore, once a certain channel starts to boil, most of the incoming liquid sodium should be diverted into other non-boiling channels in order to equalize the pressure gradient. Furthermore, it has been assumed that the flow reversal follows immediately after all channels have reached the boiling condition.

Under the R5 test condition, two-channel case have been studied by using the above sodium voiding model.

The flow coastdown started at 7.9 s in the TREAT transient time. The test section power was kept at 29 kW/pin until the power termination at 19 s. In the multi-channel calculation the sodium boiling inception occurred at 12.0 s in the central channel (channel 1) and the clad motion started at 2.8 s after the boiling inception in the same channel. The timings of various transients in the wall channel (channel 2) were slightly delayed due to the lower coolant temperature. Hence the boiling inception occurred at 12.8 s in the channel 2 and the flow reversal immediately followed. The dryout of the cladding surface started from the vicinity of the top of the fuel section and propagated downward. The predicted dryout initiation time is 13.0 s for the central channel and 13.5 s for the wall channel.

It can be seen from Figure 4 that the clad motion started at 2.8 sec (channel 1) and 3.2 s (channel 2) after the sodium boiling initiation whereas in R4 and R5 tests it was 2.75 s and 2.2 ∿ 3.2 s, respectively. The measurement of the fuel pin clad failure was based upon flowmeter response to the release of fill gas from the gas plenum. Therefore, it is expected that the experimental clad failure has occurred just prior to the initiation of clad motion. From this consideration it can be said that the simple thermal transient analysis predicts the clad melting time from the boiling initiation within reasonable accuracy. However, it is noted that the prediction of the boiling inception by considering the two-dimensional effects is about one sec earlier than the experimental data or the one-dimensional calculation.

In view of Figure 4, the initial motion of the molten clad in the central (hotter) subchannels was upward; however the extent of the upward motion was severely limited due to the sodium vapor diversion to peripheral (colder) subchannels. It was indicated that in this early stage the molten clad film was not completely rough wavy and therefore it was in the deflooding process. The flow reversal occurred to the molten clad in channel 1 at 2.9 s from the boiling inception.

At approximately 3.2 s from the boiling inception, the cladding material in the wall channel started to move (Figure 4). The film was predicted to reach the top of the heated section within 0.2 s from the initiation of clad motion in this colder channel, and freezing occurred both at the upper insulator and reflector sections. A complete blockage in channel 2 was formed within 0.5 s and the flow reversal followed immediately.

In the central channel the flow reversal from downward to upward occurred when the wall channel clad motion started. This was because the part of the sodium vapor initially diverted to the wall channel was redirected back to the central channel due to the increase in the hydraulic resistance in the wall channel. However, as can be seen from Figure 5, the overall upward motion in the central channel is considerably less than that in the wall channel. The freezing in the central channel is very limited and the complete blockage has never formed in this part. Consequently, the upper blockage for the subassembly should be a partial blockage and the most of the frozen mass should be located at the peripheral channel.

The downward flow reversal occurred almost simultaneously in channel 1 and 2 after the channel 2 was completely plugged up. After this point the molten clad motion became increasingly coherent and basically reduced to downward one-dimensional behavior. It is noted that the vapor flow existed up to the time of the lower blockage formation by the draining molten clad. At 4.2 s after the boiling initiation, the molten clad in the central channel slumped into the liquid sodium. The lower blockage was completed within 0.2 s and the extent of the initial flow blockage was relatively small (no more than 4 cm). Following the formation of the bottom plug, the draining molten clad from both the central and wall channels accumulated over the blockage up to about 20 cm. At 4.9 s from the boiling initiation the films were completely drained down. Since in the test the power was terminated at 19.0 s in TREAT time, this accumulated molten clad should have solidified in the position.

The posttest examination showed a relatively small partial blockage (∿1 cm) at the reflector section, Figure 6, which was consistent with the calculation here. In addition to uncertainties in the test bundle pressure drop at the time of clad melting and in the voiding incoherency prediction, any upper blockage formed in the test could have been remelted due to axial conduction or radiant heat transfer and might be redistributed more uniformly across the test section at the reflector section. The magnitude of the lower blockage as well as the qualitative prediction of the upper blockage are in good agreement with the posttest results and the overall physical behavior predicted by the model is quite satisfactory.

Case 2. SLSF P3A Test [8]

The P3A test subassembly contains 37 full-length initially unirradiated FFTF-type mixed oxide fuel pins. Design data for the P3A test train and test subassembly are contained in Table 2.

LOF tests in SLSF experiment P3A simulates an LMFBR unprotected flow coastdown resulting from loss of pumping power to extend current knowledge of the mechanisms involved in the initiating phase of a hypothetical core disruptive accident. The P3A LOF test was terminated at 12.9 seconds from the start of flow coastdown to preserve information regarding the mode of fuel disruption and the extent of clad melting and relocation. For fast reactors without a large positive sodium void coefficient, the current best estimate of the scenario for an LOF accident generally excludes a direct hydrodynamic disassembly in the initiating phase of the accident. The estimate is that the initiating phase proceeds in the direction of a gradual, somewhat benign meltdown and disruption of the entire core.

Coolant boiling dynamics and fuel pin dryout information for the experiment are reported in [10]. Here, a review of the experimental data for clad melting and relocation is presented and compared with analytical predictions.

a. <u>Data Analysis</u> The experimental data analyzed are the test section thermocouples (TC), hexcan TCs, inlet-outlet flowmeters and the acoustic sensors. The physical description and location of these sensors along with some of their computer generated traces during the experiment can be found in [8]. For the analysis, each sensor trace is examined for significant changes and tell-tale signs to detect boiling, dry-out, contact with molten material and gas-vapor passage. A sample TC trace is shown in Figure 8.

The TCs used for the data interpretation have been shown in Figure 7 with their data acquisition system channels numbers and axial and radial location in the test section. Furthermore, Table 3 lists the timing of the major events as sensed by these TCs. The specified time in seconds is from the initiation of the flow coastdown transient.

The major results from the data observations are summarized in the following. As much as the test section voiding information has been reported elsewhere [8,10], here we would like to point out only to those events which are pertinent for incoherency effects in clad motion within the test bundle. It follows then, that we are looking at data a few seconds later, following the net boiling initiation at 8.8 s as detected first by the acoustic detectors and test subassembly flowmeters.

TCs 12 and 23 near the fuel top indicate failure around 12.2 and 13 s respectively. These data support an early clad melting above 82.8 cm level for the edge channel (TC 12) (see Figure 7) and the upward clad motion reaching the fuel top for the second channel ring after 12.52s (TC 23).

TCs 14, 16, 24, 169 and 172 indicate failure at 12.2, 11.9, 11.9, 12.2, 12.1 s respectively. For the last four sensors failure obviously occurred somewhere above their physical level as much as failure took place abruptly.

TCs 101, 102, 103 and 21 are far up in the unheated zone and are expected to function under limited upward clad and fuel motion. These TCs indicate a big drop in temperature in the interval 13 s to 13.5 s. This may be interpreted as a void collapse or under incomplete top blockage formation close to this time. On the other hand, TCs 10, 171 and 173, although in the unheated zone also, stay level at saturation temperature. Of these, the behavior of TCs 10 and 171 may be interpreted at the void collapse filling the heated zone only partially (see Figure 7). The behavior of Ch 173 is obscure and may indicate incoherent void collapse at this level.

TC 10 indicates a sharp decrease in temperature starting at 12 s with a minimum at 13s. This suggests slowing down in vapor streaming in this period with a reduction in pressure and change in the saturation temperature. The saturation temperature is maintained at a reduced level thereafter. This may be interpreted as the top blockage formation (incomplete or venting blockage) in the period 12-13s with maximum blockage close to 13 s.

The unshown outlet flowmeter (FE 2-1) trace has continuing bursts between 10 and 20s [10]. This points to the top blockage being incomplete. Secondly, the large drop in the signal burst level of FE 2-1 between 12 and 13 s may give support to the postulated venting top blockage forming in this period.

The lower hexcan TCs 183 and 184 (see Figure 7) indicate reaching boiling only around 13.2 s. On the other hand, the higher hexcan TCs 29 and 30 show distinct dry-out as well as failure, later at 14.5 and 15.5 s respectively. This means that these TCs came in contact with molten clad, after reactor scram which indicates clad drainage beyond 13 s.

b. Cladding Motion Scenario Based On Data Based on the experimental data, discussed above subsequent to coolant boiling in the test section at 8.8 s, a scenario for the cladding motion in P3A is derived as follows:

Initial Clad Failure - Initial clad failure was indicated by the bundle-outlet flowmeter at 10.8 s and the total-loop flowmeter at 11.6 s (to include the gas rise time).

Upward Clad Movement - Extensive clad melting occurred at 11.9 - 12.2 s in the upper half of the heated section. This is indicated by TCs 12, 14 and 24. The molten cladding was carried upward by sodium vapor and started to form a partial blockage at the top.

Incomplete (Venting) Top Blockage - As the top blockage started to form, it caused increased pressure drop and reduced the saturation pressure and saturation temperature in the region above the blockage. This is indicated by TC 10, which shows a temperature drop of 50°C between 12 and 13 s. The upper blockage is believed to be incomplete (venting) because both the outlet and the loop flowmeters indicated the passage of fission gas throughout the transient.

Downward Clad Movement - Because all the thermocouples in the lower half of the test bundle failed due to melting of the leads somewhere along their length, no information can be derived from these thermocouples concerning the molten-clad movement. There are, however, two thermocouples,

(TC 29 and 30) in the hexcan which clearly indicated contact with molten materials, presumably molten cladding. From the temperature histories of these two thermocouples, one may conclude that molten cladding was moving downward and reached the fuel midplane at 12.7 s. The major portion of the molten cladding continued to move downward and reached a point 19.5 cm above the bottom of the fuel at 13.0 s. Because the major portion of the molten cladding was draining toward the bottom of the bundle, it caused TC 29 to fail one s earlier than TC 30, which was located 26 cm above TC 29.

Bottom Blockage - The inlet flowmeter showed flow oscillations around zero flow for a period of 120 s and eventually stopped at zero flow. This suggests either the formation of a complete bottom blockage well after reactor scrams at 12.9 s or a cooling phenomenon associated with the disrupted test section. Final resolution of a bottom blockage can not be made until the postmortem examinations are completed.

c.   Analytical Predictions As part of the posttest analysis, calculations for predicting cladding relocation were performed using MULCLAD code [6].

To determine the number of channels to be used in the model, the boiling information from the test data is examined. The resulting information is depicted in Figure 7. The thermocouple data delineated three distinguishable boiling curves in the test section. These are the A, B, and C curves as marked in Figure 7. The (A) curve is the boiling front for the central channel; curve (A + B) is for the middle channel and curve (B + C) is for the outer channel next to the hexcan wall. The available data demonstrated the incoherency in boiling within the test section. Near the fuel top (92 cm level in Figure 7) the boiling front for the outer channels moves out radially first before moving downward. The radial displacement takes about a second. The outer channel voiding occurs with 1.0 to 1.5 s time delay compared to the central channels. It must be remembered however, that some of the outer channel thermocouples shown in Figure 7 have been inserted behind the hexcan wall and therefore they may have time constants up to 0.3 s.

The dry-out curves necessary as input to the analytical model are based on an examination of the available data. Again the existing TC data indicated varying dry-out times between 1.0 and 1.6 s (Table 3). A typical TC trace for the experiment is shown in Figure 8. The initiation of boiling, dry-out and failure times are marked on the plot. Beginning of the saturation plateau indicates the initiation of boiling and continuing boiling culminates at dry-out at the end of the plot. At this time, a rapid temperature increase is sensed by the thermocouple without a sodium film existing to absorb the heat energy, and the thermocouple simply fails with a distinct rise. Not all thermocouples exihibit such exacting response curves since failure occurs in most instances prematurely through lead melting upon contact with molten debris.

On the basis of such data examination, average dry-out time following boiling is estimated to be in the order of a second. Input data to the analytical model for the dry-out curves are, therefore the same as the available boiling curves advanced by a second. As is evident from Figure 7, these curves are time functions and this is incorporated in the input by specifying the curve at eleven discreet segments along the channel length (92 cms to correspond to the active length of the fuel pins).

The test section power during the test is held constant until reactor scram time (12.9 s). Each analytical channel has its own power distribution with axial variation. The power curves are biased chopped cosine forms and peak to average ratio is a predetermined value of 1.25. In the input this distribution is affected by fitting a polynomial to the power curve for each channel of the model. Other non-salient features of the input information to the model can be found elsewhere [6,7].

The numerical output of the analytical model is rather large. In order to put the output into a conveniently digestable format, information of significant character is plotted out.

Figure 9 is a plot of the clad motion predicted by the 3-channel standard model. Following the initial start described in the section above, the molten clad film moves upward over yet unmelted segments. The film reaches the top of the fuel at 12.52 s for the central channels and starts forming a central blockage. The central blockage is completed for channel one at 12.78 s and at 12.79 s for channel two. The predicted blockage thickness is 7.8 cm and 6.6 cm respectively for channels 1 and 2. Following this the oncoming clad film is diverted to the third channel and the molten clad reaches fuel top for this channel at 12.8 s and starts forming an incomplete blockage. When the reactor is scrammed (12.9 s), the third channel has a 14 cm long 0.050 cm thick solidified clad film in the insulator and reflector area. The top blockage, at the time of the reactor scram, is therefore, an incomplete one (venting).

A bottom blockage is not predicted. In fact, up until scram time no clad drainage to the bottom is possible since gas velocities in the test section (Figure 10) at the time of the central blockage, are still high enough to sweep all molten cladding upward. Clad velocity predictions are shown in Figure 10.

From the plots for the clad film velocities, it is apparent that the channels one and two have similar flow dynamics. Minor differences result from the differences in the initial dry-out. Close to the formation of the central channel blockage in the upper reflector area around 3.9 s following the boiling initiation, the molten clad film in the third channel was swept upward at high velocities (up to 3 m/s) by the diverted vapor streaming from the central channels. The high velocity vapor is able to carry the third channel clad film to a higher elevation in the test section than found in the central channels. However, the clad film solidifies on the pins and the peripheral channel walls as a thin layer and does not bridge the inter-pin spacing to form a full blockage. At the time of the reactor scram (∿4.1 s from boiling initiation) clad velocities in all the channels show a tendency to slow down but are still upward in direction. As a result, until the time of the reactor scram, clad draining is not predicted although tendency toward draining has started. Possibly draining occurred following the reactor scram.

The major results from the analytical model are further condensed and tabulated in Table 4. The first column in the table is the nature of the major event specified. The second column indicates the predicted time and the axial location of the occurrence of the event. The times are given in seconds from the start of the flow reduction. In the third column the experimental observations and the interpretations of the data are summarized to corroborate the predictions. A brief examination of Table 4 shows that predictions are in general agreement with the available experimental data. For the very complex problem of molten clad motion in a highly incoherent multi-channel test section, even general agreement should be satisfying. The major sources of discrepancies in the detail, are generally the lack of precision in the dry-out data; limited data and finally our lack of understanding of the precise physical detail of the complex clad motion. The latter subject is a current fundamental research area in the reactor technology.

d.   Posttest Examination   Further substantiation of the experimental results will come from the non-destructive and destructive posttest examination of the test section. The posttest examination has begun [11] and results are expected to be available towards the end of this year. Neutron radiography has been completed and locations for cutting the test train prior to shipment have been identified [15]. Results of the present neutron radiography indicate the following information regarding fuel and cladding motion:

The fuel pellet-lower insulator interface has remained relatively planar. A 10 cm region above the lower insulators contains intact fuel and cladding. Immediately above this region, molten metal apparently contacted the outer row of pins and inner hex duct surface. Slightly below the core midplane, intact pellets at the bundle periphery can be observed. The condition of the fuel and cladding within the region extending upward ∿15 cm from the core midplane is difficult to discern from the neutron radiographs. The next 13 cm of the fuel column seems to contain a jumble of fuel pellets. Many of these pellets have relocated from a higher elevation which is now voided. The voided region (entire bundle cross section) extends upward from the pellet pile an additional 8 cm. Above this voided region, fuel columns begin and extend upward around the periphery of the bundle. At this elevation, the condition of the cladding is questionable. Molten metal appears to be cast around the cladding of these peripheral fuel columns. The central fuel pins apparently are absent. A metal blockage, beginning in the region with the metal cast around the peripheral pins, extends upward 8-10 cm. The elevations of the upper insulator pellets vary greatly for each of the pins. In fact, some of the insulators from the central pins may be absent. An object resembling an Inconel reflector rod has relocated to the void region. Some dense particles are distributed within the fuel pin reflector rod and plenum regions. However, no structural abnormalities are observable from the neutron radiographs above the fuel pin reflector rods.

V.   CONCLUSIONS

Data from the presently available seven and 37-pin bundle experiments have
been examined to study incoherency effects in clad motion in fuel bundles
under loss of flow conditions.

The observed incoherency is simulated with an analytical multi-channel
clad motion model and predictions are compared with the experimental data.
On the basis of this comparison it is found that, incoherency in fuel
bundles

- accelerates initiation of voiding and clad motion

- reduces mass of the central blockage in the bundle

- may cause wall channel clad film to penetrate farther into the flow
  channel.

- has little effect on clad slumping in the absence of fuel motion

General agreement has been established between the test data and the
analytical model. From this it is concluded that, incoherency effects can
be successfully modeled to predict the resulting complex clad motion in
multi-channel pin bundles.

REFERENCES

1   M. Ishii, W. L. Chen, and M. A. Grolmes, "Molten Clad Motion Model for
    Fast Reactor Loss-of-Flow Accidents", Nucl. Sci. Eng. 60, 435 (1976).

2   W. L. Chen, M. A. Grolmes, and M. Ishii, "A Simple Forced Diversion
    Model for Study of Thermal-Hydraulic Transients in LMFBR Subassembly",
    to be published in Nucl. Eng. and Design 45, 53 (1978).

3   M. A. Grolmes, "Heat Capacity Effects in Sodium Boiling", Trans. Am.
    Nucl. Soc. 22, 407 (1975).

4   W. L. Chen, M. Ishii, and M. A. Grolmes, "Simple Heat Conduction
    Model with Phase Change for Reactor Fuel Pin", Nucl. Sci. Eng. 60,
    452 (1976).

5   T. C. Chawla and H. K. Fauske, "On the Incoherency in Subassembly
    Voiding in FTR and its Possible Effect on the Loss-of-Flow Accident
    Sequence", Trans. Am. Nucl. Soc. 17, 285 (1973).

6   M. Ishii, W. L. Chen, and M. A. Grolmes, "Multi-Channel Cladding
    Relocation Model for Loss-of-Flow Accidents in LMFBRs", Trans. Am.
    Nucl. Soc. 26, 375 (1977).

7   C. E. Dickerman et al., "Recent Results from TREAT Tests on Fuel
    Cladding, and Coolant Motion", European Nuclear Conf. Trans., April
    21-25, 1975, Paris, France.

8   P3A Interim Posttest Report, ANL-RDP, pp. 6.9 to 6.36, November 1977.

9   H. K. Fauske, "Boiling Fuel Steel Pool Characteristics in LMFBR HCDA
    Analysis", Trans. Am. Nucl. Soc. 22, 386 (1975).

10 I. T. Hwang et al., "Sodium Voiding Dynamics and Cladding Motion in a
    37-Pin Fuel Assembly During a LOF Transient", Trans. Am. Nucl. Soc.
    28, 443-45 (1978).

11 J. W. Holland et al., "Posttest Examination and Analysis Requirements
    for Sodium Loop Safety Facility In-Reactor Experiment P3A", ANL/RAS
    77-36, September 1977.

12 D. H. Thompson, private communication, ANL/SLSF Project.

ACKNOWLEDGEMENTS

Work performed under the auspices of the U.S. Department of Energy. Efforts
of the SLSF staff who run the test; obtained data, documented it and procured
the postmortem information are greatly acknowledged. Thanks are due to
Marsha Reinke for her careful typing.

TABLE 1. EXPERIMENT SEQUENCES		
	R4	R5
Local Boiling	13.25 s	12.5 ∿ 13.5 s
Inlet Flow Reversal	14.87	14.56
Dryout Indication	15.2	14.8
Clad Failure	16	15.7
Probable Hexcan Failure	18	17.85
Power Down	25	19

TABLE II. P3A OPERATING CONDITIONS

	At Design Operating Conditions	At Boiling* Inception
Na Flowrate, lb/sec		
test subassembly	9.20	3.87
bypass	10.13	4.37
loop	19.33	8.24
through test subassembly orifice**	9.46	
through bypass restrictor**	9.87	
Test subassembly power, kW	1240	
Sodium temperatures, °F		
test subassembly inlet	792	
test subassembly outlet	1216	
mixed mean into heat exchanger	1009	

3. Element type - FTR design with the following exceptions:

    a. fuel to have the following UO_2 enrichment:

central fuel element	93.0 ± 1.0
six elements in ring 1	89.0 ± 1.0
twelve elements in ring 2	79.0 ± 1.0
eighteen elements in ring 3	58.0 ± 1.0

    b. plutonium - 25% of total fuel; enriched to 88.0 ± 0.5%
        $[(^{239}Pu + ^{241}Pu)/Pu]$

        fuel linear power, kW/ft

average	10.74
peak	13.96

total element power, kW	33.1

        coolant flowrate, lb/hr

center element	833
total subassembly	33,120

        peak coolant temperature rise, °F

center subchannel	450
subassembly mixed mean	424

TABLE III. P3A THERMOCOUPLE DATA FOR THE LOF TRANSIENT [8]

DAS Channel	Fuel Pin No.	Elevation,[a] cm	Boiling Indication, s	Saturation Temp, °C	Dryout Indication, s	Failure Time, s	Possible Cause of Failure
		Bundle TCs					
10	21	146.60	10.2	954 – 960	–	NF[b]	Upward clad motion
12	27	83.06	10	943 – 971	11.6	12.2	Local clad motion
14	31	55.11	10.2	982 – 1004	11.6	12–12.2	
21	8	192.28	10.2	927	–	NF	
23	12	90.68	10	993	11.0	13.0	Local clad melting
24	18	29.72	10.7	993 – 1004	11.9	11.9	Clad melting above junction
169	14	9.40	11.4	?	12.2	12.3	Clad melting above junction
171	30	177.04	10.2	?	–	NF	
172	32	-0.76	–	?	–	NF	Clad melting above junction
173	37	207.5	10.3	938	–	12.1	
101		225.00	10.3	932		NF	
102	Outlet	231.00	10.4	938 – 916		NF	
103		240.00	10.7			NF	
		Hexcan Outer TCs					
29		19.53	12	1004	13	14.5	Clad damage
30		44.93	12	982 – 1004	12.8	15.5	Clad damage
177		75.40	10.4	?	11.8	12.9	Contact with molten material
183		-5.1	13.1	?	–	–	
184		0	13.0	?	–	–	

[a] From the fuel bottom.

[b] NF: No failure.

TABLE IV. SUMMARY OF PREDICTIONS OF CLAD DYNAMICS BY MULCLAD

Event	Predictions	Test Observations and Data Interpretations
First Clad Melting	11.37 s, elevation 68 cm, center channel 11.74 s, elevation 83 cm, edge channel	TCs 12, 14, 16, 23, 24, 169, and 192 indicate clad failure in the time span 11.9-13.0 s, with extensive clad melting in 11.9-12.2 s period. TCs 16, 24, 169, and 172 show failure above their junction levels.
First Clad Motion	12.06 s, elevation 58 cm, center and middle channels	
Clad Film Reaches Fuel Top	12.52 s, center channel 12.80 s, edge channel	TC 23 fails prior to 13 s; TC 12 fails at 12.2 s (edge channel).
Top Blockage Complete (above fuel top)	12.78 s, center channel 12.79 s, midchannel incomplete for edge channel (film thickness 0.5 mm at scram)	TC 23 failed before 13 s; TC 10 in nonheated zone shows a sharp drop at 12 s with minimum at 13 s, indicating vapor streaming cut-off. FE 2-1, the test section outlet flowmeter shows a drop in burst activity in 12-13 s period, with large bursts thereafter to 20 s (incomplete top blockage). Acoustic sensor PE 9-1 shows first reduced noise level at 12.56 s; PE 9-2 top acoustic sensor shows reduced noise level at 12.75 s.
Blockage Thickness (includes partially open insulator region)	7.87 cm, center channel 6.62 cm, midchannel	
Clad Draining	None, until scram	Later drainage is possible on the basis of TC data 29 and 30.
Lower Blockage	None, until scram	Hexcan TCs 183 and 184 at and below fuel bottom exhibit boiling only after scram.
Molten Clad Length	82.3-28 = 54.2 cm, center channel 78.2-28 = 50.2 cm, midchannel 77.1-55.9 = 21.2 cm, edge channel	

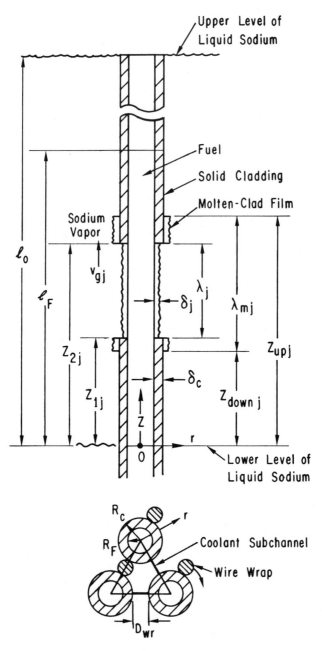

Fig. 1.   Description of the Typical Subchannel in jth Channel.

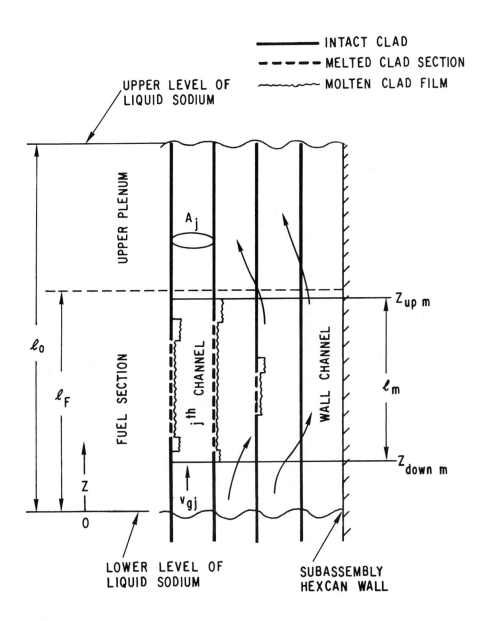

Fig. 2.   Description of the Multi-Channel System.

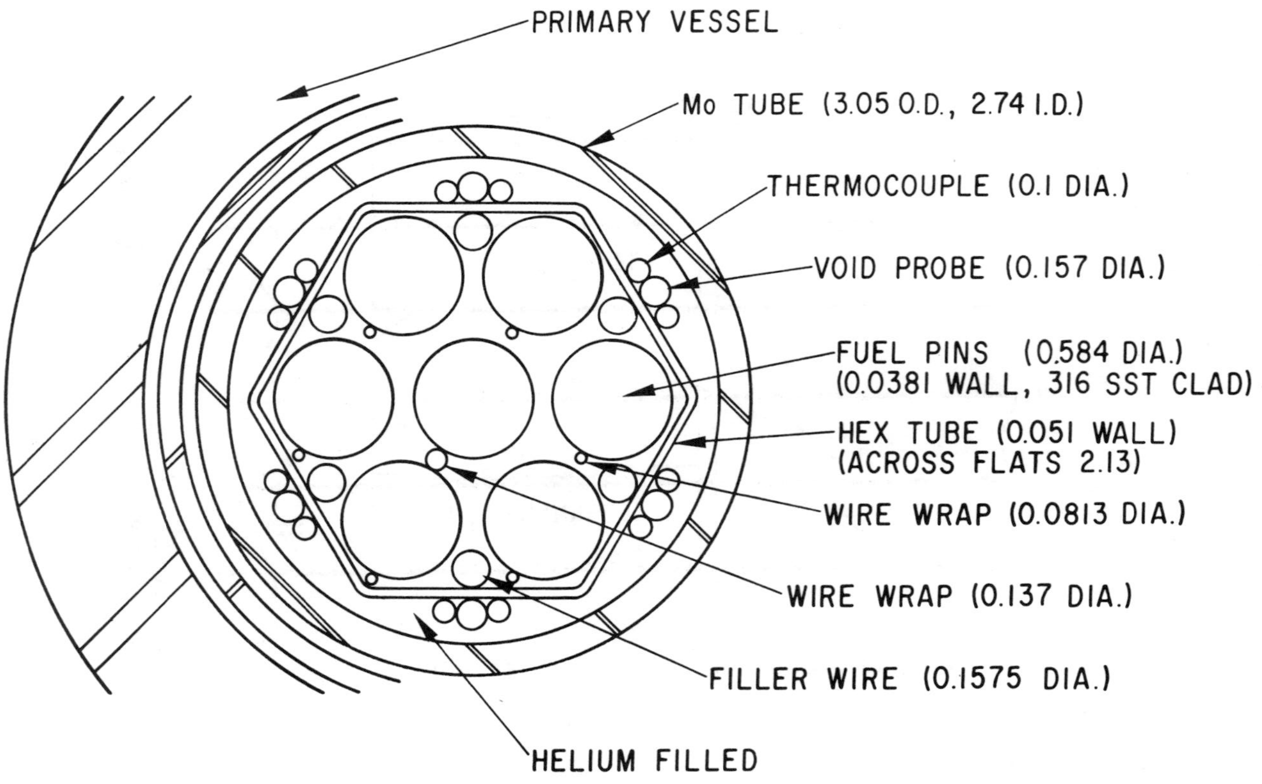

PRIMARY VESSEL

Mo TUBE (3.05 O.D., 2.74 I.D.)

THERMOCOUPLE (0.1 DIA.)

VOID PROBE (0.157 DIA.)

FUEL PINS (0.584 DIA.)
(0.0381 WALL, 316 SST CLAD)

HEX TUBE (0.051 WALL)
(ACROSS FLATS 2.13)

WIRE WRAP (0.0813 DIA.)

WIRE WRAP (0.137 DIA.)

FILLER WIRE (0.1575 DIA.)

HELIUM FILLED

ALL DIMENSIONS IN cm

Fig. 3.   Cross Section of 7-Pin Test Assembly.

1540

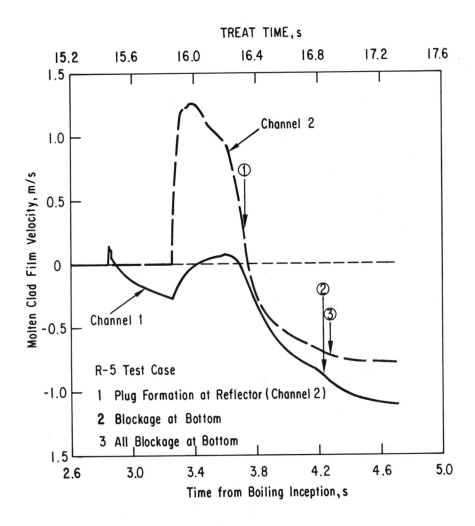

Fig. 4.   Prediction of Molten Clad Velocity for R5 Test Case
with 2-Channel Model Based on Simple Voiding Model.

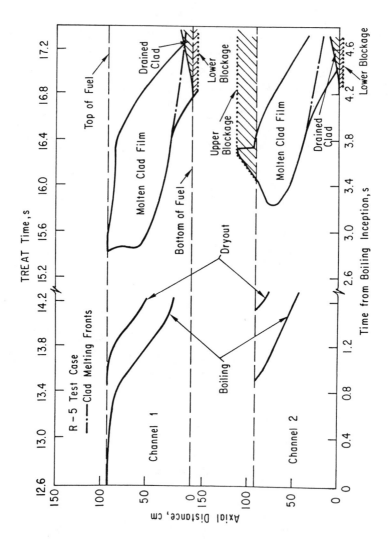

Fig. 5 – Prediction of Molten Clad Motion for R5 Test Case with 2-channel Model.

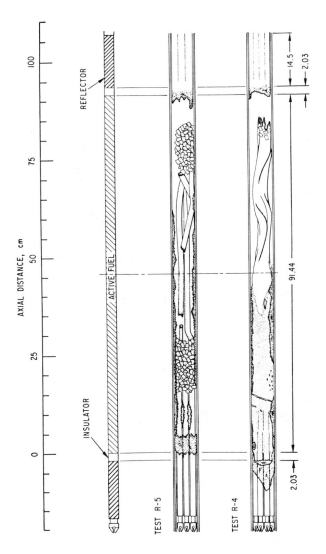

Fig. 6 – Post Transient Radiographs for R4 and R5 Loss of Flow Tests.

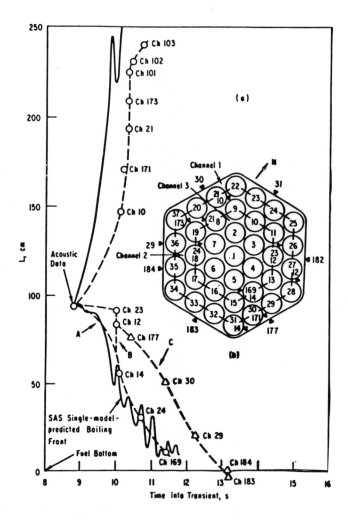

Fig. 7 — Boiling Front Prediction and the Experimental Data.
(a.) Clad Motion Channel Geometry and Thermocouple Locations in
Test Section

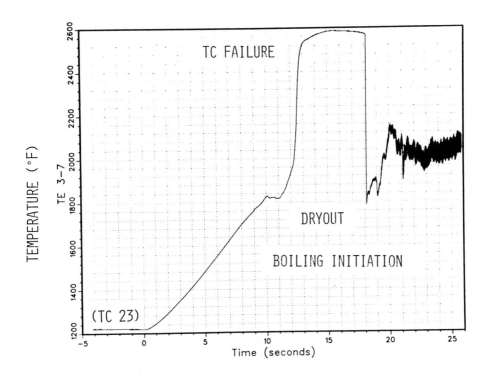

Fig. 8.   Test Section Wire Wrap Thermocouple Data (TC 23),
          Pin 12, 90.7 cm Above Bottom of Fuel.

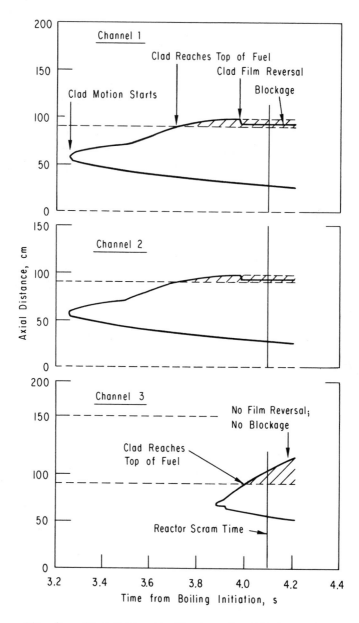

Fig. 9.   Clad Motion Predictions for P3A Loss of Flow Experiment.
(net boiling initiation at 8.8 s experiment time).

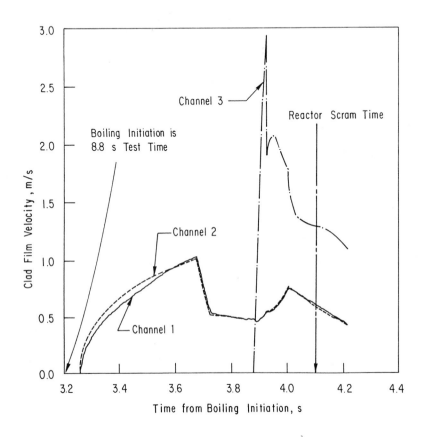

Fig. 10. Predicted Molten Clad Film Velocities During P3A Experiment. (net boiling initiation at 8.8 s experimental time).

LOCA Analysis of the Proposed PWR of Turkey

Z. BETIL and O. AKALIN
T.A.E.C., Cekmece Nuclear Research and Training Center
P.K.1, Havaalani, Istanbul, Turkey

ABSTRACT
The effort to support the Turkish Electricity Authority's activities in planning to construct the first nuclear power plant of Turkey is described. The proposed power plant will be a 600 MWe PWR, and will be constructed at the southern coast of Turkey in Akkuyu. This study is initiated with a protocol signed between the Turkish Electricity Authority and the Atomic Energy Commission, and represents the analysis of a LOCA accident of the Akkuyu nuclear power plant.

In the numerical analysis approach, the computer code BRUCH-D-02 is used. Two computer runs at the IBM-370/135 digital computer have been performed for hot and cold-leg ruptures. The results of these computations determine the pressure differences within the primary coolant system of the plant. Other thermohydraulic proporties of the system which are of importance in the design of the core structure and the pressure vessel are also determined and discussed.

The nuclear age is just starting in Turkey and the Turkish Atomic Energy Commission is giving its support for training personnel in this area and for the understanding of the nuclear problems.

INTRODUCTION
The work presented in this paper is a result of the application of the loss-of-coolant accident (LOCA) problem to the proposed PWR of Turkey. Turkish Electricity Authority plans to construct a 600 MWe net output PWR on the southern coast of Turkey. The plant will be operational in 1984. The study was carried out due to the protocol signed between the Turkish Electricity Authority and the Turkish Atomic Energy Commission.

The analysis of the loss of coolant accident problem of the
Akkuyu nuclear power plant is carried out with the code
BRUCH-D-02 [1] on the IBM-370/135 digital computer. The code
deals with LOCA analysis of pressurized water reactors. The
main objective is to estimate the pressure differences within
the primary system during a LOCA. Other thermodynamic
variables, such as total mass within various system elements,
coolant mass flow rates between various system elements,
steam quality etc., are also determined. The critical mass
flow rates, escaping from the generated break are estimated
according to the data given by Moody [2] (Table 2). The following
sections give a description of the geometric information
involved, mathematical model, method of solution and the
application of the computer code on the Akkuyu PWR blowdown.
The discussion of results are given in the last section.

GEOMETRICAL INFORMATION
The present analysis employs a two-dimensional approach
(length along the flow path and time) in the reactor primary
system. The primary coolant system is sectionalized along
the flow path into pressure nodes with variable length
increment. A total number of 15 nodes have been selected
for the simulation of the primary coolant loops [3]. These
nodes are shown in fig.1 and describe the following parts
of the primary system :
    1. The core fuel region is subdivided into 4 different
pressure nodes, designated by nodes 1,2,3,4 in fig.1 .
    2. A core leakage zone is represented by node 6 and
represents a flow path parallel to the core fuel region.
    3. A mixing plenum is described by node 6 where the
coolant flow of the different fuel channels is mixed. This
node is connected with the heat exchangers.
    4. The primary system is equipped with 2 heat exchangers.
The total volume of each heat exchanger is subdivided into
two parts. Nodes 7 and 9 simulate the heat exchanger
entrances while nodes 8 and 10 represent the heat exchanger
exits
    5. The volume between pressure vessel inlet and the
flow restriction at the upper end of the thermal shield
is represented by node 11.
    6. Node 12 describes the annulus between the core

container and the **pressure vessel.**

7. The plenum below the core entrance plate is simulated by node 13.

8. **The** by-pass flow between the pressure vessel in**l**et and the pressure vessel outlet is defined by node 15.

9. The pressurizer is represented by node 14.
The geometric information for every system element consisting of element volume, elevation, branch lengths, branch frictional loss coefficients, flow cross sectional areas of the Akkuyu nuclear power plant, is prepared as input data for the BRUCH-D-02 computer program (See Table 2).

MATHEMATICAL MODEL
For every system spatial element, a set of dependent variables is determined by the application of the continuity, energy and state equations to the element under consideration. The resulting equations are then manipulated algebraically until explicit equations for the derivatives of all dependent variables are obtained. Ref.[4] outlines the basic thermodynamic and hydrodynamic equations. In this section the determination of some of the dependent variables by the help of these equations will be given[4].

Determination of the differtial equations for pressure and mass flow rates :
Energy balance

$$\sum G_{in}h_{in} - \sum G_{out}h_{out} + Q_i = \dot{M}_i h_i + M_i \dot{h}_i - V_i \dot{P}_i \tag{1}$$

Volume balance

$$M_i v_i = \text{const.}$$

$$\dot{M}_i v_i + M_i \dot{v}_i = 0 \tag{2}$$

The specific volume of subcooled water present in a node, is a function of the pressure and the enthalpy :

$$v_i = f(P_i, h_i)$$

The derivative of specific volume with respect to time can

be represented as

$$\dot{v}_i = \varepsilon_{1i}(P_i,x_i)\dot{P}_i + \varepsilon_{2i}(P_i,x_i)\dot{h} \tag{3}$$

where the functions ε_{1i} and ε_{2i} are defined as

$$\varepsilon_{1i}(P_i,x_i) = \frac{\delta v}{\delta p} \quad , \qquad \varepsilon_{2i}(P_i,x_i) = \frac{\delta v}{\delta h}$$

Combining equations (2) and (3) the following expression is obtained :

$$\dot{M}_i v_i + M_i(\varepsilon_{1i}\dot{P}_i + \varepsilon_{2i}\dot{h}_i) = 0 \tag{4}$$

Combining equations (1) and (4) the following differential equation for the pressure in node i is obtained :

$$\dot{P}_i = \frac{\dot{M}_i(h_i - v_i/\varepsilon_{2i}) - (\sum G_{in}h_{in} - \sum G_{out}h_{out}) - Q_i}{M_i\varepsilon_{1i}/\varepsilon_{2i} + V_i} \tag{5}$$

The differential equation for the enthalpy in node i is determined from equation (4) as follows :

$$\dot{h} = \frac{\dot{M}_i v + M_i\varepsilon_{1i}\dot{P}_i}{M_i\varepsilon_{2i}} \tag{6}$$

Since the core fuel region contains a large amount of sub-cooled water, equations (5) and (6) have to be corrected. The correction has to be made for the coolant masses[4].

An appropriate approximate relationship has to be established for the specific volume in a PWR operating with large subcooling. It is determined from an integration of the partial derivatives with respect to pressure $(\delta v/\delta p)_h$ and enthalpy $(\delta v/\delta h)_p$. According to the IFC formulation the determination of the derivatives have been established on the basis of the equations of state for water and steam[5]. The curves of the derivatives which are plotted as functions of subcooling (negative quality) and the temperature of the water, are approximated by the following equations[3]:

$$\varepsilon_1 = (\delta v/\delta p)_h = a_{1,0} + a_{1,1}p + a_{1,2}h + a_{1,3}h^2 + a_{1,4}h^3 + a_{1,5}h^4,$$

$$\varepsilon_2 = (\delta v/\delta h)_p = a_{2,0} + a_{2,1}p + a_{2,2}h + a_{2,3}h^2 + a_{2,4}h^3 + a_{2,5}h^4$$

These approximations have an accuracy of $\mp 10/$ corresponding to a coolant temperature above 240°C and a pressure range from 40 bar to 170 bar.

Construction of the differential equation for the mass flow rate : A force balance along an incremental section of the coolant flow pass can be represented as

$$-A \frac{dP}{dL} dL - A\rho g \frac{dH}{dL} dL - AK \frac{w|w|}{2\rho D} dL - A\rho \frac{dw}{dt} dL = 0 \tag{7}$$

In equation (7) it is assumed that the flow area A and the velocity w are constants along the section. Assuming mass flow rate to be constant along the flow pass, the rearrangement of equation (7) yields the following momentum equation :

$$-\frac{dP}{dL} dL - \rho g \frac{dH}{dL} dL - K_K G_K G_K - G_K \int \frac{1}{A} dL = 0 \tag{8}$$

The integration and the rearrangement of the momentum equation, assuming the mass flow rate to be sectionwise constant, results in the following form :

$$G_K = \frac{1}{\int \frac{length}{flow\ area}} \quad P_i - P_j - (H_i - H_j)\rho_K g - K_K G_K G_K \quad ,$$

where the flow resistance factor K_K can be expressed as

$$K_K = f(Re) * \phi_{MNF}$$

The two phase multiplier ϕ_{MNF} is a function of pressure and quality and the Martinelli and Nelson correlation is used [6]. The density ρ_K using the homogeneous model can be expressed as

$$\rho_K = \left[v_w + x(v_D - v_w) \right]^{-1}$$

The mass flow rates at the generated rupture were calculated
according to the Moody model. The results are obtained for
both hot(the rupture is assumed between node 6 and node 7)
and cold leg ruptures(the rupture is assumed between node 8
and node 11).

METHOD OF SOLUTION
The following assumptions are made within the model :
     i. The heat addition rates to each node are assumed to
be known. They are calculated separately and taken as input
functions.
     ii. The mass flow rates escaping from the break are
calculated by a separate subroutine as function of pressure
and enthalpy. Moody model is used in the calculations.
     iii. Specific properties of steam and water are prog-
rammed as polynoms.

The mathematical model yields a set of 64 first order
differential equations which are solved by a numerical method
described in detail in reference[7]. The computation time is
quite long, about 6 hours on the IBM-370/135 digital computer.

APPLICATION OF THE COMPUTER CODE ON THE AKKUYU PWR BLOWDOWN
Akkuyu PWR data has been prepared by referring to ref.[8].
Akkuyu PWR may be characterized by the data in table 1 and
fig. 2 shows the cross section of the plant. Table 2 lists
the control volumes corresponding to the 15 nodes of the
system.

DISCUSSION OF RESULTS
This section deals with the discussion of results obtained
from the application of the code, BRUCH-D-02, on the
proposed Akkuyu PWR blowdown. Computer runs have been made
for both hot and cold leg ruptures. At the end of these
runs the thermohydraulic dependent variables which are of
importance in the design of the core structure and the
internals of the pressure vessel are obtained.

Cold leg rupture
Depressurization : Figure 3 shows the depressurization
process for the core fuel region and for nodes 6, 14 and

11. With the initiation of the break, the core pressure,drops
very rapidly to the saturation pressure of the coolant in
the core. This subcooled blowdown phase takes less than 0.5
seconds. However the depressurization rate is more less
severe during two phase blowdown. At this time large pressure
differences between nodes become evident. The gradual
depressurization during two phase blowdown after cold leg
rupture reaches saturation conditions within 10 seconds
while a rapid drop of the pressure to saturated conditions,
within 5 seconds, is achieved after a hot leg rupture.

Core quality change : The high pressure drops and decrease
in the flow inventories result in phase and then quality
changes for the core coolant. Due to the large pressure drops
the change from single phase to the two phase takes place in
less than 0.5 seconds. In fig. 4 the average quality as
function of time in different nodes has been plotted. The
quality of the coolant increases up to steam phase because
of the decreasing coolant inventory in the core and high
coolant temperature at low pressure. This increase is much
more steep in a hot leg rupture.

Flow reversal : A cold leg rupture results in a flow reversal. This event takes place in less than 30msec. . Fig.5
shows mass flow rates of different nodes after cold and hot
leg ruptures. There is no flow reversal after a hot leg
rupture. The coolant flow rate drop is also evident from the
figure and the saturation condition is reached within 10
seconds.

Temperature distribution : The results of the computation
indicate temperature distribution within the core fuel
region. Heat is produced in the core only due to the decay
of the fission products since the reactor is assumed to be
shut down after the blowdown. For this reason the central
fuel temperature and average fuel temperature drop (Fig.6) .
However an increase is detected in the average cladding
temperature. This rapid increase within 3 seconds is due to
the drop of the coolant flow rate and the change from single
phase to two phase flow.

The work presented here is the beginning of the studies
performed to support the Turkish Electricity Authority's
efforts to implement the construction of a nuclear power
plant in Turkey.The results of these theoretical studies
carried out up to now in connection with the safety of power
reactors, by the safety group at Çekmece Nuclear Research
and Training Center, provides the prerequisities for the
understanding of safety problems which are necessary for the
procedure of licencing. Turkish Atomic Energy Commission
will be active in the procedure of licencing in the near
future.

NOMENCLATURE
G_K : Mass flow rate (kg/s)
h_i : Specific enthalpy of node i (J/kg)
Q_i : Heat addition rate in node i (W)
M_i : Coolant mass in node i (kg)
V_i : Control volume of node i (m^3)
P_i : Pressure in node i (N/m^2)
v_i : Specific volume of coolant in node i (m^3)
x_i : Quality in node i
L   : Length (m)
A   : Flow area (m^2)
ρ : Density of mass flow (kg/m^3)
H   : Geometric height of the control volume center (m)
K_K : Flow resistance factor for flow rate G
w   : Velocity of the fluid (m/s^2)
D_h : Hydraulic diameter (m)
R_e : Reynolds number
Φ_{MNF}: Two phase multiplier
ε_1 : Auxiliary term
ε_2 : "   "
g   : Gravity constant (m/s^2)
v_D : Specific volume of saturated steam (m^3/kg)
v_W : Specific volume of saturated water (m^3/kg)

ACKNOWLEDGEMENT
Considerable aid of Ahmet Betil from IBM company in
application of the program to IBM-370/135 digital computer
and running a lot of computer runs is gratefully acknowledged.

REFERENCES
1 K.J. Liesch, F. Steinhoff, I. Vojtek, K. Wolfert, BRUCH-D-
  02, MRR-P-3, Juli 1973
2 F.D. Moody, Maximum two phase vessel blowdown from pipes,
  APED-4827 (1965)
3 H. Karwat. BRUCH-D, a code to investigate blowdown of PWR
  systems, Nucl. Eng. Design 9(1969)363
4 H. Karwat, A nonlinear transient study for a BWR, paper
  presented at the 2-phase flow symposium at Eindhoven,
  Sept. 1967
5 The 1967 IFC-formulation for industrial use, Formulation
  of the thermodynamic properties of ordinary water subs-
  tance(VDI-Verlag, Düsseldorf).
6 R.C. Martinelli and D.B. Nelson, Prediction of pressure
  drop during forced circulation boiling of water. Trans.
  ASME(August 1948)696
7 R. Bulirsch and J. Stoer, Numerical treatment of ordinary
  differential equations by extrapolation methods,
  Numerische Mathematik 8(1966)1.
8 TEK, Akkuyu Nuclear Power Plant Preliminary Project,
  Pressurized Water Reactor, Vol.1,2, July 1976

	TABLE 1	
	ESTIMATED THERMODYNAMIC VARIABLES FROM MOODY	
Rated thermal power (MWt)		1876
Design Pressure (MPa)		17.24
Total mass flow rate within the primary system (kg/s)		8960
Number of recirculation loops		2
Enthalpy of the lower plenum (J/kg)		1562704
Coolant weight (kg)		69920

TABLE 2
CONTROL VOLUMES CORRESPONDING
TO FIFTEEN NODES OF SYSTEM

Pressure nodes	Control volumes(m^3)	Pressure nodes	Control volumes(m^3)
1	2.77	9	7.20
2	2.77	10	7.20
3	2.77	11	5.25
4	2.77	12	9.04
5	5.20	13	4.67
6	8.85	14	24
7	7.20	15	6.50
8	7.20		

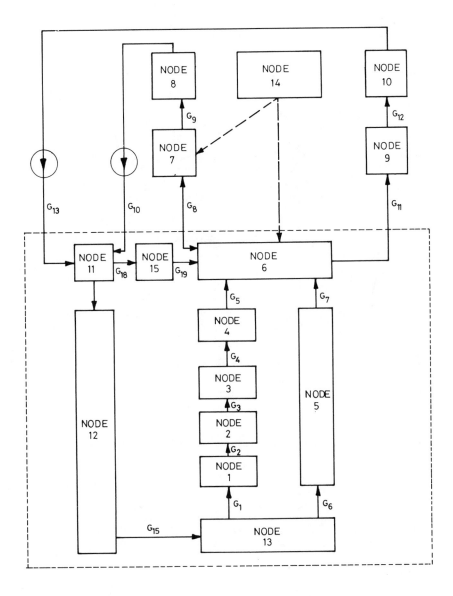

Fig.-1. Pressure node distribution

1559

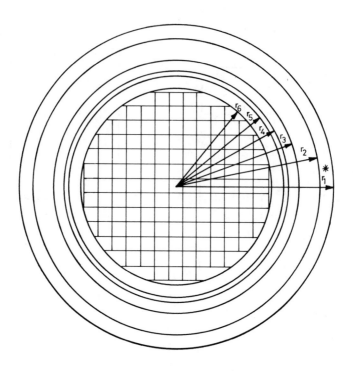

Fig. - 2 Cross sectional view of the Akkuyu nuclear power plant.

* r_1 : Pressure vessel outer diameter (1796.5 mm)
r_2 : Pressure vessel inner diameter (1676.5 mm)
r_3 : Thermal column outer diameter (1506.5 mm)
r_4 : Thermal column inner diameter (1441.5 mm)
r_5 : Core vessel outer diameter (1411.5 mm)
r_6 : Core vessel inner diameter (1386.5 mm)

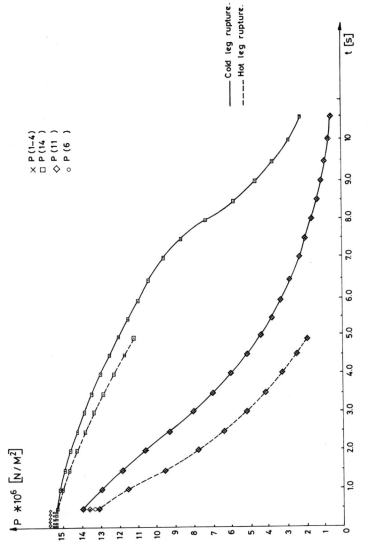

Fig.3.- Pressure distribution as function of time in different nodes after cold and hot leg rupture.

—— Cold leg rupture.
---- Hot leg rupture.

× P (1-4)
□ P (14)
◇ P (11)
○ P (6)

P *10⁶ [N/M²]

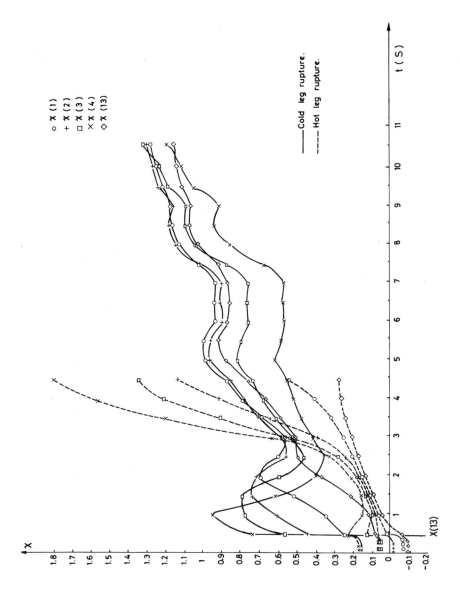

Fig. 4 — Average quality as function of time in different nodes after cold and hot leg rupture.

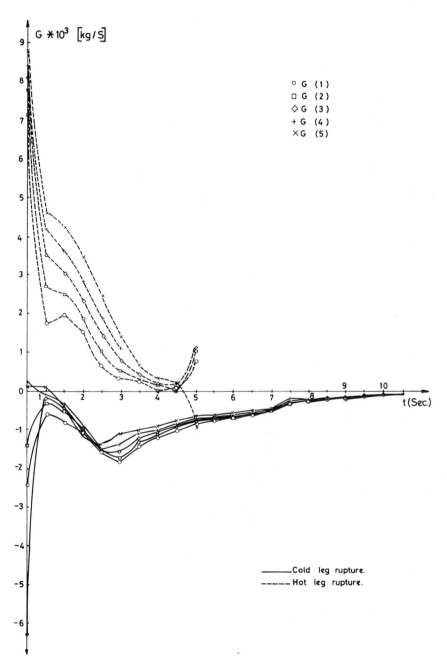

Fig. 5 _ Mass flow rates of different nodes after cold and hot leg rupture.

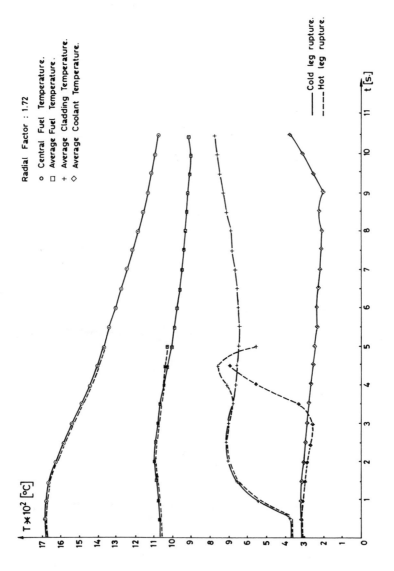

Fig. 6 – Temperature distribution in fuel element type 2 (radial factor: 1.72) as
function of time after cold and hot leg rupture.

Development of a Nonequilibrium ECC Mixing Model for Use in RELAP4/MOD7

S. R. FISCHER, H. CHOW, and G. Van ARSDALL
EG&G Idaho, Inc.
Idaho Falls, Idaho 83401, USA

H. STADTKE
Joint Research Centre Ispra Establishment
Ispra, Italy

ABSTRACT

A general model to simulate the nonequilibrium phenomena associated with the mixing of subcooled water with saturated steam has been developed and is operational on preliminary versions of RELAP4/MOD7. This ECC mixing model incorporates a separate liquid energy balance into the RELAP4 equation set. Condensation rates are computed for each control volume through use of a simple flow regime dependent constitutive package.

The nonequilibrium mixing model has been used to perform numerous calculational simulations of the Creare ECC bypass and LOFT facility experiments. Comparisons of RELAP4/MOD7 code predictions with experimental measurements have indicated that nonequilibrium effects should be accounted for in the analysis of LOCA transients.

INTRODUCTION

RELAP4[1,(a)] is a computer code that has been written specifically to analyze the thermal hydraulic behavior of light water nuclear reactors subjected to various postulated loss-of-coolant (LOCA) transients. The code is quite general in nature and thus can be used to analyze the two-phase flow and heat transfer characteristics of various experimental blowdown and reflood facilities.

The RELAP4 code provides for the solution of the time-dependent one-dimensional conservation of mass, momentum, and energy equations written for fluid control volumes. The code generally assumes homogeneous fluid conditions and thermodynamic equilibrium between phases within a control volume. Special models have been incorporated within the basic code framework to relax or remove some of the homogeneous equilibrium assumptions for special circumstances; that is, formation of a well-defined mixture level, superheating of vapor during reflood or slip between liquid and vapor phases in gravity dominated flow. The addition of these non-homogeneous or nonequilibrium models to the RELAP4 code has greatly improved the capability of the code to predict the complex thermohydraulic phenomena occurring during the blowdown, refill, and reflood phases of a postulated LOCA in a light water reactor.

(a) RELAP4/MOD6 is the current publicly released version of the code and is available through the National Energy Software Center, Building 208, Room C-230, 9700 S. Cass Avenue, Argonne, Illinois 60439.

The assumption of thermodynamic equilibrium can be unrealistic for the refill phase of a postulated LOCA transient during which highly subcooled water is injected into the reactor vessel from the ECC accumulator. As a result of the injection of subcooled water, liquid temperatures in some parts of the system may greatly differ from saturation or the vapor temperature. For example, experimental results from LOFT[2] indicate that water delivered to the lower plenum can be substantially subcooled. However, the thermodynamic equilibrium condition inherent in RELAP4 forces the subcooled ECC water and steam to mix instantly, thereby rapidly depressurizing the system. Consequently, poor code-data comparisons for the refill characteristics of the cold leg, downcomer and lower plenum can result.

A model is needed to properly calculate the nonequilibrium processes that occur during refill. Nonequilibrium condensation models have been incorporated into several of the advanced system and component LOCA codes such as TRAC[3], K-TIF[4], RELAP5[(b)], and DRUFAN[5]. Other nonequilibrium models have been discussed and proposed by Saha[6], Jones and Saha[7], and Hughes et al[8]. These models are, for the most part, based on simple empirical type correlations relating a condensation rate J and liquid thermal subcooling $(T_{sat} - T_\ell)$:

$$J = \phi \ (T_{sat} - T_\ell)$$

Wolfert[5] and Hughes[8] attempt to calculate the condensation rate by computing meaningful interfacial surface areas and heat transfer coefficients based on flow regime considerations. DRUFAN[5] utilizes simple correlations for bubbly flow at low void fractions $(\alpha < 0.3)$ and for dispersed flow at high void fractions $(\alpha > 0.7)$. Condensation rates at intermediate void fractions are apparently determined through interpolation. Hughes et al[8] recommend a somewhat more complex set of correlations for interfacial areas and heat transfer coefficients.

One major drawback in the aforementioned nonequilibrium condensation models is that they all require specification of empirical constants which must be determined through comparisons of code calculations with experimental data. Clearly, such simplistic models cannot be expected to be universally applicable to all of the mixing situations likely to occur during reactor transients. Enhanced mixing resulting from turbulence, fluid interactions with reactor internals, liquid injection techniques, and pipe roughness should ideally be taken into account. However, with the present state of knowledge, only an approximation to the physical situation can be anticipated.

A simple nonequilibrium model has been formulated as a part of the development of RELAP4/MOD7. The nonequilibrium model allows the coexistence of subcooled liquid and saturated steam. This coexistence implies that the

---

(b) RELAP5 will be available through the National Energy Software Center, Building 208, Room C-230, 9700 S. Cass Avenue, Argonne, Illinois 60439 about May 1979.

model is restricted to dealing with the thermal nonequilibrium of two-phase steam-water mixtures where the departure from equilibrium is associated only with subcooling of the liquid phase. That is, the model addresses physical situations such as that occurring during ECC injection when subcooled water partially mixes with saturated or nearly saturated steam. This mixing of subcooled water with steam occurs not only in the cold leg injection section of a PWR but also in the down-comer during periods of reverse core steam flow. The model is expected to be applicable or useful for the analysis of PWR upper head injection or hot leg injection systems and for BWR top spray systems. During the upper head spray cooling phase of a hypothetical BWR LOCA, conden-sation of steam on subcooled water droplets may play an important role in determining water delivery to the reactor core. Nonequilibrium occurring in such situations is assumed to approach equilibrium through interfacial heat and mass transfer between phases.

In the following section, Model Description, the standard RELAP4 equili-brium assumptions are reviewed and the nonequilibrium model and its implementation scheme are discussed. In the section Constitutive Relations for Interfacial Heat Transfer, correlations for the interfacial area and heat transfer coefficients used in determining the condensation rate are presented. Comparisons of experimental data with calculations utilizing the nonequilibrium model are given in the section Mixing Model Assessment. The results of this development effort are discussed and summarized in the Summary.

MODEL DESCRIPTION

RELAP4 Equilibrium Model

In the RELAP4 code the thermohydraulic behavior of a nuclear reactor system is described by solution of the mass and energy conservation equations for each fluid control volume and by one-dimensional momentum balances across the interfaces (junctions) between control volumes. The determination of the thermodynamic state of the fluid within a control volume is based on the following assumptions.

    (1) Homogeneous fluid conditions exist provided phase separation models are not applied.

    (2) The flow of fluid is one-dimensional through volumes and across junctions.

    (3) For two-phase mixtures ($0 < x < 1.0$) pressure and temperature equilibrium exist between phases; that is

$$P_g = P_\ell = p \text{ and } T_g = T_\ell = T.$$

    (4) For single-phase fluid, the state can be subcooled $T_\ell \leq T_{sat}$ for $x = 0$, or superheated $T_g \geq T_{sat}$ for $x = 1$.

By neglecting potential and kinetic energy terms and assuming no air present, the conservation rate equations for mass and energy for volume i can be written as

$$\dot{M}(i) = \sum_j [w_g(j) + w_\ell(j)], \tag{1}$$

$$\dot{U}(i) = \sum_j [w_g(j) \ h_g(j) + w_\ell(j) \ h_\ell(j)] + \dot{Q}_{wall} \tag{2}$$

The junction mass flow rates $w_g(j)$ and $w_\ell(j)$, are positive for flow into the control volume i and negative for flow out of the control volume.

The specific volume $v(i) = V(i)/M(i)$, and specific internal energy $u(i) = U(i)/M(i)$, can be obtained once Equations (1) and (2) are integrated and solved. As a result of the equilibrium assumptions, all thermodynamic quantities are completely determined by $v(i)$ and $u(i)$. Mass and energy transfer between phases are, therefore, implied by the equilibrium conditions. When subcooled water is injected into a volume containing a two-phase mixture, the injected liquid instantaneously attains the saturation state (provided there is sufficient amount of vapor) independent of the injection rate, the degree of subcooling, and the volume conditions. This process results in unrealistically high depressurization rates.

Nonequilibrium Condensation Model

The primary purpose of the nonequilibrium condensation model is to allow the coexistence of saturated steam and subcooled liquid within a control volume. This coexistence means that the mass and energy transfer rate between phases is no longer determined only by overall mass and energy conservation principles. An additional constitutive equation is needed to calculate the condensation rate depending on the extent of the departure from equilibrium.

The basic assumptions invoked in the nonequilibrium model are as follows:

(1) The two-phase mixture within a control volume is heterogeneous although each phase is homogeneous. That is, incoming liquid completely mixes with the resident liquid and incoming vapor completely mixes with the resident vapor.

(2) For two-phase mixtures, pressure equilibrium is assumed between phases and vapor is always assumed to be at saturated conditions; that is,

$$p_g = p_\ell = p \text{ and } T_g = T_{sat}(p).$$

(3) The liquid phase may be subcooled. The degree of subcooling is determined in part by the mass and energy transfer between phases.

(4) The condensation rate is governed by the degree of liquid subcooling, the interfacial area per unit volume A_{in}, and an interfacial heat

transfer coefficient h_{in}. Specifically, the mass of vapor which condenses per unit time, $\dot{M}_{cond}$, is given by

$$\dot{M}_{cond}(i) = \{h_{in}(i) \, A_{in}(i) \, [\, T_{sat}(i)$$

$$- T_\ell(i)]\}V(i) / [h_{gs}(i) - h_{\ell s}(i)]. \tag{3}$$

For this simplified nonequilibrium model, thermodynamic quantities of each phase can be calculated based on the separate mass balances of liquid and vapor, the overall energy balance, the constant volume assumption and the equations of state[5]. The mass balance rate equations are

$$\dot{M}_g(i) = \sum_j w_g(j) - \dot{M}_{cond}(i), \tag{4}$$

$$\dot{M}_\ell(i) = \sum_j w_\ell(j) + \dot{M}_{cond}(i). \tag{5}$$

The overall energy balance equation is the same as Equation (2). The independent state variables can be chosen as quality (x), pressure (p), and liquid specific enthalpy (h_ℓ). The thermodynamic properties of the vapor phase are functions of p only and those of the subcooled liquid are functions of p and h_ℓ.

An implicit implementation of the nonequilibrium model into RELAP4 would require a solution scheme completely different from that coded presently. Furthermore, the main feature of RELAP4, simplicity, would disappear. To minimize changes to the existing code, the method described in the following subsection has been utilized to interface the nonequilibrium condensation model with the existing RELAP4 solution scheme.

Implementation Scheme

For a nonequilibrium control volume with subcooled water, the condensation rate is given by Equation (3) with the aid of the constitutive model described in the next section. The rate of pressure change, $\dot{p}(i)$, and the rate of change in total liquid enthalpy, $\dot{H}_\ell(i)$, can be obtained from Equations (2), (4), and (5) as

$$\dot{p} = (A - B \, v_{\ell,h})/C, \tag{6}$$

$$\dot{H}_\ell = \sum_j w_\ell(j) \, h_\ell(j) + \dot{M}_{cond} \, h_g - M(x\tilde{h}_{g,p} - v)\dot{p} + \dot{Q}_{wall}. \tag{7}$$

Here the volume index (i) has been omitted for conciseness, M is the total fluid mass in the control volume, and

$$A = \dot{M}_{cond}(v_g - v_\ell) - [v_g \sum_j w_g(j) + v_\ell \sum_j w_\ell(j)],$$

$$B = \dot{M}_{cond} (h_g - h_\ell) + \sum_j w_\ell(j) (h_\ell(j) - h_\ell)$$

$$+ \sum_j w_g(j) (h_g(j) - h_g) + \dot{Q}_{wall},$$

$$C = M [x\tilde{v}_{g,p} + (1-x)v_{\ell,p} - (x\tilde{h}_{g,p} - v)v_{\ell,h}],$$

$$\tilde{v}_{g,p} = d\, v_g/dp,$$

$$\tilde{h}_{g,p} = d\, h_g/dp,$$

$$v_{\ell,p} = (\frac{\partial v_\ell}{\partial p})_{h_\ell},$$

$$v_{\ell,h} = (\frac{\partial v_\ell}{\partial h_\ell})_p.$$

Note that, Equation (6) indicates that condensation does not necessarily result in a decrease in pressure.

In order to utilize the equilibrium scheme of RELAP4, the nonequilibrium model is introduced through an equivalent equilibrium system for which the same depressurization rate is achieved by introducing an effective heat addition rate $\dot{Q}^*$ (which represents the sum of the wall heat transfer rate and the energy transfer rate necessary to ensure the nonequilibrium depressurization rate). The overall conservation rate equations for a control volume in the equivalent equilibrium system then become

$$\dot{M}^* = \sum_j w_g(j) + \sum_j w_\ell(j), \tag{8}$$

$$\dot{U}^* = \sum_j w_g(j) h_g^*(j) + h_\ell^* \sum_j w_\ell(j) + \dot{Q}^*. \tag{9}$$

Here the superscript (*) is used to explicitly specify the equivalent system. Equations (8) and (9) differ from Equations (1) and (2) in that junction liquid enthalpy $h_\ell(j)$ is replaced by the saturated liquid enthalpy h_ℓ^* of the control volume and $\dot{Q}_{wall}$ by $\dot{Q}^*$.

By equating $\dot{p}^*$ to $\dot{p}$, the condensation rate $\dot{M}_{cond}^*$ (rate of mass transfer from vapor to liquid) and the effective heat addition $\dot{Q}^*$ can be found from Equations (8) and (9) as

$$\dot{M}^*_{cond} = \{M^* [x \, d \, v^*_g/dp^* + (1-x) \, dv^*_\ell/dp^*] \, \dot{p}$$

$$+ v^*_g \sum_j w_g(j) + v^*_\ell \sum_j w_\ell(j)\}/(v^*_g - v^*_\ell), \tag{10}$$

$$\dot{Q}^* = - \dot{M}^*_{cond} (h^*_g - h^*_\ell) + M^* [x \, d \, h^*_g/dp^*$$

$$+ (1-x) \, d \, h^*_\ell/dp^* - v^*] \, \dot{p}. \tag{11}$$

By comparing Equation (10) with Equation (6), note that $\dot{M}_{cond}$ nearly equals $\dot{M}^*_{cond}$ when x is not too small, since $v^*_\ell \approx v_\ell$, and $\partial v^*_\ell/dp$, $(\partial v_\ell/\partial p)_{h_\ell}$, and $(\partial v_\ell/\partial h_\ell)_p$ are very small.

At each time step, $\dot{p}$ and $\dot{Q}^*$ are calculated according to Equations (6) and (11), respectively, for each of the nonequilibrium volumes. Once $\dot{Q}^*$ is known, the thermodynamic state of the equivalent system can be determined by the usual RELAP4 solution scheme. The thermodynamic state of vapor for the nonequilibrium system is assumed to be the same as that of the equivalent system, as are the pressure and mass of the liquid. The total liquid enthalpy is advanced explicitly in each time step by using Equation (7) with $\dot{M}_{cond}$ replaced by $\dot{M}^*_{cond}$.

CONSTITUTIVE RELATIONS FOR INTERFACIAL HEAT TRANSFER

A constitutive model for calculating the interfacial area per unit volume (A_{in}) and interfacial heat transfer coefficient (h_{in}) for energy transfer between subcooled liquid and saturated vapor is discussed in this section. For the present model, simple expressions are obtained for h_{in} and A_{in} in the bubbly flow and dispersed droplet flow regimes. Figure 1 shows the bubbly and dispersed flow regimes, which are based in part on the modified Bennett[9] vertical flow regime map, as specified by mass flux (G) and void fraction (α). An interpolation scheme has been developed to obtain the $h_{in} A_{in}$ product across the transition region.

For bubbly flow the rate of bubble collapse is assumed to be governed by the convection of latent heat away from the vapor-liquid interface into the liquid phase. Assuming spherical bubbles of uniform size, the interfacial heat transfer coefficient and interfacial area per unit volume can be expressed as[8,10-13]

$$h_{in,b} = [2 \, v_r \, k_\ell \, \rho_\ell \, c_{p\ell}/(\pi r_b)]^{1/2}, \tag{12}$$

$$A_{in,b} = 3\alpha/r_b. \tag{13}$$

Here v_r is the relative velocity between the vapor and liquid phase; k_ℓ, ρ_ℓ and $c_{p\ell}$ are, respectively, the thermal conductivity, density and specific heat of the liquid phase, and α is the void fraction. To account for turbulence effects at increased mass flow rates, $h_{in,b}$ is further multiplied by a factor proportional to $(G)^{0.125}$.

For dispersed flow, with liquid droplets uniformly distributed in a continuous vapor phase, the condensation rate is assumed to be controlled by the conduction of latent heat away from the droplet surface into the droplet bulk. For spherical droplets with uniform radii the heat conduction into the droplet bulk is[3,8]

$$h_{in,d} = C \, k_\ell / r_d, \tag{14}$$

where the constant C is taken to be 8.067[8]; the corresponding interfacial area is

$$A_{in,d} = 3(1-\alpha)/r_d. \tag{15}$$

The bubble radius r_b and droplet radius r_d are computed based on a Weber number criterion using Zuber's churn-turbulent drift expression[12,13]. The critical Weber number is assumed to be 8.0 for bubbles[12] and 12.0 for droplets[14].

The interpolation procedure in the transition region is derived using the following approach. Suppose that control volume V is divided into two parts: one part contains fluid in bubbly flow with void fraction α_b and volume V_b and the remainder of the volume contains fluid in dispersed flow with void fraction α_d and volume V_d. Then, the volume of the bubbly and dispersed regions can be computed as

$$V_b = (\alpha - \alpha_b) \, V / (\alpha_d - \alpha_b), \tag{16}$$

$$V_d = (\alpha_d - \alpha) \, V / (\alpha_d - \alpha_b). \tag{17}$$

By substituting $(V_b + V_d)$ for V in Equation (3), one can see that the heat transfer in the transition region can be calculated by linear interpolation of $h_{in} A_{in}$ at α_b and at α_d. The void fractions α_b and α_d are assumed to be the intercepts of the line of constant G with the flow regime boundaries. The interpolation scheme may also be extended to include a weighting factor for $h_{in} A_{in}$.

MIXING MODEL ASSESSMENT

The nonequilibrium ECC mixing model, as implemented into RELAP4/MOD7, has been evaluated with the Battelle[15] and Creare[16] 1/15-scale PWR results, the Westinghouse 1/3-scale cold leg ECC injection data[17], and the LOFT L1-4 test[2]. The RELAP4/MOD7 mixing model, when used in conjunction with the slip model, has effectively described the nonequilibrium refill behavior of the Battelle data. Application of the mixing model also resulted in a good comparison with the Westinghouse results. Based

on the success of simulating quasi-steady state nonequilibrium separate
effect tests, additional assessment of the mixing model was performed
using experimental results that were more indicative of the actual
phenomena expected during the refill period of a PWR LOCA. For these
comparisons the Creare transient reverse core steam tests and LOFT L1-4
test were used.

The Creare test facility, Figure 2, is a 1/15-scale model of a PWR that
has been designed to explore the effects of ECC subcooling, ECC flow rate,
and various reverse core and intact cold leg steam flow rates on refill of
a four-loop reactor. The system consists of intact blind flanged cold
legs with corresponding ECC and steam flow injectors, a scaled pressure
vessel, and a simulated containment. The typical test sequence, as
utilized in our comparison, consisted of establishing a reverse core steam
flow through the system, allowing the system to equilibrate, injecting
the ECC water, and within two seconds of the ECC injection initiating a
decreasing reverse core steam flow transient. For each test the liquid
level in the lower plenum and reverse core steam flow rate versus time
were recorded.

To simulate the Creare facility the RELAP4/MOD7 model shown in Figure 3
was developed. The model consisted of a seven-volume, eight-junction
system with the three intact cold legs lumped into a single control
volume, a two-volume downcomer, and a time-dependent volume simulating
a containment. The RELAP4/MOD7 flow regime dependent slip model was
specified for all downcomer junctions along with complete phase separation
in the lower plenum. Thermal nonequilibrium was assumed for all volumes
except the simulated core and containment. The model was initialized by
impressing a given reverse core steam flow on an initially stagnant system
at atmospheric pressure. When the system equilibrated, the ECC was
injected and the reverse core steam flow ramp initiated.

In Figure 4 a representative RELAP4 computed refill calculation for test
H1 is compared with the test data. For this test the system was initialized to 192.4 kPa lower plenum pressure with 0.324 kg/s reverse core
steam flow prior to the injection of a 3.79 ℓ/s ECC flow and initiation
of a 10 s steam ramp decay. As shown, the RELAP4 calculation shows
reasonably good agreement with the experimental refill rate for this
highly subcooled test, but is at variance by approximately 2 s in
the prediction of delivery initiation. This anomaly, which was not
observed in the Battelle comparisons, is believed due to a hot wall delay
effect which was not modeled for the Creare facility. While in the
Battelle facility the pressure vessel was composed primarily of non-
metallic materials and, therefore, possessed marginal stored energy, the
Creare vessel was totally metallic in construction and consequently the
higher stored energy of the system translated into substantial vapor
generation and a significant hot wall time delay.

Results of Creare test H37, another highly subcooled but also very high
ECC injection run, is compared with data in Figure 5. In this run, a
testing sequence similar to that of test H1 was followed, however, the
initial system steam flow and pressure were reduced to 0.238 kg/s and

144 kPa, respectively, with a 17 s steam decay ramp while the ECC
flow was increased to 5.68 ℓ/s. As with test H1 the results again
duplicated the refill rate while deviating in the prediction of delivery
initiation.

Table I presents the results of code simulations of other Creare tests.
As may be observed, the tests represent a range of initial steam and
ECC flow rates, transient duration, initial system pressures, and initial
subcoolings. The comparisons indicate that the RELAP4 calculated refill
rates generally agree well with the data. The same delivery initiation
problem previously noted was observed for most of the tests.

Based on the successful application of the mixing model to a range of
separate effects tests an effort was undertaken to investigate the effec-
tiveness of the model in describing the nonequilibrium phenomena associated
with PWR system LOCA. For this task the nonnuclear LOFT L1-4 experiment
was modeled. The system, Figure 6, consisted of a simulated pressure
vessel and associated core simulator connected to an intact and broken
loop. The intact loop simulates the three unbroken loops of a PWR and
includes a steam generator, pressurizer, primary coolant pumps, and ECC
injection site with associated accumulator, HPIS, and LPIS. The broken
loop consists of a hot leg, steam generator and pump simulators and a
cold leg each with an adjustable break plane orifice connecting to a containment back pressure simulator. For the L1-4 test an initially isothermal system was subjected to a 200% offset cold leg shear pipe break
initiated by a simultaneous opening of the broken loop quick opening
valves. Critical system parameters were recorded during the initial
blowdown phase and the subsequent ECC injection period.

The RELAP4 model of the L1-4 system, which is depicted in Figure 7, consisted of 49 volumes, 55 junctions, and 47 heat slabs. The nonequilibrium
calculation was specified for all intact cold leg volumes upstream of the
primary pump juncture, all volumes of the pressure vessel except the core
simulator, and all volumes of the broken cold leg. The system was initialized to a steady state isothermal condition from which the blowdown
and subsequent ECC injection were initiated.

Figure 8 presents the experimental data and calculated results for the
core simulator pressure. For the first 25 s after rupture both
equilibrium (standard RELAP4) and nonequilibrium calculations are in
good agreement with the experimental data. Beyond 25 s, the nonequilibrium calculation is seen to deviate only slightly from the
experimental result; on the other hand, the pressure trace of the
equilibrium calculation falls considerably below the measured pressure.
Clearly, the rapid depressurization in the equilibrium calculation due
to the instantaneous mixing of steam and subcooled water can be overcome
by using the nonequilibrium model.

Figure 9 shows the fluid density in the intact loop cold leg. In the
equilibrium calculation, the density begins to increase shortly after
the ECC water is injected into the cold leg. Due to the equilibrium
mixing assumption, the cold leg quickly fills with water and becomes

subcooled. Volumes downstream of the injection section become full of water and subcool as the transient proceeds. The sequential "water packing" of volumes is characteristic of a standard RELAP4 calculation of the ECC injection phase of a LOCA transient. The nonequilibrium calculation predicts a large quantity of steam in the cold leg at all times. This higher void fraction is more reasonable and typical of the data, although the experimental density fluctuations which reflect the sensing of intermittent fluid slugs is not predicted.

In Figure 10 the fluid temperature in the intact loop cold leg is shown. Since only a limited amount of steam condenses, the temperature of the ECC liquid is somewhat subcooled and corresponds to a temperature between saturation and the injection temperature. Since the vapor is nearly saturated, the measured (mixture) temperature should fall between the saturated temperature and the subcooled liquid temperature due to the fact that the thermocouple senses intermittent slugs of subcooled liquid in a steam environment.

The total mass of fluid in the reactor vessel is shown in Figure 11. Both the equilibrium and nonequilibrium calculations yield reasonable results. The nonequilibrium calculation does show better agreement with the experimental data after the injection of ECC water.

SUMMARY

A simple model to simulate the nonequilibrium phenomena associated with the mixing of subcooled water with saturated steam has been developed and is operational on preliminary versions of RELAP4/MOD7. The model has been implemented through the use of an equivalent equilibrium system which yields the same depressurization rate as the true nonequilibrium system. The liquid enthalpy is computed explicitly and the interfacial heat transfer between phases is determined using empirical correlations.

Use of the nonequilibrium model to simulate the Creare 1/15-scale ECC bypass tests and the LOFT L1-4 test indicate that the model can reasonably predict the nonequilibrium phenomena occurring during the refill phase of a LOCA. Results from these and other simulations clearly indicate the need for consideration of nonequilibrium effects during refill. Discrepancies between calculated and experimental behavior indicate the need for continued development of constitutive relations for modeling ECC mixing phenomena.

NOMENCLATURE

A_{in} interfacial area per unit volume

$c_{p\ell}$ liquid specific heat at constant pressure

h_{in} interfacial heat transfer coefficient

h_g vapor specific enthalpy

h_{gs} — specific enthalpy of saturated vapor

H_ℓ — total liquid enthalpy in a control volume

$\dot{H}_\ell$ — dH_ℓ/dt

i — volume number

j — junction number

h_ℓ — liquid specific enthalpy

$h_{\ell s}$ — specific enthalpy of saturated liquid

G — mass flux

k_ℓ — thermal conductivity of liquid

M — total fluid mass in a control volume

$\dot{M}$ — dM/dt

$\dot{M}_{cond}$ — condensation rate in a control volume

p — pressure

$\dot{p}$ — dp/dt

$\dot{Q}_{wall}$ — wall heat transfer rate

$\dot{Q}^*$ — effective heat addition to a control volume taking into account wall heat transfer and condensation effects

r_b — bubble radius

r_d — droplet radius

T — temperature

T_g — vapor temperature

T_ℓ — liquid temperature

T_{sat} — saturated temperature

U — total energy of the fluid in a control volume

$\dot{U}$ — dU/dt

V — total volume of a control volume

v — specific volume of the fluid

v_ℓ - liquid specific volume

v_g - vapor specific volume

v_r - relative velocity between liquid and vapor phases

w_g - junction mass flow rate of vapor

w_ℓ - junction mass flow rate of liquid

x   - quality

α - void fraction

ρ_ℓ - liquid density

REFERENCES

1. K. R. Katsma et al, RELAP4/MOD5 - A Computer Program for Transient Thermal Hydraulic Analysis of Nuclear Reactors and Related Systems, Vols. I, II, III, ANCR-NUREG-1335 (1976).

2. D. L. Batt, Experiment Data Report for LOFT Nonnuclear Test L1-4, TREE-NUREG-1084 (July 1977).

3. TRAC-P1A - An Advanced Best-Estimate Computer Program for PWR LOCA Analysis, NUREG CR-0063, LA-7279-MS, Vol. 1 (June 1978).

4. A. A. Amsden and F. H. Harlow, K-TIF: A Two-Fluid Computer Program for Downcomer Flow Dynamics, LA-6994, NRC-4 (January 1978).

5. K. Wolfert, "The Simulation of Blowdown Processes with Condensation of Thermodynamic Nonequilibrium Phenomena," Specialists Meeting on Transient Two-Phase Flow sponsored by the OECD/Nuclear Energy Agency, Toronto, Canada, August 3-4, 1976.

6. P. Saha, "Direct Contact Condensation," Reactor Safety Research Programs Quarterly Progress Report (October 1 - December 31, 1977), BNL-NUREG-50785 (Feburary 1978), pp 198-203.

7. O. C. Jones and P. Saha, "Nonequilibrium Aspects of Water Reactor Safety," Thermal and Hydraulic Aspects of Nuclear Reactor Safety, Vol. 1: Light Water Reactors, O. C. Jones and S. G. Bankoff (eds.), ASME (1977), pp 249-288.

8. E. D. Hughes et al, An Evaluation of State-of-the-Art Two-Velocity, Two-Phase Flow Models and Their Applicability to Nuclear Reactor Transient Analysis, EPRI NP-143 (February 1976).

9. A. E. Bennett, G. F. Hewitt et al, Flow Visualization Studies of Boiling at High Pressure, AERE-R-4874 (1967).

10. E. Rukenstein, "On Heat Transfer Between Vapor Bubbles in Motion and the Boiling Liquid from Which They are Generated," Chem. Eng. Sci. 10, 22 (1959).

11. D. Moalem and S. Siderman, "The Effect of Motion on Bubble Collapse," Int. J. Heat and Mass Transfer, 16, 2321 (1973).

12. M. Ishii, One-Dimensional Drift-Flux Model and Constitutive Equations for Relative Motion Between Phases in Various Two-Phase Flow Regimes, ANL-77-47 (1977).

13. N. Zuber and J. A. Findlay, "Average Volumetric Concentration in Two-Phase Flow System," J. Heat Transfer 87, 453 (1965).

14. E. O. Moeck, Annular-Dispersed Two-Phase Flow and Critical Heat Flux, AECL-3656 (1970).

15. R. A. Cudnik, L. J. Flanigan, W. A. Carbiener, R. O. Wooton and R. S. Denning, Penetration Behavior in a 1/15-Scale Model of a Four-Loop Pressurized Water Reactor, BMI-NUREG-1973, NRC-2 (June 1977).

16. C. J. Crowley et al, Downcomer Effects in a 1/15-Scale PWR Geometry - Experimental Data Report, NUREG-0281, NRC-2 (May 1977).

17. G. R. Lilly and L. E. Hochreiter, Mixing of Emergency Core Cooling Water with Steam: 1/3-Scale Test and Summary, EPRI 294-2 Final Report (June 1975).

TABLE I. RESULTS COMPARISONS FOR 1/15-SCALE CREARE TESTS						
	Initial Conditions		ECC Conditions		Refill Rate	
Test No.	Steam Flow (kg/s)	Plenum Pressure (kPa)	Flow (ℓ/s)	Temp (K)	Test (ℓ/s)	RELAP4 (ℓ/s)
H1	0.324	192.4	3.79	300.8	2.09	2.01
H3	0.334	167.5	3.79	301.1	2.02	1.53
H37	0.238	144.1	5.68	300.0	1.50	1.87
H75	0.171	146.2	3.79	338.9	2.95	1.89
H104	0.211	177.9	3.79	375.0	1.22	1.22
H117	0.284	271.0	3.79	300.8	0.83	1.19
H121	0.331	422.0	3.79	300.8	1.15	1.06

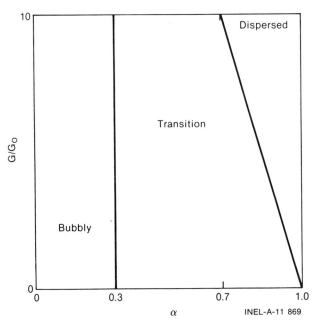

Fig. 1   Flow Map $G_0 = 1.356 \times 10^3$ Kg/s - m^2; for $G > 10G_0$, G is set equal to $10G_0$

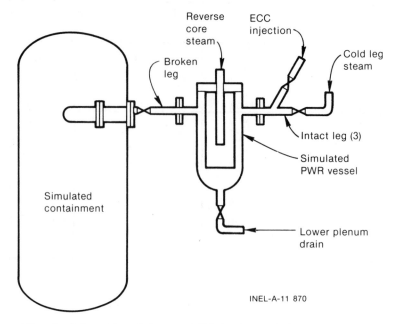

Fig. 2   Schematic of Creare 1/15-Scale Facility

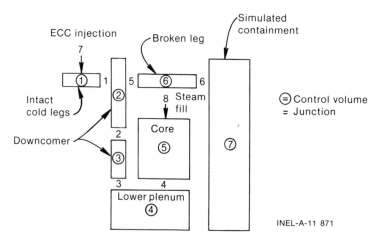

Fig. 3   RELAP Model of Creare 1/15-Scale Facility

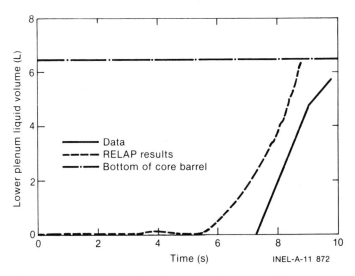

Fig. 4   Creare Test No. H1 Lower Plenum Refill Comparison

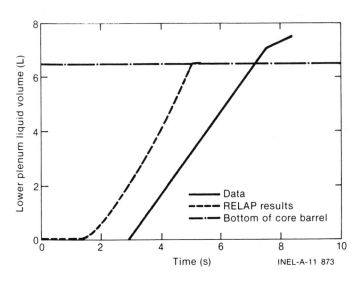

Fig. 5   Creare Test No. H37 Lower Plenum Refill Comparison

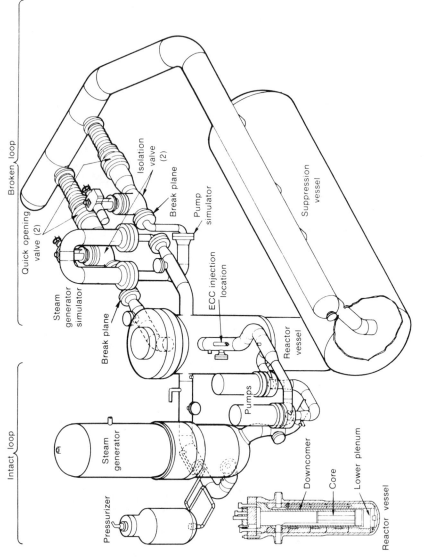

Broken loop

Isolation valve (2)

Break plane

Quick opening valve (2)

Pump simulator

Steam generator simulator

Break plane

ECC injection location

Suppression vessel

Intact loop

Steam generator

Pressurizer

Reactor vessel

Pumps

Downcomer

Core

Lower plenum

Reactor vessel

Fig. 6 LOFT Major Components

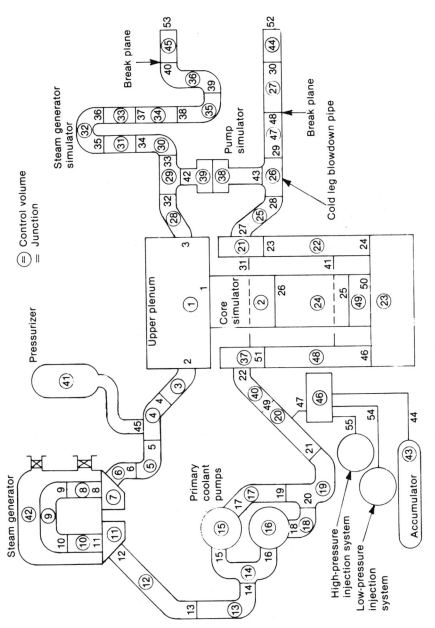

Fig. 7 RELAP4 Model for LOFT L1-4 Analysis

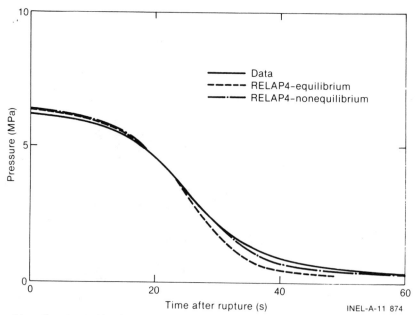

Fig. 8   Core Simulator Pressure, LOFT L1-4

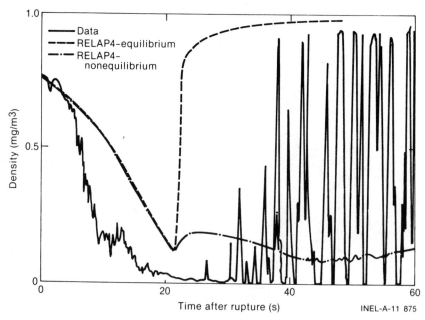

Fig. 9   Average Density in Intact Loop Cold Leg, LOFT L1-4

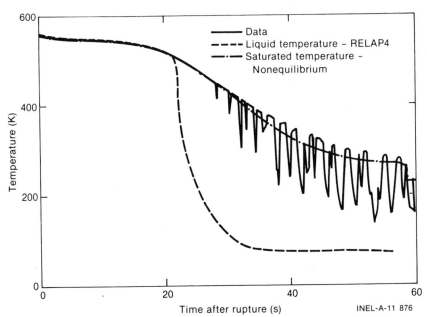

Fig. 10 Temperature in Intact Loop Cold Leg, LOFT L1-4 Data and
RELAP4 Nonequilibrium Calculation

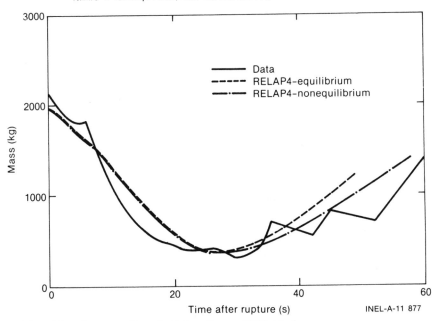

Fig. 11 Reactor Vessel Water Mass, LOFT L1-4

Heat Transfer Considerations for the First Nuclear Blowdowns

J.W. SPORE, M.M. GILES, and D.R. EVANS
EG&G Idaho, Inc.
Idaho Falls, Idaho 83401, USA

ABSTRACT

The first nuclear blowdowns were carried out in the Power Burst Facility
at the Idaho National Engineering Laboratory as the LOC-11 series of experiments[1]. This test series was designed to simulate a blowdown
transient in a pressurized water reactor (PWR) so that nuclear fuel performance could be investigated under conditions representative of the
PWR 15 x 15 fuel element design.

Post-test calculations using the RELAP4 computer program[2] were performed for the LOC-11B and LOC-11C tests. Comparisons between calculations and experimental data revealed that the ability to accurately
model (1) critical heat flux (CHF) during low core flow conditions,
(2) initial stored energy in the fuel rods, and (3) radiative heat
transfer between fuel rods and shrouds, was required to adequately
represent the fuel rod thermal behavior. Pre-test calculations performed
using RELAP4 with licensing-type heat transfer and fuel rod models
resulted in peak cladding temperatures several hundred K higher than
measured, thus providing further evidence of the need to accurately
model heat transfer and fuel rod behavior.

INTRODUCTION

This paper presents results of the first nuclear blowdown tests (LOC-11A,
LOC-11B, LOC-11C) ever conducted. The Loss-of-Coolant Accident (LOCA)
Test Series is being conducted in the Power Burst Facility (PBF) reactor
at the Idaho National Engineering Laboratory, near Idaho Falls, Idaho
for the Nuclear Regulatory Commission. The objective of the LOC-11 tests
was to obtain data on the behavior of pressurized and unpressurized fuel
rods when exposed to a blowdown similar to that expected in a pressurized
water reactor (PWR) during a hypothesized double-ended cold-leg break.
The data are being used for the development and assessment of analytical models that are used to predict the thermal and hydraulic response of
a PWR during a blowdown transient.

TEST DESCRIPTION AND CONDUCT

The tests were conducted with four, separately shrouded, PWR-type fresh
fuel rods. The fuel rods were of 15 x 15 design, except for the active

length, which was 0.91 m. The fuel rod plenum volume was scaled proportionally to the active fuel length. Two rods were initially pressurized
to 0.1 MPa (Rods 611-1, 611-4) and one each to 2.11 MPa (Rod 611-3) and
4.82 MPa (Rod 611-2). (However, the 4.82 MPa rod contained a small leak
and its posttest pressure was 1.0 MPa). A fluted flow shroud was selected
to minimize the chance of complete flow blockage if uniform ballooning
occurred. The coolant flow area was about twice the value associated
with a single PWR rod. Four screws, located at two axial elevations,
centered each fuel rod. Figure 1 illustrates the blowdown system and
a test fuel rod within a fluted shroud.

Valves were used to isolate the experimental hardware from the PBF loop
coolant system and thereby provide a controllable flow path during blowdown. Test conduct began with PBF loop isolation from the in-pile tube
and a simultaneous reactor scram. Blowdown then commenced and was controlled by quick (∿ 100 ms) opening blowdown valves. Valve operation
was controlled by a time sequential programmer. The break planes were
formed by converging-diverging nozzles with a cylindrical throat section
having equal length and diameter measurements. The design was patterned
after that used in the Semiscale program at the Idaho National Engineering Laboratory to optimize predictive capability. The throats were
sized to control the flow and depressurization rates. The coolant
ejected from the system and the fission products carried from the fuel
were collected in a blowdown tank. A quench system provided coolant
for terminating the cladding temperature excursion and ending the test.

The fuel rod instrumentation consisted of cladding surface thermocouples,
fuel centerline thermocouples, linear variable differential transformers,
plenum pressure transducers, and plenum temperature thermocouples. The
test train instrumentation consisted of flow turbines located at each
end of the fuel rod flow shrouds, coolant temperature thermocouples,
coolant pressure transducers, and thermocouples on the outer surface
of the fuel rod flow shroud.

Piping measurement spools were installed for determination of the initial
inlet and blowdown coolant conditions. Each spool contained temperature,
pressure, and flow rate measuring devices. The spools in the blowdown
piping also contained a shielded and chopped three-beam gamma densitometer to determine coolant density, and inlet screens to straighten and
disperse the flow.

The LOC-11 tests consisted of three separate blowdowns from nuclear power
operation. The first test (Test LOC-11A) was conducted after a power
calibration, two cycles of full power operation for fuel rod precondi-
tioning, and an additional six hours at full power. Initial test conditions were a coolant inlet pressure of 14.9 MPa, temperature of 591 K,
flow rate of 0.91 ℓ/s, and a peak power of 54.7 kW/m. Spurious system
blowdown and isolation valve cycling occurred because of an inductive
feedback from a liquid level indicator in the blowdown tank interrupting
the electrical signals required to activate proper valve sequencing. As

a result, additional coolant entered the blowdown system from the PBF loop, thus delaying the onset of critical heat flux (CHF) for six to eight seconds after blowdown initiation. Peak measured cladding temperatures did not exceed 830 K. Test LOC-11A served as a facility checkout test and is not considered further.

Tests LOC-11B and LOC-11C were conducted with axial peak powers of 45.5 and 69.9 kW/m, inlet coolant pressures of 15.2 and 15.3 MPa, inlet coolant temperatures of 593 and 596 K, and flow rates per rod of 0.99 and 0.98 ℓ/s, respectively. During Test LOC-11B, blowdown system siolation and reactor scram occurred at time zero, with one blowdown valve opening in the hot- and cold-leg piping at about 0.9 second, as planned. The delay in valve opening allowed for a 0.9-second stagnation period prior to blowdown. Blowdown was programmed to begin about 0.1 second after isolation and reactor scram during Test LOC-11C, rather than the 0.9-second delay used for Test LOC-11B. CHF occurred 3.2 seconds after isolation during Test LOC-11B, and peak measured cladding temperatures reached 880 K. During Test LOC-11C, CHF occurred 1.6 seconds after isolation, and the peak measured cladding temperatures reached 1030 K.

EXPERIMENTAL DATA COMPARISONS

Pretest calculations were performed for the LOC-11 Test at the originally-planned peak power of 55 kW/m, using the RELAP4/MQD5 computer program. In these calculations, a number of the assumptions required for licensing of commercial nuclear reactors were employed. (The principal effects of these assumptions were to force early CHF, to calculate a high value for initial stored energy, and to neglect radiative heat transfer from fuel rod to shroud).

Post-test calculations using a special version of the RELAP4/MOD6 computer program[a] were made at the actual test conditions, as far as possible, and employing assumptions intended to accurately model the heat transfer and fluid flow processes occurring within the reactor system. The following paragraphs discuss comparisons between experimental data and RELAP4 calculations.

Critical Heat Flux

Figure 2 compares measured values for cladding surface temperature, shroud inlet and outlet volumetric flow rate, and cladding elongation for Test LOC-11C. It is seen that the CHF condition, as indicated by a sudden rise in cladding temperature and a sudden elongation of the cladding, occurs at the second occurrence of zero flow within the shroud.

---

[a] RELAP4/MOD6, Update 4, EG&G Idaho, Inc. Configuration Control Number H003321B.

In the RELAP4/MOD5 pretest calculations, the calculated occurrence of CHF was at the initial occurrence of zero flow. This was because the CHF correlations used were based on experimental data at high flow, and extrapolating these correlations to low flow gave a too-small CHF value. The licensing assumptions made in this calculation inhibited any tendency there may have been to return to nucleate boiling. In the RELAP4/MOD6 program, the CHF logic was improved over that of RELAP4/MOD5 by using the modified Zuber correlation[3] for low-flow conditions. With RELAP4/MOD6, the CHF condition was calculated to occur at 1.2 s, and the second occurrence of zero flow was calculated to occur at 1.4 s. In RELAP4/MOD6, for mass fluxes greater than or equal to 1356 kg/m^2·s, the high-flow correlations (the W-3 correlation[4] for subcooled fluid, the Hsu-Beckner modification[5] of the W-3 correlation for saturated and two-phase fluid) are used. For mass fluxes less than 271 kg/m^2·s, the low-flow correlation (modified Zuber) is used. For mass fluxes between 271 and 1356 kg/m^2·s, interpolation on mass flux between the appropriate high-flow correlation, evaluated at 1356 kg/m^2·s, and the low-flow correlation is used. Reduction of the value of mass flux below which the low-flow correlation is used to 67.8 kg/m^2·s did not appreciably improve the time of CHF in the RELAP4 calculations.

The modified Zuber correlation has no mass flux dependence and has only ·a moderate pressure dependence. The principal parameter in the correlation is the void fraction. Since the development of void fraction depends on the rate of phase separation, the ability of the RELAP4 slip model to calculate phase separation effects is of significance. The early occurrence of CHF in the RELAP4 calculations indicates calculation of a more rapid rate of void formation than actually occurred. Sensitivity studies, in which adjustments are made to the RELAP4 slip model parameters, will help to evaluate whether improved calculation of CHF time can be achieved by simple adjustment of the RELAP slip model parameters.

Additional understanding concerning the physical processes occurring during CHF in the LOC-11 tests is evidently needed. More experimental data and theoretical investigation will lead to such understanding.

As an illustration of the importance of calculating the timing of CHF, a calculation was performed in which the occurrence of CHF in RELAP4 was forced to coincide with that obtained experimentally. Figure 3 shows a comparison of three RELAP4 calculations, the pretest MOD5 calculation, the post-test MOD6 calculation, and the post-test MOD6 calculation with correct CHF time. The improvement in agreement with improved calculation of CHF time is evident. Thus, it is seen that significant progress in calculating CHF time, relative to RELAP4/MOD5, was obtained in the development of RELAP4/MOD6.

Initial Stored Energy

It is well known that initial stored energy within the fuel rod has a significant effect on cladding temperature during a blowdown transient. However, the standard RELAP4 program cannot model the radial power generation profile that exists in the LOC-11 fuel rods. Therefore, the capability to model a radial power generation profile was added to RELAP4. Also of significance is the centerline thermocouple hole within the LOC-11 fuel rods. An early post-test RELAP4/MOD6 calculation was run neglecting the centerline thermocouple hole, and a later calculation was run considering the hole. Table I compares the early post-test with the final post-test calculated values for centerline temperature with the measured value. As can be noted, the final post-test calculation gave the best value for centerline temperature, indicating the necessity of modeling the thermocouple hole.

Radiative Heat Transfer

In Figure 4, calculated cladding temperatures are compared with experimental data for two calculations: one neglecting radiative heat transfer from fuel rod to shroud, and one in which this effect is considered. It is evident that radiative heat transfer significantly affects cladding temperature and that considering radiative heat transfer significantly improves agreement between calculations and experimental data.

CONCLUSIONS

The results of this study support the conclusion that accurate calculation of core thermal response in nuclear fuel during blowdown requires accurate modeling of critical heat flux under low flow conditions, initial fuel rod stored energy, and, when significant, radiative heat transfer. It is further concluded that additional work concerning modeling of critical heat flux is needed to improve agreement between RELAP4 calculations and experimental data.

REFERENCES

1. J. R. Larson, J. M. Broughton, J. W. Spore, L. K. Sepold, PBF LOCA Test Series Test LOC-11 Test Results Report, NUREG/CR-0618 TREE-1329 (March 1979).

2. K. R. Katsma, RELAP4/MOD5 A Computer Program for Transient Thermal-Hydraulic Analysis of Nuclear Reactors and Related Systems User's Manual, ANCR-NUREG-1335 (September 1976).

3. R. A. Smith and P. Griffith, "A Simple Model for Estimating Time to CHF in a PWR LOCE," Transactions of the American Society of Mechanical Engineers, Paper No. 76-HT-9 (1976).

4. L. S. Tong, "Prediction of Departure from Nucleate Boiling for an Axially Non-Uniform Heat Flux Distribution," Journal of Nuclear

Energy, 21 (1967) pp. 241-248.

5. L. S. Tong, "Heat Transfer in Reactor Safety", Paper No. KS-21,
    Proceedings of Sixth International Heat Transfer Conference,
    Toronto, Canada (August 7-11, 1978).

TABLE I

CALCULATED AND EXPERIMENTAL FUEL ROD CENTERLINE
TEMPERATURES FOR LOC-11C

Case	Centerline Temperature, K
Post-test MOD6 (no centerline hole)	2675
Post-test MOD6 (centerline hole)	2450
Experimental Data	2500

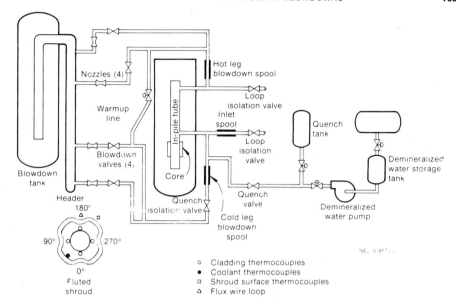

Fig. 1   PBF Blowdown System and Test LOC-11 Fuel Rod Orientation

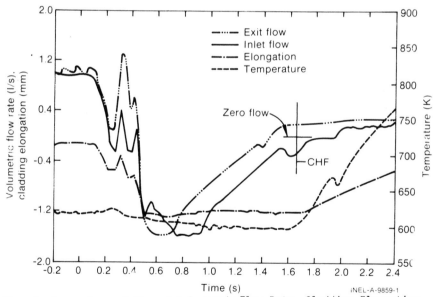

Fig. 2   Comparison of Shroud Volumetric Flow Rate, Cladding Elongation, and Cladding Surface Temperature During LOC-11C

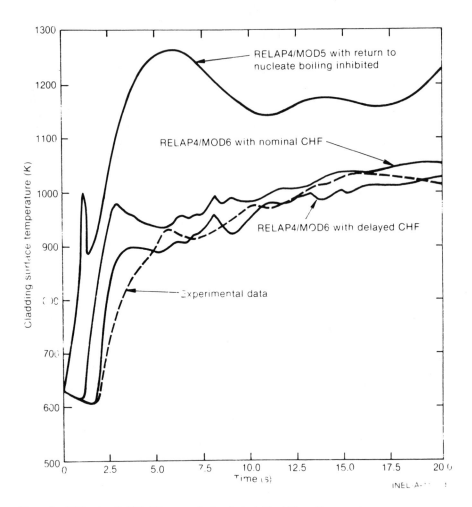

Fig. 3 Effect of CHF Time on Calculated Cladding Temperature

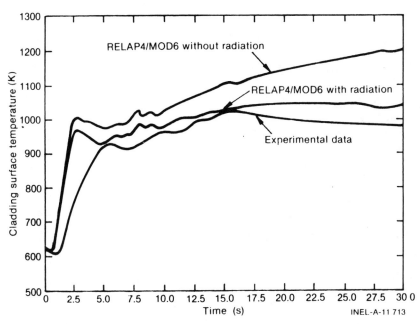

Fig. 4 Effect of Radiative Heat Transfer on Calculated Cladding Temperature

Discharge of a Flashing Liquid through Tubes

D.W. SALLET, S.R. ROD, M.E. PALMER, and W. NASTOLL
Mechanical Engineering Department
The University of Maryland
College Park, Maryland 20742, USA

M. GÜHLER
Fachhochschule für Technik Mannheim
Mannheim, Germany

ABSTRACT

This paper describes an extensive, primarily experimental investigation of the discharge of a flashing liquid from a finite reservoir through orifices and tubes to the atmosphere. The L/D ratios chosen were 0.33 (orifice), 3, 12, 36 and 120. Detailed experimental results are presented, including time-varying mass flow rate, pressure and tempera- ture data for the flow of initially saturated Freon-12 from a 20 liter vessel through 1.59 mm (1/16 in), 3.18 mm (1/8 in) and 4.76 mm (3/16 in) diameter outlets. The nominal initial pressures were 0.5 MPa (72 psia) and 2.0 MPa (280 psia). The experimental mass flow rates were compared to several theoretical models of two-phase flow.

NOMENCLATURE

A	cross sectional area (m^2)
C	orifice coefficient
D	diameter (m)
G	mass flux (kg/sm^2)
G_{max}	maximum mass flux (kg/sm^2)
h	enthalpy (J/kg)
K	slip ratio
L	length of tube (m)
m	mass (kg)
$\dot{m}$	mass flow rate (kg/s)
p	pressure (N/m^2)
s	specific entropy (J/kg K)
t	time (s)
v	specific volume (m^3/kg)
x	quality

Subscripts

  e   exit section
  f   saturated liquid property
  g   saturated vapor property
  o   stagnation

INTRODUCTION

The thermal and fluid dynamic behavior of saturated liquids subjected to
sudden depressurization due to accidental or intentional venting is of
interest in many areas of thermal engineering, particularly in the safety
analysis of such equipment as water and liquid-metal-cooled nuclear
reactors, high pressure steam generators, and heat exchangers. An area of
growing concern is the safety analysis of rail tank cars transporting such
hazardous material as propane, chlorine, and vinyl chloride. These
materials, gases at atmospheric conditions, are transported at high
pressure; when subjected to rapid depressurization, whether intentionally
by the activation of a safety valve, or due to a puncture, venting rates
and the rate of pressure relief are of much importance.

The design adequacy and sizing of tank car safety valves is the subject
of an ongoing analytical and experimental research program at the
University of Maryland. Included in the program are analyses of the impact
of thermodynamic models on predicted critical flow rates of liquified gases
[1] and [2], visualization experiments for the sudden depressurization
incident [3], and continuing experimental and theoretical efforts involving
the heat transfer and fluid flow aspects of flashing liquid venting rates.
Detailed experimental and theoretical results are presented in an interim
program report [4]; a summary of the safety valve sizing problem is also
available [5]. The non-steady aspects of one- and two-phase depressurization of pressure vessels containing liquified gases was recently addressed
by Sallet, Palmer and Rod [6] and the flow through actual pressure relief
valves is described in reference [7].

The phenomena of two-phase choked flow have been the subject of continuing
research during the past several decades. There is little need to survey
the literature in this area; the development of the subject through 1971
is adequately summarized in [8]. Many important later works are contained
in reference [9]. Of particular interest are the two-phase flow models
by Fauske [10], Moody [11], Levy [12] and Masena [13]. A comparison of
mass flow rates predicted with these models is given in [4].

Essentially, the venting rate depends on fluid properties, nozzle
geometry, degree of superheat, and exit quality. Homogeneous equilibrium
models under-predict the mass flow rate of orifices and short pipes. Nonequilibrium models and slip flow models are generally more successful,
although no single model is adequate for all quality regimes and nozzle
geometries. At high quality, the differences between the several

available critical flow rate models is relatively small.

The subject of the present paper is a detailed description of fundamental experiments on critical flow rates of initially saturated liquids through orifices and short pipes from finite vessels. The flow path in an actual pressure relief valve is exceedingly complex, and even an experimental simulation of the real flow would be difficult. The approach taken in the present work is to determine critical flow rates for tubes of various L/D with selected pressure ratios and fluids of interest. With this information, a small number of full scale tests with actual valve designs will yield "equivalent L/D ratios" or two-phase multipliers to facilitate valve sizing over the entire spectrum of commodities and pressures experienced in the rail transport environment.

After a description of the test apparatus and instrumentation used in the study, pressure, temperature, and flow rate results for the blowdown of an initially near-saturated liquid through large and small orifices and short pipes will be presented and discussed. Comparison of the results to limiting theoretical predictive schemes will be made and conclusions drawn.

EXPERIMENTAL APPARATUS

The principal components of the apparatus are shown in Figure 1. The pressure vessel is a 20 liter cylindrical steel canister of 30.5 cm inner diameter and 39 cm height. The steel instrumentation plates which are welded to the top and bottom of the pressure vessel are 15.25 cm in diameter. Installed in the top plate are a manually operated valve for controlled venting of the tank, a pressure measuring probe and three of the six thermocouples used in the experiments. On the bottom plate are mounted a manually operated valve for filling the tank with the test fluid, an electrical-resistance heating element, three additional thermocouples and the exit pipe assembly, shown in greater detail in Figure 2. The pressure vessel with all fittings installed withstands an internal pressure of 500 psig.

An aluminum ring is attached to the vessel at its midplane. The entire assembly is supported by positioning the ring on three load cells built into a supporting frame and tripod. The mass of the test assembly is measured with these load cells, which are located in the same elevation plane and spaced 120° apart on the frame.

The fluid venting assembly (see Figure 2) consists of a pneumatically actuated globe valve (0.5 s from completely closed to completely open) at the outlet of which is mounted either an orifice plate or a plate equipped with a venting tube of short or intermediate length. The entire channel from the bottom of the pressure vessel to the exit plate has a constant diameter of 3.81 cm so that the actual exit pipe (maximum test diameter of 4.76 mm) effectively has a square-edged entrance. Below the vent outlet a thrust plate is mounted to deflect the exiting fluid stream and thus guarantee a zero net axial thrust on the system. This is necessary because the mass of the system is measured by the load cells, which actually measure the weight of the test assembly, i.e. the total axial force of the system. A pressure tap is included near the outlet of the exit pipes and special arrangements are made to measure the pressure at the orifice as described later in more detail.

INSTRUMENTATION

The system mass is measured using three load cells. The output from each cell is to an individual bridge amplifier. The amplified signals are combined and the signal sum is recorded during the tests on an x-y plotter as a function of time. The impulse of the exiting mass is compensated for by use of a deflector plate.

Pressure measurements are obtained with a diaphragm type strain gauge transducer (quoted accuracy $\pm$ 0.5%) installed in the pressure probe assembly shown in Figure 3. This assembly consists of a pressure transducer mounted at the end of a fluid-filled piston chamber. The reason for employing the piston assembly is mainly because the transducer was found to be very sensitive to temperature gradients, although the temperatures at the transducer stayed well within the recommended temperature range. The time response to the pressure measurement with the pressure probe assembly stayed well below 1 millisecond.

The pressures of interest are the vessel stagnation pressure and the vent exit pressure. With regard to the former, experiments with two transducers, one at each end of the vessel, resulted in coinciding p(t) curves when hydrostatic pressure differences were taken into account. Therefore all further runs were conducted with only one transducer, at the top of the vessel. The outputs from the pressure transducers which measure the stagnation pressure and the exit section pressure or rather the near-exit section pressure were amplified and graphed by a two-channel strip chart recorder with built in bridge amplifiers. When discharge was to take place through pipes of various L/D, (length to diameter ratio), the pressure was measured approximately 4 mm before the exit of the tube through a pressure tap 1 mm in diameter.

When an orifice was to be used as the vessel outlet, the exit section pressure was obtained by employing a split orifice assembly, shown in figure 4. A gasket separating two thin orifice plates maintains a very narrow gap. Pressure is measured via a pressure tap in an annular space open to the gap. Precise alignment of the two plates is achieved with carefully machined locating pins.

In preliminary experiments with the split orifice, two distinct pressure readings, both reproducible, were obtained for the same discharge conditions, the only variable being the orifice plate separation. It was found that for a too-large plate spacing flow separation occurs before the second orifice plate, yielding an erroneous pressure reading. This finding was supported by temperature measurements within the split orifice assembly. With the proper gap size, no flow separation occurred prior to the second orifice plate and the measured pressure was indeed the exit section pressure at the orifice.

Transient local temperatures within the vessel were measured with six ice-point-referenced thermocouples (ASTM type T; Copper-Constantan) whose locations are noted in Figure 1. To obtain rapid time response, micro-thermocouples with a wire diameter less than 0.25 mm and welded beads were used. Thermocouple output in the initial series of tests was to a multi-channel digital printer which sampled the sensors sequentially. The output of each thermocouples was recorded every five seconds and signals from selected sensors were continuously graphed on a two-channel strip chart recorder. Subsequent tests were conducted with two selected thermocouples monitored continuously on the strip chart recorder. This type of temperature monitoring was adequate because only minor temperature variations were noted among thermocouples located in the main portion of the pressure vessel during blowdown. Sampling one centrally located thermocouple and one close to the bottom of the vessel was therefore sufficient to determine the vessel temperature to the required accuracy. Temperatures measured with the above described system are estimated to be accurate within 0.5 C.

EXPERIMENTAL PROCEDURE

The experimental procedure consists of the following activities. First, the mass measurement system is calibrated and checked for linearity. A weight is suspended from each load cell sequentially and the gain of each bridge amplifier is adjusted so that all three load cell outputs yield the same deflection on the recorder for an equal load. This ensures linearily in that the sum of signals indicates the true system mass even though the test assembly is eccentrically loaded. Then with the pressure vessel in place on the load cells, several equal weights are added to the vessel until the total system weight exceeds the estimated weight of the vessel fully charged with the test fluid, dichlorodifluoromethane (Freon-12). The recorder gain is then adjusted so that the planned charge of fluid will cause maximum deflection, thus assuring maximum sensitivity. Linearity is checked further by comparing the recorder deflection per unit mass (9mm/g) of each weight unit added. Since the system is calibrated before each test, errors are introduced only by deviations from linearity, reproducability and the precision of the reading of recorded output. The total error in the mass determination is established to be less than $\pm$ 0.5%.

The instantaneous mass flow rate $\dot{m}(t)$ is calculated by numerical differentiation of the m(t) curve. Second order polynomials are curve fitted to given small segments of the m(t) curve and the derivative of the polynomial is evaluated at the centerpoint of the chosen interval to give the mass flow rate at that point. Cumulative errors in this data reduction technique do not exceed $\pm 1.0\%$.

A deadweight tester is employed to calibrate the pressure measurement
system before each run and linearity and reproducability are checked by
sequentially adding, then removing weights from the tester. Considering
temperature-induced errors, transducer nonlinearity and precision of
reading, the overall error in pressure measurements is estimated to be
less than ± 2%.

The vessel is then filled with Freon-12 from a pressurized supply canister
at ambient temperature. Controlled venting allows the vessel to be filled
to any desired level; the resulting expansion of the fluid into the system
causes slight subcooling. The vessel is left at rest for a time to allow
local temperatures to equalize and convection to cease, if a test is to be
run with the system initially at ambient temperature (Freon-12 saturation
pressure around 70 psig); if a high pressure test is to be run, the heating element is switched on for a time to bring the system to the desired
state (e.g. 282 psig at 69 C). For heated tests, a small initial temperature gradient is induced within the vessel. This cannot be avoided since
the system will not return to complete thermal equilibrium until it cools
back to ambient temperature.

The data recording devices are started simultaneously with the opening
of the globe valve. After the experiment, mass, pressure and temperature
measurement systems are rechecked for proper calibration. The recorded
data is processed at a convenient later time.

RESULTS AND DISCUSSION

The experimental results which were selected to be reported in this paper
are given in Figures 5 through 9. Figure 5 shows mass flow rates as a
function of time for flow through 1/16 inch (1.59 mm) diameter and 3/16
inch (4.76 mm) diameter orifices and tubes. The mass flow rates decrease
with increasing tube length, as would be expected. While there is a
relatively small decrease in mass flow rate when the L/D of the tube is
increased from 36 to 120 there is a significant decrease in mass flow rate
when the L/D ratio is increased from less than 3 to 12. This is due to
non-equilibrium which is more severe in flow through orifices and short
tubes. In comparing the flow rates given in Figure 5a with 5c, and 5b
with 5d, it is seen that for orifice flow (L/D = 0.3 and L/D = 1.0) the
mass flow rate indeed increases by a factor of 9 as the orifice diameter
increases from 1/16 inch (1.59 mm) to 3/16 inch (4.76 mm); this comparison
is only valid if made at a time when the stagnation pressures are the same.

The pressure histories for the different discharge experiments are given
in non-dimensional form in Figure 6. Again the effects of tube diameter,
initial pressure and different L/D ratios are presented. The initial
pressures are given in Table 1. When comparing the low pressure test
series (Figure 6a and 6c) it is noted that the exit pressures for the
1/16 inch (1.59 mm) diameter tubes do not vary nearly as much as those for
the 3/16 inch (4.76 mm) diameter tubes. This may be caused by the higher
heat transfer rate per unit volume at lower diameter and by the location

of the pressure tap. The pressure tap was always 4 mm from the end of the tube, i.e. 0.8 diameters for the 3/16 inch (4.76 mm) tubes and 2.5 diameters for the 1/16 inch (1.59 mm) tubes. This comparison is not possible for the high pressure test series because of the transient behavior. Pressure traces for L/D ratios of 36 and 120 for tubes of 1/8 inch (3.18 mm) diameter at low stagnation pressure were very similar to those observed for the 3/16 inch (4.76 mm) diameter tubes (Figure 6c).

Figure 7 shows the stagnation temperature histories measured in the vessel as the venting proceeded. The temperature gradient shown in Figure 7a was typical of the venting tests. The temperatures shown in Figures 7b, c and d are those recorded by thermocouple To, i.e. the thermocouple closest to the exit of the vessel. The high rate of decrease in temperature when short venting tubes of 3/16 inch (4.76 mm) diameter are used (see Figures 7c and d) are due to the high evaporative cooling associated with large mass flow rates.

The experimental mass flow rates were compared with 4 simple models. All of these models are based on the following assumptions: 1. the flow is in thermal equilibrium; 2. frictional losses are negligible; 3. each phase flows at a unique average velocity; 4. the flow process is isentropic. Moody [11] derived from energy considerations the following mass flux equation on the basis of the just stated assumptions:

$$G = \sqrt{2 \; \frac{h_0 - (1-x_e)h_{fe} - x_e h_{ge}}{[K(1-x_e)v_{fe} + x_e v_{ge}]^2 \; [x_e + (1-x_e)/K^2]}} \qquad (1),$$

where $\quad x_e = (s_0 - s_{fe})/(s_{ge} - s_{fe}).$

The two homogeneous flow models are given by equation (1) with no slip (K = 1). The two Moody flow models are also given by equation (1) where the slip ratio K is equal to the cube root of the ratio of liquid to vapor density at the exit. The noncritical models use the measured stagnation and the measured exit section pressures, assuming saturated liquid stagnation conditions. For the critical models only the measured stagnation pressures were used in equation (1); the exit pressures used were those which yield a maximum mass flux found through trial and error calculations.

Figures 8 and 9 show that mass flux predictions based on Moody's slip flow model are always higher than those assuming homogeneous flow. While the low pressure mass flow rates are bounded by the two types of models (see Figure 8), the high pressure mass flux are generally not. It appears that for flow through very short tubes and orifices a non-equilibrium flow model would be more appropriate. The non-critical homogeneous flow model predicts well for long tubes with large diameter (see Figures 8d and 9d). Other effects such as heat-transfer and bubble size appear to play a more significant role in tests with smaller tube diameters.

The primary goal of this contribution was to present experimental results describing the flow of a flashing fluid from a vessel through orifices and tubes to the atmosphere. While extensive experiments have been performed with water as a medium, relatively few investigations have been made with commercial liquified gases. The data presented in this paper is only part of a much larger body of data which will be available in a forthcoming DOT report.

ACKNOWLEDGEMENT

This work was supported by the U. S. Department of Transportation under Contract DOT-FR 64181.

REFERENCES

1. D. W. Sallet, M. Palmer, and F. K. Wu, "Thermodynamic Properties of Liquified Petroleum Gases (LPG)", Federal Railroad Administration Report FRA-ORD 76/299, 1977.

2. M. W. Palmer, D. W. Sallet, and F. K. Wu, "The Influence of Thermodynamic Properties on the Calculation of Homogeneous Mass Flow Rates", ASME Paper 78-WA/HT-36, December 1978.

3. M. Gühler, R. Hannemann, and D. W. Sallet, "Unsteady Two-Phase Blowdown of a Flashing Liquid from a Finite Reservoir", Proceedings of the 1978 ICHMT International Seminar, Dubrovnik, Yugoslavia, 1978.

4. D. W. Sallet, M. E. Palmer, and K. F. Wu, "The Mass Flow Rates of Liquified Propane Gas (LPG)" Federal Railroad Administration Report FRA-ORD 76/302, 1978.

5. D. W. Sallet, "On the Sizing of Pressure Relief Valves for Pressure Vessels Used in the Transport of Liquified Gases", ASME Paper 78-WA/HT-39, December 1978.

6. D. W. Sallet, M. E. Palmer, and S. R. Rod, "The Non-Steady Flow of Fluids from Pressure Vessels", ASME Paper to be presented at the Third National Congress, Pressure Vessel and Piping Division, San Francisco, June 24-29, 1979.

7. D. W. Sallet, J. R. Weske, and M. Gühler, "The Flow of Liquids and Gases Through Pressure Relief Valves", ASME Paper to be presented at the Third National Congress, Pressure Vessel and Piping Division, San Francisco, June 24-29, 1979.

8. Y. Y. Hsu and R. W. Graham, Transport Processes in Boiling and Two-Phase Systems, Hemisphere, Washington, 1976, Chapter 11.

9. R. T. Lahey, and G. B. Wallis, eds., Non-Equilibrium Two-Phase Flows, ASME, New York, 1975.

10. H. K. Fauske, "Contribution to the Theory of Two-Phase, One-Component Critical Flow", Argonne National Laboratory, ANL-6633 1962, 164 pages.

11. F. J. Moody, "Maximum Flow Rate of a Single Component Two-Phase Mixture", J. Heat Transfer,87, (1965), pp. 134-142.

12. S. Levy, "Prediction of Two-Phase Critical Flow Rate", J. Heat Transfer, 87,(1965), pp. 53-58.

13. W. A. Massena, "Steam-Water Critical Flow Using the Separated Flow Model", G. E. report HW-65739, 1960, 11 pages.

Thermocouple — **Height Above Base Plate**

Thermocouple	Height Above Base Plate
T_0	6 cm
T_1	12 cm
T_2	19 cm
T_3	26 cm
T_4	33 cm
T_5	39 cm

Figure 1: Test Apparatus.

TABLE 1
INITIAL STAGNATION PRESSURES (P_{oi}).

TEST	EXIT PIPE I.D.	L/D	P_{oi} (MPa)
Low Pressure	1.59 mm	1*	0.612
"	"	3	0.661
"	"	12	0.612
"	"	36	0.601
"	"	120	0.555
High Pressure	1.59 mm	1*	1.72
"	"	3	1.93
"	"	12	1.81
"	"	36	1.85
"	"	120	1.81
Low Pressure	4.76 mm	0.33+	0.562
"	"	3	0.643
"	"	12	0.562
"	"	36	0.591
"	"	120	0.574
High Pressure	4.76 mm	0.33+	2.20
"	"	3	2.01
"	"	12	1.99
"	"	36	1.93
"	"	120	2.03

*For the 1.59 mm case, L/D = 1 is the orifice.
+For the 4.76 mm case, L/D=0.33 is the orifice.

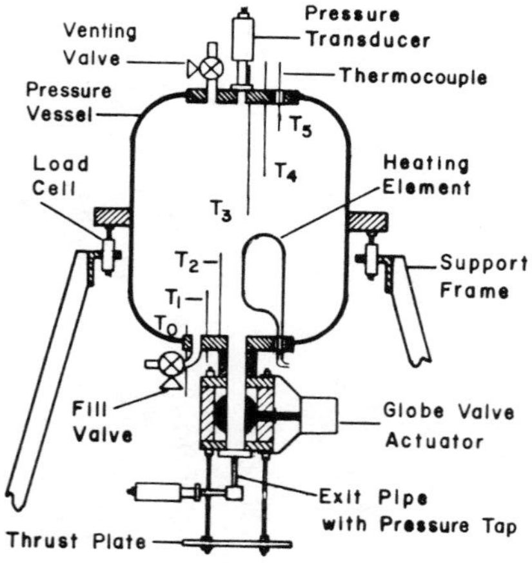

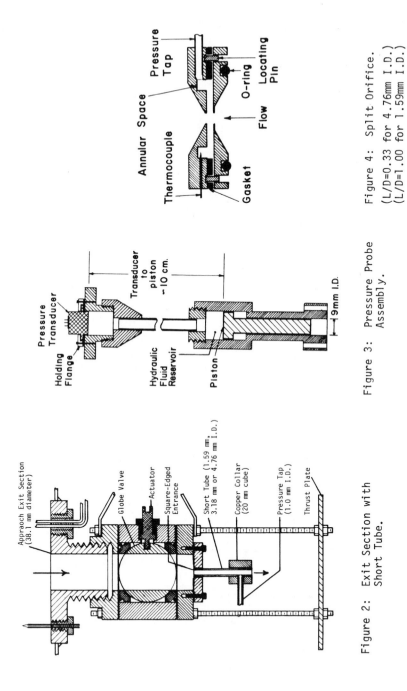

Figure 4: Split Orifice.

(L/D=0.33 for 4.76mm I.D.)
(L/D=1.00 for 1.59mm I.D.)

Figure 3: Pressure Probe Assembly.

Figure 2: Exit Section with Short Tube.

1607

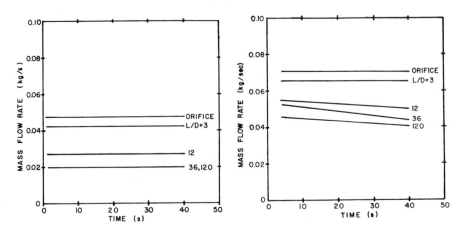

(a) 1.59mm I.D. Low Pressure Tests   (b) 1.59mm I.D. High Pressure Tests

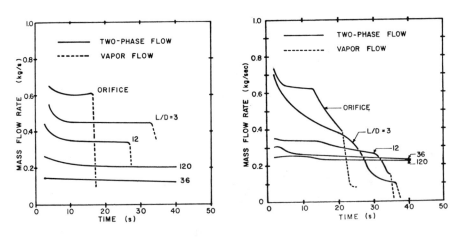

(c) 4.76mm I.D. Low Pressure Tests   (d) 4.76mm I.D. High Pressure Tests

Figure 5:   Experimental Mass Flow Rates.

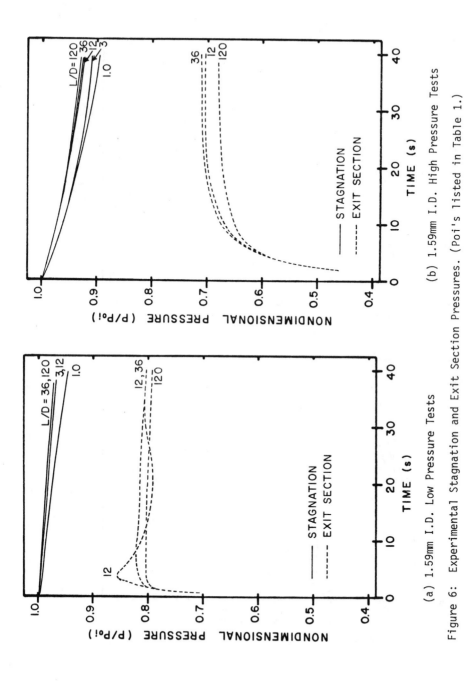

(a) 1.59mm I.D. Low Pressure Tests

(b) 1.59mm I.D. High Pressure Tests

Figure 6: Experimental Stagnation and Exit Section Pressures. (Poi's listed in Table 1.)

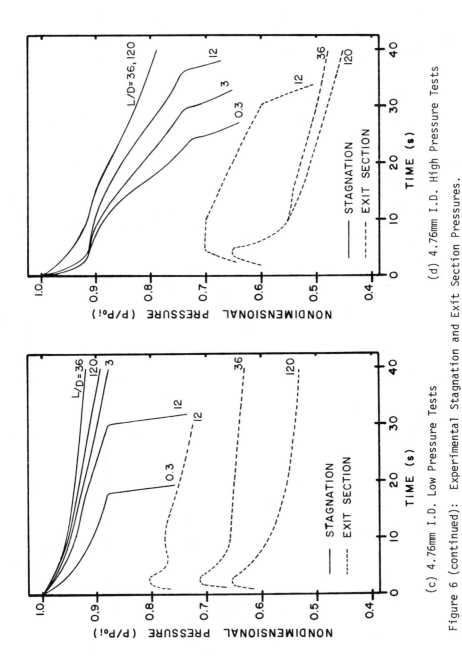

(c) 4.76mm I.D. Low Pressure Tests

(d) 4.76mm I.D. High Pressure Tests

Figure 6 (continued): Experimental Stagnation and Exit Section Pressures.

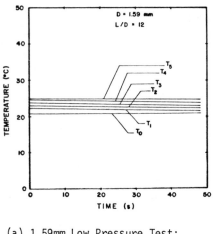

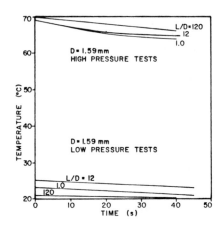

(a) 1.59mm Low Pressure Test; L/D = 12, All Thermocouples

(b) 1.59mm Low Pressure and High Pressure Tests

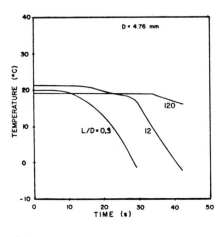

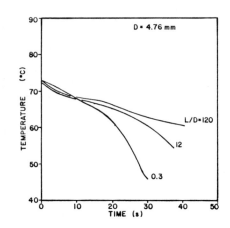

(c) 4.76mm Low Pressure Tests

(d) 4.76mm High Pressure Tests

Figure 7: Experimental Stagnation Temperatures.

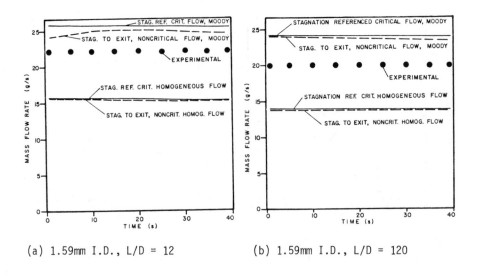

(a) 1.59mm I.D., L/D = 12   (b) 1.59mm I.D., L/D = 120

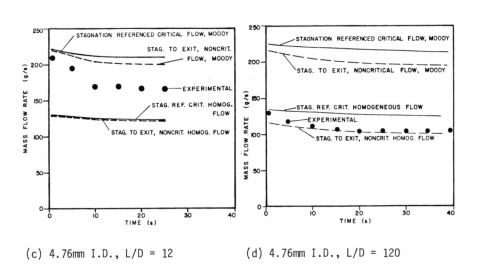

(c) 4.76mm I.D., L/D = 12   (d) 4.76mm I.D., L/D = 120

Figure 8: Predicted and Measured Mass Flow Rates for Low Pressure Tests.

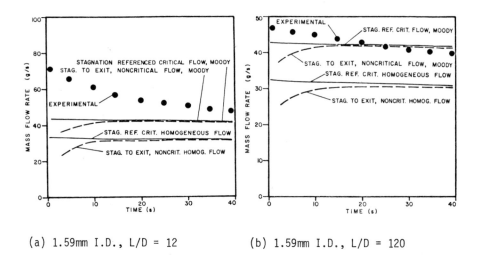

(a) 1.59mm I.D., L/D = 12   (b) 1.59mm I.D., L/D = 120

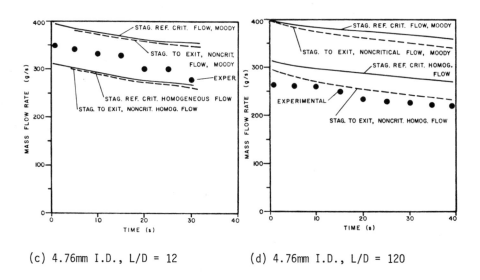

(c) 4.76mm I.D., L/D = 12   (d) 4.76mm I.D., L/D = 120

Figure 9: Predicted and Measured Mass Flow Rates for High Pressure Tests.

Flooding Correlations for BWR Bundle Upper Tieplates and Bottom Side-Entry Orifices

K.H. SUN
Nuclear Safety and Analysis Department
Electric Power Research Institute
Palo Alto, California 94303, USA

ABSTRACT

The fluid flow associated with countercurrent flooding is important for the determination of heat transfer in a Boiling Water Reactor (BWR) in the hypothetical loss-of-coolant accidents (LOCA). Available flooding data obtained for simulated full-scale BWR bundle upper tieplates and bottom core inlet side-entry orifices are analyzed. It is found that the flooding phenomena occurring at the tieplates can be characterized by the Kutateladze parameters which compare the dynamic head with the surface tension force in a two-phase flow system. For the case of side-entry orifices where the gas and liquid phases counterflow horizontally at the orifice location, a Bond number was used to account for the effect of different orifice sizes. Flooding correlations are derived which are relevant to BWR performance characteristics during LOCA.

INTRODUCTION

During the postulated loss-of-coolant accident of boiling water reactors, steam is generated in the fuel bundle due to heat transfer from the core to the cooling water, and in the lower plenum due to flashing and heat transfer from the vessel wall to the water. The updrafting steam flow in the core can limit the flow from the upper plenum into the bundle. Likewise, the updrafting steam flow from the lower plenum can limit the water flow from the bundle to the lower plenum. These phenomena are often referred to as Counter-Current Flow Limitation (CCFL) or flooding. For typical BWR bundles, flooding can occur at the bundle upper tieplates and bottom side-entry orifices. Since flooding restricts the flow, its characteristics are important for the determination of water inventories in different regions of a BWR during LOCA.

Considerable efforts have been made to develop theories for
the description of the flooding mechanisms (see e.g. Summary
Report [1]). For practical applications in nuclear technology, calculations of the flooding process depend largely on
empirical correlations [2, 3]. The most common type of correlation is the Wallis correlation [4] which has been used
extensively for correlating data from circular tubes [4, 5]
and annuli [2]. For BWR tieplates which have honeycomb type
multi-passage geometries, a geometric length is difficult to
ascertain, and a correlation was suggested [3, 6, 7] by
using parameters similar to the Kutateladze number. It
replaces the geometric length in the Wallis correlation by
the characteristic length $[\sigma/g(\rho_f-\rho_g)]^{1/2}$. The correlation
form was later obtained by applying the kinematic wave
theory and the Taylor instability critical wavelength to a
gas-liquid interface in an idealized potential flow
system [8]. Various investigations of flooding with no
liquid penetration [2, 9, 10, 11] also showed that the
Kutateladze number is a relevant parameter for correlating
the critical gas flooding velocity.

Flooding data from full scale simulated BWR bundles became
available recently through the BD/ECC program*. Tobin [12]
performed flooding experiments in a simulated 7x7 fuel
bundle, in which the upper tieplate was simulated by sleeves
mounted on rods to preserve the same flow area. The data
was shown to be correlated well by the Kutateladze type correlation [3]. Jones [6] conducted experiments with a prototypical 8x8 tieplate in a simulated fuel bundle. He concluded that the flooding characteristics are influenced
moderately by the method of liquid injection, but strongly
by the steam inlet geometry. It was observed that the subcooling of the water injected above the tieplate was a governing factor for the onset or collapse of flooding, but
exerted little effect on the counter-current flow characteristics below the tieplate. Jones [13] also performed a
series of flooding tests for the TLTA** core inlet side-
entry orifices. He observed that different orifice sizes

---

*The BD/ECC program is jointly sponsored by the U.S. Nuclear
Regulatory Commission, the Electric Power Research Institute, and the General Electric Company. The objective is to
provide system, components, and core response data for the
latter stages of blowdown with actuation of the emergency
core cooling system.

**Two Loop Test Apparatus, a major facility in the BD/ECC
program.

and the number of orifices led to different flooding
characteristics.

Naitoh et al. [14] obtained flooding data for a simulated
8x8 tieplate which has a flow area about 8% smaller than the
protypical ones. Similar to Jones' findings [8], he
observed the same effect of subcooling and no effect of
water injection method and water head above the tieplate.
The steam injection effect was not assessed since he did not
vary the steam inlet geometry.

The objective of the present study is to analyze the available flooding data from simulated full-scale BWR fuel bundles in Wallis-Kutateladze type parameters. Correlations
which are relevant to BWR performance during LOCA are
derived.

ANALYSIS

Basic Correlation Forms

Wallis [4] considered that the phenomena of counter-current
flooding is governed by the balance of inertia and buoyancy
forces and defined the dimensionless volumetric fluxes for
the two-phase flow components as:

$$j_g^* = [\rho_g j_g^2 / gD(\rho_f - \rho_g)]^{1/2} \text{ and } j_f^* = [\rho_f j_f^2 / gD(\rho_f - \rho_g)]^{1/2} \qquad (1)$$

where ρ is the density, j is the volumetric flux which is
equal to the mass flow rate divided by the density and the
open flow area, g is gravity, and D is the geometric
length. The subscripts g and f designate gas and liquid,
respectively.

He then correlated the experimental data into the empirical
equation as:

$$(j_g^*)^{1/2} + m(j_f^*)^{1/2} = c \qquad (2)$$

where m and c are coefficients determined empirically from
experiments and were shown to vary with the system inlet and
exit geometries [5].

The Wallis correlation can be modified by replacing D by the
characteristic length, $[\sigma/g(\rho_f - \rho_g)]^{1/2}$, which has been widely
used for applications in boiling and two-phase flow [15].
Thus, Eq. (2) becomes [3, 6, 7]

$$(K_g)^{1/2} + m \ (K_f)^{1/2} = C \qquad\qquad\qquad (3)$$

where K_g, the Kutateladze number, and K_f are defined as

$$K_g = \rho_g^{1/2} j_g / [g g_c \sigma (\rho_f - \rho_g)]^{1/4}$$

and $\qquad\qquad\qquad\qquad\qquad\qquad\qquad\qquad (4)$

$$K_f = \rho_f^{1/2} j_f / [g g_c \sigma (\rho_f - \rho_g)]^{1/4}$$

and σ is the surface tension. The K parameters in Eq. (4) and the j^* parameters in Eq. (1) can be related by the equation

$$K_{g,f} = j_{g,f}^* (D^*)^{1/2} \qquad\qquad\qquad (5)$$

where D^*, the Bond number (see e.g. Ref. [15]), is defined as

$$D^* = D[\sigma / g (\rho_f - \rho_g)]^{-1/2} \qquad\qquad\qquad (6)$$

Tobin's steam-water flooding data for a simulated 7x7 tieplate [12] was correlated by Sun and Fernandez [3] by using Eq. (3) with

$$(K_g)^{1/2} + (K_f)^{1/2} = 1.79 \qquad\qquad\qquad (7)$$

The limiting condition of Eq. (7) at $K_f = 0$ coincides with Pushkina and Sorokin's experimental findings for various tube sizes in their air-water experiments [9] and with Lovell's air-water data for large D^* [11].

Equations (3), (4), and (5) will be used to correlate the available 8x8 tieplate data of Jones (6) and of Naitoh et al. [14], and the side-entry orifice data of Jones [13]. Since the description of their test facilities are well-documented in References [6, 13, and 14] respectively, they are not discussed in detail here, except for some unique features which could have an effect on the flooding characteristics.

Flooding Correlations for BWR 8x8 Bundle Upper Tieplates

In Jones' experiments [6], a prototypical 8x8 tieplate, as shown in Fig. 1, was used. There were three modes of water injection above the tieplate, namely, the spillover injection (water spills over the top of the channel), the bypass slots injection (water is injected through the slots at the bundle bypass region), and the cross flow injection (horizontal jets are injected into the flow channel) with two different hole sizes. In addition, two 6-inch extension pieces were mounted above the tieplates in few tests to vary the static head above the tieplate. The bundle steam flow was simulated by three injection methods: the capped sparger (the sparger is capped at the end to direct steam flow horizontally), the clarinet sparger (a diffuser at the end of sparger), and the lower tieplate sparger (steam flow through the lower tieplate). The lack of physical understanding of the motion and condensation in the churn-turbulent flow region in the upper plenum and the lack of local thermal-hydraulic measurement make it almost impossible to characterize the effect of different water injection modes on the flooding phenomenon. Likewise, the effect of different steam injection methods on the local flow conditions in the bundle cannot be quantified.

Jones concluded in general that the flooding results were only moderately affected by the water injection mode, but strongly affected by the steam injection methods. Jones' data are plotted separately on $(K_g)^{1/2}$ vs. $(K_f)^{1/2}$ coordinates, as shown in Figs. 2, 3, and 4, for the three different steam injection methods. It is shown that although the data scatter as a result of different inlet water flow rate, inlet water subcooling, and water injection mode, the data appear to be consistent and can be correlated by

$$(K_g)^{1/2} + (K_f)^{1/2} = 1.89 \pm 6\% \qquad (8)$$

for capped steam sparger,

$$(K_g)^{1/2} + (K_f)^{1/2} = 2.10 \pm 13\% \qquad (9)$$

for clarinet steam sparger, and

$$(K_g)^{1/2} + (K_f)^{1/2} = 2.07 \pm 8\% \qquad (10)$$

for lower tieplate steam sparger. The uncertainty bands for the empirical coefficients were determined from the

individual correlations for each specific test case for a
given steam injection method.

While no local thermal-hydraulic measurements were made in
Jones' tests to ascertain the effect of different steam
spargers, the bundle pressure drop measured during flooding
indicated that the pressure drop for the capped sparger is
significantly larger than those for the clarinet and tieplate spargers. This could be interpreted that for the
capped sparger, the steam is injected from the sparger in
the form of high velocity jets in a direction normal to the
longitudinal direction of the rod bundle and this is likely
to produce the most nonuniform velocity distribution among
the three methods. For the same steam flow rate, the non-
uniformity of steam velocity can cause high velocities in
local positions, which can lead to local flooding inside the
bundle. As a result, slugs may be formed inside the bundle
and entrainment of water to the tieplate may be sufficient
to reduce the downward water flow. Consequently, the correlation coefficient is smaller for the capped sparger than
the other two.

The steam injection method used by Naitoh et al. [14] is
different from those of Jones'. The steam was injected to
the bottom of a 4.51 m (14.8 ft) long bundle with seven
spacers below the tieplate. The bundle is more than twice
the length of Jones' bundle which is 1.95 m (5.91 ft) long
with two spacers. Although the steam injected during the
test was normal to the rod bundle, the length of the bundle
and the spacers are expected to flatten the nonuniformity of
the velocity distribution. Indeed, the comparison of the
data of Naitoh et al. with Jones' data for the clarinet and
tieplate spargers on the $(K_g)^{1/2}$ vs. $(K_f)^{1/2}$ coordinates, as
depicted in Fig. 5, shows good agreement. By excluding
Jones's data for the capped sparger, the existing flooding
data for 8x8 BWR tieplates may be represented by the correlation form,

$$(K_g)^{1/2} + (K_f)^{1/2} = 2.08 \tag{11}$$

where the uncertainty band for the empirical coefficient is
+14% and -12%.

Flooding Correlation for BWR Bundle Side-Entry Orifices

Figure 6 shows the cross-sectional view of the core inlet side-entry orifices used in the TLTA loop [13]. During the experiments, water at near-saturation temperature was injected into a pool above the flow tube and spilled into the flow tube while steam was injected from below. The steam and water counterflow horizontally at the most restrictive area, the orifice, where the flooding phenomenon occurs. Three different orifice sizes (6.17 cm, 3.76 cm, and 3.19 cm) of the TLTA-3 configuration and two different sizes (one 4.06 cm orifice and two 2.87 cm orifices) of TLTA-1 configuration were tested.

Figure 7 depicts the $(K_g)^{1/2}$ vs. $(K_f)^{1/2}$ plot of all the side-entry orifice data. It is shown that the orifice diameter and configuration clearly have an effect on the flooding characteristics. Close examination of the trend of data indicates that each set of data is systematically parallel to the others with a slop -0.59. To account for the effect of orifice geometry by comparing with the two-phase flow characteristic lenth $[\sigma/g(\rho_f-\rho_g)]^{1/2}$, a Bond number of the form,

$$L^* = L[\sigma/g(\rho_f-\rho_g)]^{-1/2} \qquad (12)$$

where L, the circumference of the orifice or orifices, is considered to be relevant because the orifice diameter can not characterize a multi-orifice configuration. Indeed, the plot of the empirical coefficients for each case in Fig. 7 against the Bond number, as illustrated in Fig. 8, shows that the coefficients can be represented by a simple linear function of L^*, i.e.,

$$f(L^*) = 2.14 - 0.0080 \, L^* \qquad (13)$$

for the available data range of 40 <L* <80. Judging from physical understanding, one would expect that f(L*) approaches a constant for very large L* where the flooding mechanisms are localized and the orifice size is no longer relevant.

The combination of Eq. (13) with Eq. (3) and the slope -.59 leads to the correlation,

$$(K_g)^{1/2}/f(L^*) + 0.59 \, (K_f)^{1/2}/f(L^*) = 1 \qquad (14)$$

for the side-entry orifices. Fig. 9 shows that all sixty-four data for different orifice sizes and configurations can

be collapsed together by the use of Eq. (14). It is not
clear how the Bond number is related to the Kutateladze
numbers physically when the gas and liquid phases counterflow horizontally at the orifice location. It may be due to
a Taylor instability type phenomenon (see e.g. ref. [15])
associated the annular or slug flows condition at the
orifice.

SUMMARY AND CONCLUSIONS

The available flooding data to date for simulated BWR fuel
bundles have been analyzed and summarized in Table 1. The
data for 7x7 bundle tieplate, though limited in quantity and
some test conditions, can be well correlated by Eq. (7).
Jones' data for the 8x8 bundle with a capped steam sparger
appear to be strongly affected by water entrainment inside
the bundle. Jones' 8x8 bundle data for the clarinet and
lower tieplate steam spargers are in general agreement with
the data of Naitoh et al. and are represented by Eq. (11).
The side-entry orifice data for five different sizes and two
different geometric configurations are correlated by
Eq. (14).

The following conclusions are made as a result of the   .
present study:

1.   Considering the available data for BWR bundle tie-
      plates, the gross gas and liquid flow rates asso-
      ciated with flooding at the tieplates can be char-
      acterized by a simple bundle-average correlation
      with K_g and K_f as the governing parameters. The
      effect of possible flooding at local tieplate sub-
      channels appears to be of secondary importance.

2.   For steam-water countercurent flooding at BWR 8X8
      bundle upper tieplates, the following correlation
      may be applicable:

$$(K_g)^{1/2} + (K_f)^{1/2} = 2.08$$

3.   For steam water countercurrent flooding at BWR
      bundle bottom core inlet side-entry orifices, the
      governing parameters are K_g, K_f, and L^* which is a
      Bond number with respect to the circumference of
      the orifice or orifices. The following correlation
      is appropriate based on the available data:

$$(K_g)^{1/2} + 0.59 \ (K_f)^{1/2} = 2.14 - 0.80 \times 10^{-2} \ L^*$$

for $40 < L^* < 80$.

NOMENCLATURE

c	empirical coefficient
D	geometric length
D*	Bond number with respect to the tube diameter
g	gravity
j	volumetric flux
$j_{g,f}$	dimensionless parameters, defined in Eq. (1)
$K_{g,f}$	dimensionless parameters, defined in Eq. (4)
L	circumference
L*	Bond number with respect to the circumference
m	empirical coefficient

Greek Symbols

ρ	density
σ	surface tension

Subscripts

g	designates gas
f	designates liquid

REFERENCES

1. C. L. Tien and C. P. Lui, "A Survey on Vertical Two-Phase Counter-Current Flooding," Electric Power Research Institute, Report NP-984 (1979).

2. J. A. Block and V. E. Schrock, "Emergency Cooling Water Delivery to the Core Inlet of PWR's During LOCA," ASME Sym. on the Thermal and Hydraulic Aspects of Nuclear Reactor Safety, Vol. 1, p. 151 (1977).

3. K. H. Sun and R. T. Fernandez, "Counter-Current Flow Limitation Correlation for BWR Bundles During LOCA," ANS Transation, Vol. 27, p. 605 (1977).

4. G. B. Wallis, One-Dimensional Two-Phase Flow, McGraw-Hill, Inc. (1969).

5. D. Bharathan, "Air-Water Counter-Current Annular Flow in Vertical Tubes," EPRI Report NP-786 (1978).

6. D. D. Jones, "Subcooled Counter-Current Flow Limiting Characteristics of the Upper Region of a BWR Fuel Bundle," General Electric Company, Nuclear Systems Products Division, BD/ECC Program, NEDG-NUREG-23549 (1977).

7. C. L. Tien, "A Simple Analytical Model for Counter-Current Flow Limiting Phenomena with Condensation," Letters in Heat Transfer and Mass Transfer, Vol. 4, p. 231 (1977).

8. K. S. Chung, "Flooding Phenomena in Counter-Current Two-Phase Flow Systems," Ph.D. Thesis, Dept. of Mechanical Engineering, University of California, Berkeley (1978).

9. O. L. Pushkina and Y. L. Sorokin, "Breakdown of Liquid Film Motion in Vertical Tubes," Heat Transfer - Soviet Research, Vol. 1, 5, 56 (1969).

10. G. B. Wallis and S. Makkenchery," The Hanging Film Phenomenon in Vertical Annular Two-Phase Flow," J. Fluid Engineering, Technical Briefs, Vol. 96, Ser. 1, 3, p. 297 (1974).

11. T. W. Lovell, "The Effect of Scale on Two-Phase Counter-Current Flow Flooding in Vertical Tubes," M.S. Thesis, Thayer School of Engineering, Dartmouth College (1977).

12. R. Tobin, "CCFL Test Results, Phase 1 - TLTA 7x7 Bundle," General Electric Company, Nuclear System Products Division, BD/ECC Program, GEAP-21304-5 (1977).

13. D. D. Jones, "Test Report TLTA Components CCFL Tests," General Electric Company, Nuclear System Products Division, BD/ECC Program, NEDG-NUREG-23732 (1977).

14. M. Naitoh, K. Chino, and R. Kawabe, "Restrictive Effect of Ascending Steam on Falling Water During Top Spray Emergency Core Cooling," J. of Nuclear Science and Technology, Vol. 15, 11, p. 806 (1978).

15. Y. Y. Hsu and R. W. Graham, "Transport Processes in Boiling and Two-Phase Systems," McGraw-Hill, Inc. (1976).

Table 1

SUMMARY OF SIMULATED BWR FUEL BUNDLE FLOODING DATA AND CORRELATIONS

Source of Data	Geometry	Test Conditions	Correlations
Tobin BD/ECC program [12]	7x7 bundle upper tie-plate (simulated by sleeves with same flow area)	o Saturated steam & water o near-atmospheric pressure o steam flow from 36 ~ 99 gm/s o water inlet flow from 549 ~ 972 cm³/s	$(K_g)^{1/2} + (K_f)^{1/2}$ $= 1.79 \pm 2\%$
Jones BD/ECC program [6]	8x8 bundle upper tie-plate	o saturated steam o water temperature from 38°C ~ 96°C o steam flow from 0 ~ 126 gm/s o near-atmospheric pressure o inlet water flow rate 315 ~ 946 cm³/s o three inlet water injection methods (bypass slots, cross flow, and spillover) o three steam injection methods (capped sparger, clarinet sparger, and lower tieplate sparger)	$(K_g)^{1/2} + (K_f)^{1/2}$ $= 1.89 \pm 6\%$ for capped sparger $(K_g)^{1/2} + (K_f)^{1/2}$ $= 2.10 \pm 13\%$ for clarinet sparger $(K_g)^{1/2} + (K_f)^{1/2}$ $= 2.07 \pm 8\%$ for tieplate sparger

Table 1 (cont.)

Source of Data	Geometry	Test Conditions	Correlations
Jones BD/ECC program [13]	Bundle bottom core inlet side-entry orifices	o inlet water flow ~505 cm³/s o inlet steam flow from 0 ~38 gm/s o saturated steam & water o near-atmospheric pressure o five different orifice sizes	$(K_g)^{1/2} +$ $0.59\ (k_f)^{1/2}$ $= -2.14 +$ $0.0080\ L*$
Naitoh et al. [14]	8x8 bundle upper tie-plate	o steam flow from 43 ~ 83 gm/s o near-atmospheric pressure o water temperature from 27°C ~ 97°C o inlet water flow 117 ~ 1033 cm³/s o two inlet water injection methods (spray nozzles and straight pipe) o steam inlet from bottom of bundle	$(K_g)^{1/2} + (K_f)^{1/2}$ $= 2.06 \pm 6\%$

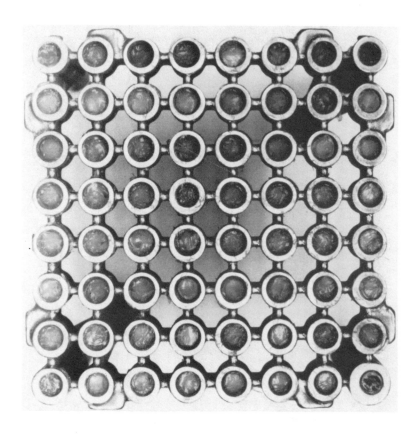

Figure 1.   Bottom view of a prototypical 8 × 8 BWR fuel bundle upper tieplate.

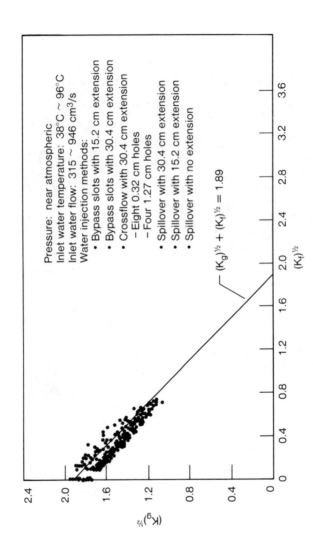

Figure 2. Flooding data for a 8 × 8 upper tieplate in a simulated BWR fuel bundle with steam injection from a capped sparger (BD/ECC program, Jones [6]).

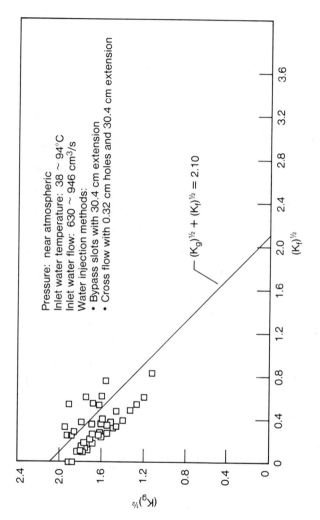

Figure 3.   Flooding data for a 8 × 8 upper tieplate in a simulated BWR fuel bundle with steam injection from a clarinet sparger (BD/ECC program, Jones [6]).

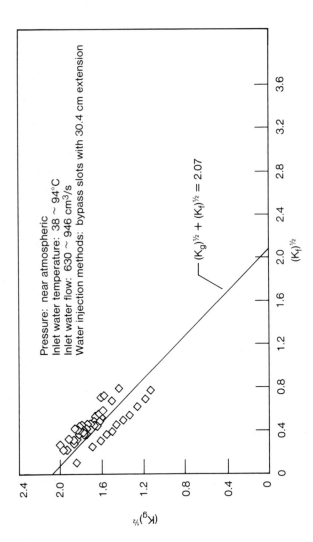

Figure 4.   Flooding data for a 8 × 8 upper tieplate in a simulated BWR fuel bundle with steam injection from a lower tieplate sparger (BD/ECC program, Jones [6]).

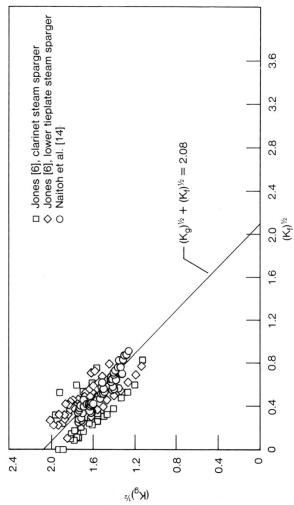

Figure 5.   Comparison of data of Jones [6] with data of Naitoh et al. [14] for flooding at a 8 × 8 tieplate in a simulated BWR fuel bundle.

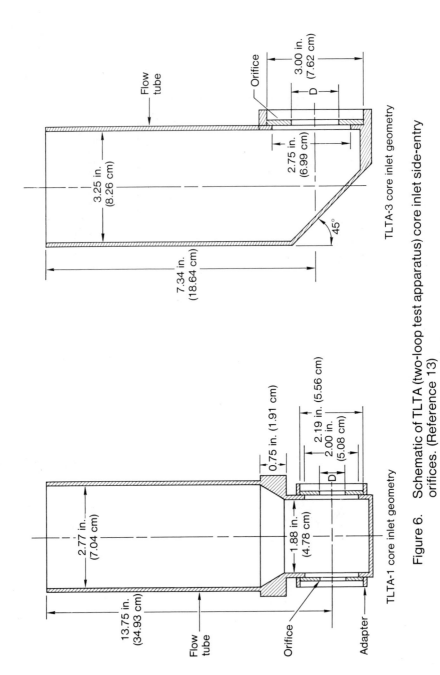

Flow tube

Orifice

3.00 in.
(7.62 cm)

D

2.75 in.
(6.99 cm)

3.25 in.
(8.26 cm)

45°

7.34 in.
(18.64 cm)

TLTA-3 core inlet geometry

0.75 in. (1.91 cm)

2.19 in. (5.56 cm)

2.00 in.
(5.08 cm)

D

2.77 in.
(7.04 cm)

1.88 in.
(4.78 cm)

13.75 in.
(34.93 cm)

Flow tube

Orifice

Adapter

TLTA-1 core inlet geometry

Figure 6. Schematic of TLTA (two-loop test apparatus) core inlet side-entry orifices. (Reference 13)

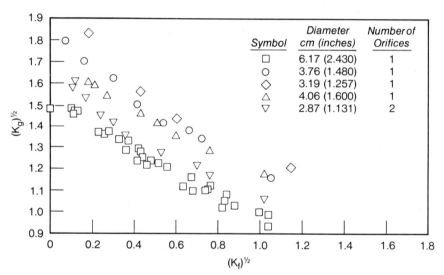

Figure 7.   Flooding data from simulated BWR bundle bottom side-entry orifices.

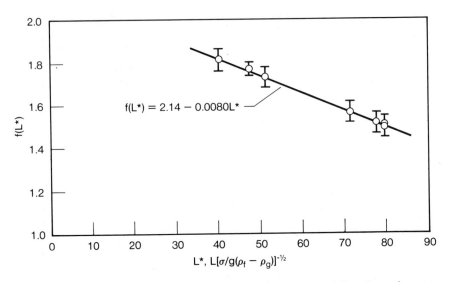

Figure 8.   Flooding coefficient as a function of Bond number.

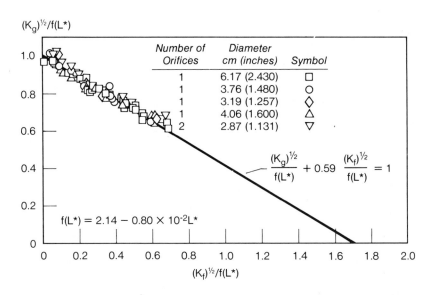

Figure 9.   Correlation of flooding data from simulated BWR bottom
             side-entry orifices.

Thermal Hydraulics of Accelerator Breeder Systems for Regeneration of Reactor Fuel Assemblies*

W.S. YU and J.R. POWELL
Brookhaven National Laboratory
Department of Nuclear Energy
Upton, New York 11973, USA

ABSTRACT

Accelerator breeder systems have been designed [1,2] that can pre-enrich or regenerate fissile material in situ in fabricated fuel assemblies, with the assemblies subsequently used directly in existing reactor types (e.g., LWR and CANDU). Such systems have the potential to reduce uranium lifetime requirements for existing reactors by a factor of four or more, and to considerably increase the overall burnup of fuel assemblies, while operating in a non-reprocessing mode to minimize proliferation concerns. The thermal hydraulic characteristics of the LAFR [Linear Accelerator Fuel Regenerator] system are a very important determinant of overall performance. In the LAFR concept [1], the primary 1.5 GeV proton beam interacts with falling jets of liquid Pb–Bi, producing spallation and evaporation neutrons ($E_A \sim 5$ MeV), which generate fissile material in a surrounding blanket of pressure tubes containing fuel assemblies. To maintain high fissile material production rate, as well as to minimize power peaking, the coolant for these fuel assemblies should not significantly moderate neutrons from the primary Pb–Bi target. In addition, fuel assemblies must be compatible with both the LAFR coolant and water, since the latter is the coolant in LWR and CANDU.

These restrictions appear to dictate that two-phase mixtures (steam and liquid) of either D_2O or H_2O be the primary coolant option for a LAFR. Thermal-hydraulic analyses have been carried out to determine desirable operating ranges for these coolants in a LAFR. The following limits are taken: 700°F maximum clad temperature on fuel elements (oxidation limits); ≤20% equivalent liquid density for two-phase mixtures; coolant temperature range corresponds to a thermal power efficiency ≥20%; and pressure drop of ≤10% of base pressure.

The following conclusions are obtained with regard to the thermal-hydraulic behavior of the LAFR for PWR and CANDU fuel.

1. Two-phase flow is a feasible coolant option for fuel element heat fluxes up to 1 x PWR (or CANDU) average value, which is the maximum design value for a LAFR.

2. Two-phase flow pressure drops are low (typically 10–30 psi) and film temperature drops very low (typically ~ 10°F) for PWR fuel, with inlet velocity

---

* Work performed under the auspices of The Department of Energy.

range (50 to 75 ft/sec). A somewhat higher inlet velocity range (75 to 100 ft/sec) and pressure drop (50-100 psi) is necessary for CANDU fuel, however, to prevent dry out.

I. INTRODUCTION

The energy crisis seems to stay. The oil embargo made the American public conscious of the widening gap between energy consumption and domestic production, and of our unaccustomed but growing dependence on foreign supplies. It is our judgment that nuclear energy is an important element of our total energy system and will become even more so in the future.

However, nuclear energy as produced in Light Water Reactors (LWR) is wasteful in the long run, and at the rate of use presently projected, our economically recoverable uranium resources will be gone in a few decades. The development and commercialization of the Liquid Metal Fast Breeder Reactor (LMFBR) has been slower and costlier than first estimated. The reprocessing facilities required for the LMFBR system are now seen as presenting a risk of nuclear weapons proliferation, and the future commercialization of fast breeder reactors in this country is in doubt.

For these reasons, a program has been initiated by DOE to evaluate fuel cycles and alternative nuclear energy systems which could be made more proliferation resistant and which at the same time could help to stretch the uranium resources. This program is conducted under DOE's Non-Proliferation Alternative Systems Assessment Program (NASAP), organized for that purpose.

Under NASAP funding, the Department of Nuclear Energy at Brookhaven National Laboratory has investigated the use of particle accelerators for producing fissile material in conjunction with proliferation resistant systems. During this study, a linear accelerator fuel regenerator (LAFR) system was considered.

The concept of LAFR involves the use of a high energy proton or deuteron beam from a linear accelerator impinging on a primary Pb-Bi target that is surrounded by a lattice blanket of metal-clad rods of fertile-fissile material cooled by an appropriate fluid. The system is characterized by maximizing the total production rate of fissile material in the lattice as well as minimizing the radial variation of fissile fuel production. The fertile-fissile elements of interest are natural and depleted uranium oxides, and thorium metal. For best performance, the blanket coolant should moderate the source neutrons to the minimum possible extent, thus hardening the neutron energy spectrum within the lattice. The lattice consists of fabricated fertile fuel assemblies whose reactivity would be increased through irradiation to the desired level for subsequent burn up in a separate power reactor. After burn up in the reactor, the fuel elements could be recycled through the accelerator-regenerator for reenrichment, and then used again in the power reactor. This process would be repeated until fission product buildup and radiation damage to cladding was excessive. No reprocessing would be required.

In the course of this study, particular attention was given to engineering feasibility with regard to the thermal hydraulics of the system. The results of preliminary investigation including neutronics and system economics [1] indicate promising production of fissile fuel without reprocessing is technically feasible without major departures from existing technology. The existing LWR nuclear power economy can be retained with almost no modification; uranium resources can be extended substantially over that of the throw-away LWR cycle; there would be no need for reprocessing; even greater fuel-stretching benefits can be achieved in the U-233 cycle; in conjunction with HWR's and/or with reprocessing, the system can be developed to maturity in a reasonable length of time ($\sim$20 years) with predictable performance and reasonable R&D.

II. DESCRIPTION OF LAFR

The conceptual design of a linear accelerator fissile fuel production facility consisting of a 1.5-GeV proton linear accelerator using a flowing liquid lead-bismuth primary target surrounded by a blanket or secondary target containing fertile uranium material was described in a Brookhaven Report [1]. The LAFR consists of two distinct parts: the 1.5-GeV linear accelerator or LINAC, and the target-blanket assembly with its power generation system. Figure 1 shows the design principle of the target. It consists of a primary lead-bismuth target stopping the entire proton beam, and a secondary target (blanket) containing the fertile uranium material.

The primary target consists of multiple falling liquid lead-bismuth columns or jets so arranged as to provide for an evenly distributed neutron source. This is accomplished by providing a variable target density with respect to target depth, and by stepping the target to intercept different parts of the proton beam at different points within the neutron source area. The liquid lead-bismuth jets operate in the vacuum of the containment vessel, which is directly connected to the accelerator via the beam transport system. No window material is required between the accelerator and the target.

The uranium fertile material in the blanket consists of PWR or HWR fuel assemblies located in individual pressure-tubes. These surround the primary target neutron source in a manner consistent with minimization of neutron leakage, parasitic absorption, and mechanical design constraints. The assemblies of fuel, coolant, and moderator, are designed to remain highly subcritical under any circumstance. During an irradiation cycle, fuel shuffling is required to achieve good control of reactivity buildup. For this reason, the blanket will need instrumentation to monitor the fuel being irradiated.

Neutron multiplication occurs in the blanket, generating thermal energy. This energy, as well as that generated by the proton beam in the lead-bismuth target, is used to generate electric power by a conventional steam-turbine system.

The safety considerations applicable to the target are the same as those for a PWR, with the notable exception that the target of the fuel re-generator is subcritical. However, the entire target-blanket and primary coolant systems are housed in a containment building similar to that of a conventional PWR, with all the safety features of a PWR.

The LAFR would produce fissile fuel in fabricated fuel rods, by means of an external source of neutrons. The LAFR could stretch the nuclear fuel re-source by a factor of ∿4 or more without resorting to reprocessing, thus providing a long term supply of fuel to the LWR power system. Subsequent use of the LAFR with protected reprocessing could stretch the fuel supply by a factor of nearly 200 over that estimated from the U-235 availability alone. It would achieve the same purpose as the FBR but with the notable exception that the LAFR can also efficiently produce U-233 from thorium, thus opening up use of the thorium fuel resource. The LAFR is not a power reactor nor a breeder: it is a fuel generator. It would avoid the dis-advantage of severely depleting the natural uranium resource which is the case with diffusion plants. One LAFR could support three or more LWR's. Further, the fuel regenerator would not impose new technology on the utility company, which would continue to operate LWR's. The characteristics of this system with respect to the neutron spallation-evaporation process, neutron multiplication and target blanket calculations are given in references [1] and [2]. A schematic chart for a LAFR system is shown in Figure 2.

III. BLANKET AND TARGET DESIGN

Figure 3 shows an overall view of the target-blanket configuration used for enriching or regenerating PWR fuel assemblies. The primary proton beam, entering from the beam transport region at the left of Figure 3 strikes a series of liquid metal Pb-Bi columns that fall from the jet spray nozzles at the top of the target-blanket assembly. The proton beam, initially circular in shape, is converted into a narrow ellipse by the final set of beam transport magnets. This elliptical beam enters a thin vertical slot in the target-blanket assembly and interacts with the liquid Pb-Bi columns. Instead of defocusing the beam in this fashion, we are also considering the possibility of sweeping the beam vertically to cover the entire target area.

A practical target-blanket assembly has to satisfy three fundamental con-straints:

1. The power density in the blanket fuel assemblies must be compatible with available cooling methods.

2. The neutron source current at the target-blanket interface should be as uniform as possible. This minimizes power peaking and variations in fissile material build-up.

3. The neutron leakage from the target-blanket assembly should be small, so that leakage losses do not significantly reduce the fissile fuel production rate.

Because of the short range of protons in Pb-Bi ($\sim$90 cm at 1.5 GeV), a Pb-Bi target at normal density would generate excessively high blanket power densities in the first part of the target unless a very large target area were used. This would then cause a very large neutron leakage in the backward direction, as well as a very non-uniform neutron source distribution. The maximum neutron current from a Pb-Bi target consistent with good cooling capability in the blanket is on the order of 10^{14} n/cm^2 sec. For the example of 450 MW of beam power and a neutron yield of 45 per proton at 1.5 GeV, the surface area of the corresponding target would be 100 m^2. A single disk Pb-Bi target of 100 m^2 area and 90 cm thick would not be feasible, because of the high neutron leakage and non-uniformity of the source.

A practical Pb-Bi target-blanket assembly thus requires that the interaction distance of the primary protons in the target be much greater than the stopping distance in liquid Pb-Bi. This is possible if the effective Pb-Bi density along the target path is much less than that of the liquid. Figure 4 shows a cross sectional view of the target-blanket assembly with the Pb-Bi liquid colums. The effective density of the liquid columns increases with distance along the beam path. This spatial distribution compensates for the decrease in neutron production rate as proton energy is lost by interactions with the Pb-Bi columns. In addition to varying the spatial density of the Pb-Bi colums along the proton beam path, the Pb-Bi colums can be "stepped" forming a wedge or triangle pattern to intercept successive portions of the primary beam. These two techniques, used either in conjunction or separately, should allow one to shape the neutron source function along the beam path to any desired level.

The PWR fuel assemblies are contained in 12 inch ID Zircaloy pressure-tubes as shown in Figure 5. The pressure-tubes are headered at the target-blanket assembly. Fuel assemblies are loaded and unloaded from the top of the pressure-tubes into fuel handling casks. The pressure-tubes project through the tube sheet at the top of the assembly, and are welded to the tube sheet to provide a vacuum tight seal. Plugs at the top of each pressure-tube can be removed for the insertion or withdrawal of fuel assemblies.

Coolant flows up through the crescent-shaped regions between the square PWR fuel assembly and the round pressure-tubes, and then down through the assembly, cooling the fuel elements. The pressure drop of the coolant acts to keep the fuel assembly centered on the guide structure in the bottom of the pressure-tube. A shroud structure is necessary to prevent short circulating of the coolant flow from the inlet flow regions to a PWR fuel

assembly, since the assembly has no external box around it. Such a
shroud is shown in the cross sectional view of Figure 5 with attached ribs
that support it in the pressure-tube.

Since there is no window between the accelerator and the target-blanket
assembly, the pressure-tubes must be vacuum tight and there must be a
vacuum envelope surrounding the pressure-tube assembly. This envelope
will in effect be a relatively large vacuum tank, on the order of 10
meters in length, ∿4 meters high and ∿3 meters wide, with the external
pressure nominally at 1 atm. Because of the relatively thick structure
required to carry external pressure over large flat areas, the reflector
and thermal shield will probably have to be placed inside the vacuum en-
closure, rather than outside as shown in Figure 4. Design of this portion
of the target-blanket assembly will not be examined in detail until neu-
tronic studies define the nature of the reflector and shielding required.

The vapor pressure of Pb-Bi inside the vacuum tank will be ∿10^{-5} Torr. A
precise value is difficult to estimate since different portions of the Pb-
Bi jets will be at different temperatures (e.g., the inlet temperature at
the spray nozzle might be ∿300°C, and the outlet temperature ∿500°C), and
the pressure-tubes will be at relatively lower temperatures, i.e., ∿300°C.
The colder surfaces will tend to act as condensing "cold fingers" for Pb-
Bi vapor, so that the actual vapor pressure will depend on local position
within the target-blanket assembly. There will be some transport of Pb-
Bi vapor up the accelerator tube, but this can be easily condensed by
cooling panels and returned to the liquid Pb-Bi circuit.

Other configurations of the LAFR are possible, depending on the type of
fuel assembly to be enriched and/or regenerated. Figure 6 shows a target-
blanket assembly based on CANDU-type fuel assemblies. As in the CANDU reactor, the pressure-tubes are horizontally arranged. The proton beam
enters through the narrow slot between the banks of pressure-tubes. Unlike
the CANDU reactor, however, there is no moderator between pressure-tubes,
so a calandria vessel is not required. Fuel assemblies would be loaded
and unloaded at the ends of the pressure-tubes by a fuel handling mechanism
similar to that in CANDU reactors. This mechanism is not shown in Figures
6 and 7. If it proves sensible to load and unload fuel on line, as in
CANDU reactors, there would be substantial benefits in terms of operating
plant factor.

As in the PWR version of the LAFR, described earlier, variable density
Pb-Bi jets would be used to shape the neutron source distribution to the
desired value (Figure 7).

IV. COOLANT OPTIONS

Coolant options for the blanket fuel assemblies are summarized in Table I
together with their relative advantages and disadvantages. Only four
options appear to be practical:

1. Liquid D_2O

2. Two-Phase D_2O

3. Two-Phase H_2O

4. Helium

Liquid H_2O does not appear to be acceptable because it will strongly moderate neutrons from the target, causing excessive fission power, excessive power peaking, and variation in fissile content in the blanket fuel assemblies. Sodium does not appear to be acceptable, although it is an attractive coolant, since it may not be possible to maintain a protective film on the Zircaloy cladding of the LWR fuel elements if they are subjected to a sequence of different coolant environments. That is, each cycle in the LAFR would involve exposure to sodium followed by exposure to water in a PWR.

Helium is an attractive coolant option. However, because of the potential for oxidative corrosion with oxygen and water impurities in the helium, the maximum operating clad temperature in He will probably be comparable to that in a PWR, that is, on the order of ~700°F. Under these conditions, the thermal efficiency of the power cycle with the coolant will be considerably lower than that obtained with two-phase or liquid water coolants. Studies are being carried out to determine what cycle efficiency is achievable, and whether this would be acceptable for a LAFR.

If liquid D_2O is acceptable from the neutronics standpoint, it would be relatively easy to use as the blanket coolant. Pressure drops would be acceptable and thermal cycle efficiency would be acceptable and thermal cycle efficiency would be comparable to that in HWR's, i.e., ~30%. The additional cost of D_2O coolant would not significantly affect overall system economics. The D_2O inventory in a LAFR is much less than in an existing CANDU reactor, first because it is not required as a moderator and second, because the thermal power of the target-blanket assembly is only ~40% that of a CANDU reactor. In addition, since one LAFR regenerates fuel for three LWR reactors, the cost of D_2O for a LAFR, expressed as an equivalent additional fuel cycle cost for the LAFR/LWR system, will be negligible (i.e., much less than one mill/KWh).

If liquid D_2O proves not desirable for reasons of neutronics, two-phase (vapor plus liquid) mixtures are an attractive option. Either H_2O or D_2O two-phase mixtures could be used. The effective density of the two-phase mixture will be ~10% that of the liquid, and both H_2O and D_2O two-phase mixtures should result in relatively "hard" neutron spectra.

In general, two-phase mixtures appear to have excellent characteristics for cooling the LAFR blanket. Two-phase mixtures are desirable because they do not moderate neutrons very well, compared to liquid coolants, and retain good heat transfer/transport capability.

The only reservation with regard to the use of two-phase coolants is the question of how possible is local "dryout" of fuel element surfaces. The excellent heat transfer properties of two-phase coolants depend on evaporation of thin liquid films on the heat transfer surfaces, which are continually replenished by transfer of liquid from the two-phase mixture. Experience with two-phase coolant mixtures indicates that this does not appear to be of serious concern unless very high exit qualities (>0.8) are employed. The exit quality of the two-phase mixtures in a LAFR would be kept well below 0.8, so that "dryout" should not occur.

The LAFR and its associated heat exchangers, piping, pumps, etc., would be located in a containment shell similar to that for LWR's. Figures 8 and 9 show one possible arrangement of a LAFR for the regenerating of PWR fuel assemblies. Penetrations through the containment vessel for the accelerator beam tube and steam lines could be closed by fast acting isolation valves, if necessary. Construction of the LAFR and the inside containment for its associated systems would be similar to that for LWR's.

Overall containment requirements will probably be comparable to those for LWR's though the lower thermal rating of the LAFR's, as well as the use of separate pressure-tubes for the fuel assemblies, may result in somewhat less demanding requirements.

The thermal energy from the LAFR reactor is taken equal to 1350 MWt and is obtained as a combined output from the blanket (900 MWt) and the Pb-Bi target (450 MWt). The hot Pb-Bi exiting the reactor is used to heat the feedwater (@2600 psia) which has been previously heated by the regenerative system up to near the saturation temperature ($\sim$670°F) (Figure 10).

V. OBJECTIVES

For the LAFR system, in order to maintain high fissile material production rate, as well as minimize power peaking, the coolant for these fuel assemblies cannot significantly moderate neutrons from the primary Pb-Bi target. In addition, fuel assemblies must be compatible with both the LAFR coolant and water, since the latter is the coolant in LWR and CANDU.

These restrictions appear to require that a two-phase mixture (steam and liquid) of either D_2O or H_2O be the primary coolant option for a LAFR. The thermal-hydraulic limitations of these coolants in the LAFR fuel assemblies are important in the determination of economic and technical feasibility of the LAFR concept. Thermal-hydraulic analyses have been carried out to determine whether or not this coolant option is practical and what operating ranges are permissible in a LAFR. This presentation reports the findings of the thermal-hydraulic behavior of the two-phase mixture coolant in either PWR or CANDU fuel elements for a LAFR. The key questions examined in this study are:

1. Is adequate cooling of the blanket fuel assemblies achievable at low overall densities of two-phase mixtures (e.g., 10% of liquid density)?

2. Are two-phase pressure losses acceptable for the range of heat fluxes expected in the blanket?

2. Can hot spots occur due to local dryout?

VI. ANALYSES

Two-phase mixtures are examined as a function of heat flux and other thermal-hydraulic variables to determine whether or not they meet these limiting criteria. PWR and CANDU fuel assembly data used in the analyses are summarized in Table II.

The ranges of independent input variables used in the analysis are as follows:

P_o = Average heat flux from fuel pins in the blanket fuel assembly (expressed as a multiple of the average heat flux in either PWR or CANDU elements).

= 0.25, 0.5, 0.75, 1.0 x (average PWR or CANDU heat flux)

X_i = Inlet steam quality to channel

= $\dfrac{\text{Mass of Steam}}{\text{Mass of steam and water}}$

= 0.3, 0.5, 0.7

v_i = Inlet velocity of two-phase mixture to channel

= 25, 50, 75, 100 ft/sec

P_{2p} = Inlet pressure of two-phase mixture to channel

= 1000 psia

The following dependent variables are calculated for the above range of input variables:

X_o = Exit quality of two-phase mixture from channel.
(calculated from overall enthalpy balance, assuming pressure drop is negligible)

v_o = Exit velocity of two-phase mixture from channel
(calculated from overall mass balance)

ΔP_{2p} = Two-phase pressure drop across channel
       (based on average quality in the channel)

α_o = Exit steam volume fraction from channel
       (based on average quality in the channel)

$\bar{h}$ = Average heat transfer coefficient in channel
       (based on average quality)

ΔT_F = Film temperature drop
       (based on average heat transfer coefficient in channel)

The following correlations are used:

1. Pressure Drop

The Martinelli-Nelson two-phase friction factor [3,4] is used to determine the pressure drop. The two-phase pressure drop is expressed in
terms of the single-phase liquid pressure drop as,

$$\left(\frac{\Delta P}{\Delta L}\right)_{TPF} = \left(\frac{\Delta P}{\Delta L}\right)_{LPF} \phi_{\ell tt}^2 \tag{1}$$

where the correlation parameter $\phi_{\ell tt}$ is a function of

$$X_{tt} = \left(\frac{\rho_g}{\rho_\ell}\right)_{sat}^{1/(2-n)} \left(\frac{\mu_\ell}{\mu_g}\right)^{n/(2-n)} \left(\frac{1-x}{x}\right) \tag{2}$$

n is determined empirically from $f = C/Re^n$, and n=0.20-0.25 for turbulent
flow.

2. Void Fraction

The steam volume fraction, α, is calculated from the Bankoff Correlation
[5] of slip ratio,

$$S = \frac{1-\alpha}{K-\alpha} = \text{slip ratio} \tag{3}$$

$$K = K_j + (1-K_j)\alpha^\gamma \tag{4}$$

$$\gamma = 3.33 + 0.18 \times 10^{-3} P + 0.46 \times 10^{-6} P^2 \tag{5}$$

$$K_j = 0.71 + 10^{-4} P \tag{6}$$

P = pressure (psia)

The steam fraction is determined from the relationship;

$$\alpha = \frac{1}{1 + S\dfrac{\nu_f}{\nu_g}\dfrac{1-x}{x}}$$

where, V_f = specific volume of water

V_g = specific volume of steam

x = flow quality

3. Heat-Transfer Coefficient

The heat-transfer correlation of Schrock and Grossman with Wright constants [6] is used to determine the two-phase heat-transfer co-efficient;

$$h = 6700 \left[\frac{\phi s}{GH_{fg}} + 0.00035 \left\{ \left(\frac{x}{1-x} \right)^{0.9} \left(\frac{\rho f}{\rho g} \right)^{0.5} \left(\frac{\mu g}{\mu f} \right)^{0.1} \right\}^{0.66} \right]$$
$$\left[\left(\frac{0.023 \, k_f}{D} \right) \left(\frac{DG(1-x)}{\mu_f} \right)^{0.8} (Pr)^{0.4} \right] \quad (7)$$

The physical properties are evaluated at saturation conditions, where,

H_{fg} = heat of vaporization, Btu/lb.

ρ = density, lb/ft^3

k = thermal conductivity, Btu/hr/ft/°F

VII. RESULTS

Thermal-hydraulic calculations have been carried out for the blankets of accelerator-reactor systems based on the geometry of PWR (Figure 3), and CANDU (Figure 6) fuel assemblies. The following results are obtained with regard to the thermal-hydraulic behavior of LAFR for PWR fuel as shown in Figures 11-15:

1. Two-phase flow is a feasible coolant option for fuel element heat fluxes up to 1 x PWR average value, which is the maximum design value for a LAFR. As shown in Figure 11, steam volume fractions are reasonable for an inlet quality of 0.3 and the range of heat fluxes and inlet velocities considered.

2. In Figure 12, the results show that the two-phase flow pressure drops in the PWR pressure tubes are low, in the range of 10-30 psi for all parameters studied. The film temperature drops as given in Figure 13, are also low (typically ∿10°F). From Figure 14, the results show that the optimum inlet velocity should be in the range of 50 to 75ft/sec. A steam volume fraction of 0.80 corresponds to an effective density equivalent to ∿20 percent that of the liquid. Results show effective density for the two-phase mixture is generally about 10 percent that of

the liquid, which is well within the limiting criterion. Dryout of the fuel assembly surface does not appear to be of concern, since exit quality as shown in Figure 14 can be kept well below 0.8, the point of maximum heat transfer coefficient (Figure 15), by suitable choice of coolant flow conditions. The coolant temperature operating range corresponds to a power cycle efficiency of ∿30 percent, which considerably exceeds the allowable lower limit of 20 percent.

The following results are obtained for the LAFR with CANDU fuel elements as shown in Figure 16-20:

1. Two-phase flow appears adequate for cooling of CANDU fuel assemblies for heat fluxes up to 1 x the average CANDU value. Steam volume fractions are in a reasonable range at inlet quality of 0.3. However, a somewhat higher inlet velocity range of 75 to 100 ft/sec is necessary to prevent dryout.

2. Two-phase flow pressure drops, though higher for CANDU fuel elements, typically 50 to 100 psi, are still considered manageable. They are given in Figure 17. Film temperature drops are shown in Figure 18 and are again very low (typically ∿10°F). Optimum inlet velocity is in the range of 75 to 100 ft/sec and is concluded from Figure 19. Effective density for the two-phase mixture is well within the limiting criterion. The favorable heat-transfer coefficients are shown in Figure 20 for CANDU fuel elements.

VIII. DISCUSSION AND CONCLUSIONS

Returning to the questions about the two-phase cooling of the blanket listed earlier, the following answers can be formulated:

1. Adequate cooling of the blanket fuel assemblies appears achievable at low overall two-phase coolant densities, i.e., ∿10% of liquid density, at least up to fuel pin heat fluxes that are comparable to average PWR and CANDU heat fluxes (∿200,000 BTU/hr/ft^2). In any case these heat fluxes would appear to be upper limits, regardless of coolant choice, so as to ensure good cooling and safe operation. Since the blanket area can be readily designed to keep maximum heat fluxes at below this limit, there appears to be no problem in achieving adequately low coolant densities with two-phase mixtures.

2. Two-phase flow pressure drops with PWR assemblies are quite low and have no significant impact on power generation efficiency or coolant properties. With CANDU assemblies, two-phase flow pressure drops are considerably higher, because of lower coolant/fuel volume ratio and longer pressure-tubes. The length considered in the CANDU cases examined, 19.5 feet, appears to be an upper limit to pressure tube length for maximum heat flux in the assemblies on the order of 200,000 BTU/hr/ft^2. If heat fluxes are lower, pressure tubes can be correspondingly longer. If longer pressure-tubes are not possible at high heat fluxes, it probably

would be necessary to use split flow headering, with the pressure-tube fed at its middle with inlet coolant.

The coolant would then exit at each end of the pressure tube. There appears to be no fundamental reason why this would not be feasible, but it would involve a more complex piping arrangement. With this flow, the length of the blanket pressure-tubes could be doubled, so that pressure-tubes could be $\sim$40 ft long at heat fluxes of $\sim$200,000 BTU/hr/ft^2.

3. Gross dryout of the fuel assembly is of no concern, since outlet qualities of the two-phase mixture can readily be in the range of 0.4 to 0.7, depending on coolant flow conditions. The question of localized dryout is a much harder question to answer, since it is affected by fuel element geometry, evenness of flow, etc. Ultimately, experiments on fuel assemblies would be required to assure that dryout could not occur. The margin of safety is measured by going to low inlet qualities and high inlet velocities. For PWR fuel assemblies, an inlet quality of as low as 0.2 and a flow velocity of 75 ft/sec yields a pressure drop of $\sim$36 psi, which is acceptable. The effective moderator density (Figure 11 and 16) would be higher, however, on the order of 20% of liquid density. This probably would be acceptable from the standpoint of neutronics. Outlet quality under these conditions would be $\sim$0.3, so that the margin of safety would be considerable. Conditions for CANDU fuel are similar, with an inlet quality of $\sim$0.2 corresponding to outlet quality of $\sim$0.4. It thus appears that a large margin of safety against local dryout can be provided. Experiments on electrically heated simulated fuel assemblies can be carried out to determine local heat transfer conditions, and these should demonstrate that local dryout is not a problem.

For the range of LAFR designs considered, two-phase coolant appears feasible. The choice between two-phase mixture coolant or other coolant options will probably be primarily determined by economics, and will depend strongly on the particular parameters of a given LAFR design.

REFERENCES

1. P. Grand and H. C. Kouts, "Conceptual Design and Economic Analysis of a Light Water Reactor Fuel Regenerator," BNL Report 50838, May 1978.

2. P. Grand, J. R. Powell, M. Steinberg, and H. Takahashi, "Linear Accelerator Driven and Regenerative Reactor Systems," Brookhaven National Laboratory, Submitted to 1978 Annual ANS Meeting, San Diego, CA, June 18-22, 1978.

3. L. S. Tong, Boiling Heat-Transfer and Two-Phase Flow, p. 79, John Wiley & Sons, Inc., New York, London, Sydney.

4. C. J. Hsu, Brookhaven National Laboratory, private communication.

5. S. G. Bankoff, "A Variable Density Single-Fluid Model for Two-Phase Flow", Trans, ASME, 82, 265 (1960).

6. V. E. Schrock and L. M. Grossman, Forced Convection Boiling Studies, Final Report on Forced Convection Vaporization Project, TID-14632 (1959).

7. Steam/Nuclear Installtions for Electric Utilities.

8. UE&G, ERDA, 770630, COO-2477-4.

	TABLE I	
	BLANKET COOLANT OPTIONS	
OPTION	ADVANTAGES	DISADVANTAGES
HELIUM	NON-REACTIVE NON-MODERATING	LOW THERMAL CYCLE EFFICIENCY WITH ZIRCALOY CLAD TEMPERA- TURE LIMITATIONS
D_2O LIQUID	INTERMEDIATE MODERATION NO DRYOUT CONCERN	ADDITIONAL COST -
2 PHASE	LOW MODERATION	POSSIBLE DRYOUT CONCERN
H_2O LIQUID	LOW COST, NO DRYOUT CONCERN	STRONGLY MODERATES NEUTRONS
2 PHASE	LOW MODERATION	POSSIBLE DRYOUT CONCERN
SODIUM	LOW PRESSURE HIGH THERMAL EFFICIENCY NON-MODERATING	REACTIVE NOT COMPATIBLE WITH ZIRCALOY - CAN ONLY BE USED IN FUEL PRODUCER

TABLE II

FUEL ASSEMBLY DATA

	PWR [7]	CANDU [8]
ASSEMBLY (OR CHANNEL)	205	380
FUELS/ASSEMBLY (OR/BUNDLE)	208	37
BUNDLE/CHANNEL	–	12
LENGTH/CHANNEL, FT	12	19.5
EQUIVALENT DIAMETER, FT OF FLOW CHANNELS	0.042	0.0290
FREE FLOW AREA/ASSEMBLY (OR/CHANNEL), FT^2	0.30	0.0360
HEAT–TRANSFER AREA/ASSEMBLY (OR/CHANNEL), FT^2	281	96.17
AVERAGE HEAT FLUX, $BTU/FT^2/HR$	$197{,}000 \times \begin{cases} 1.0 \\ 0.75 \\ 0.5 \\ 0.25 \end{cases}$	$193{,}000 \times \begin{cases} 1.0 \\ 0.75 \\ 0.5 \\ 0.25 \end{cases}$
VOLUME RATIO OF COOLANT/ FUEL IN FUEL ASSEMBLY	1.5	0.8

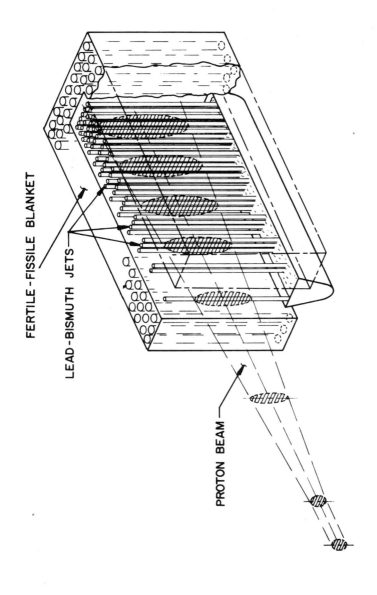

FERTILE-FISSILE BLANKET

LEAD-BISMUTH JETS

PROTON BEAM

Fig. 1 – Design Principle of the Target

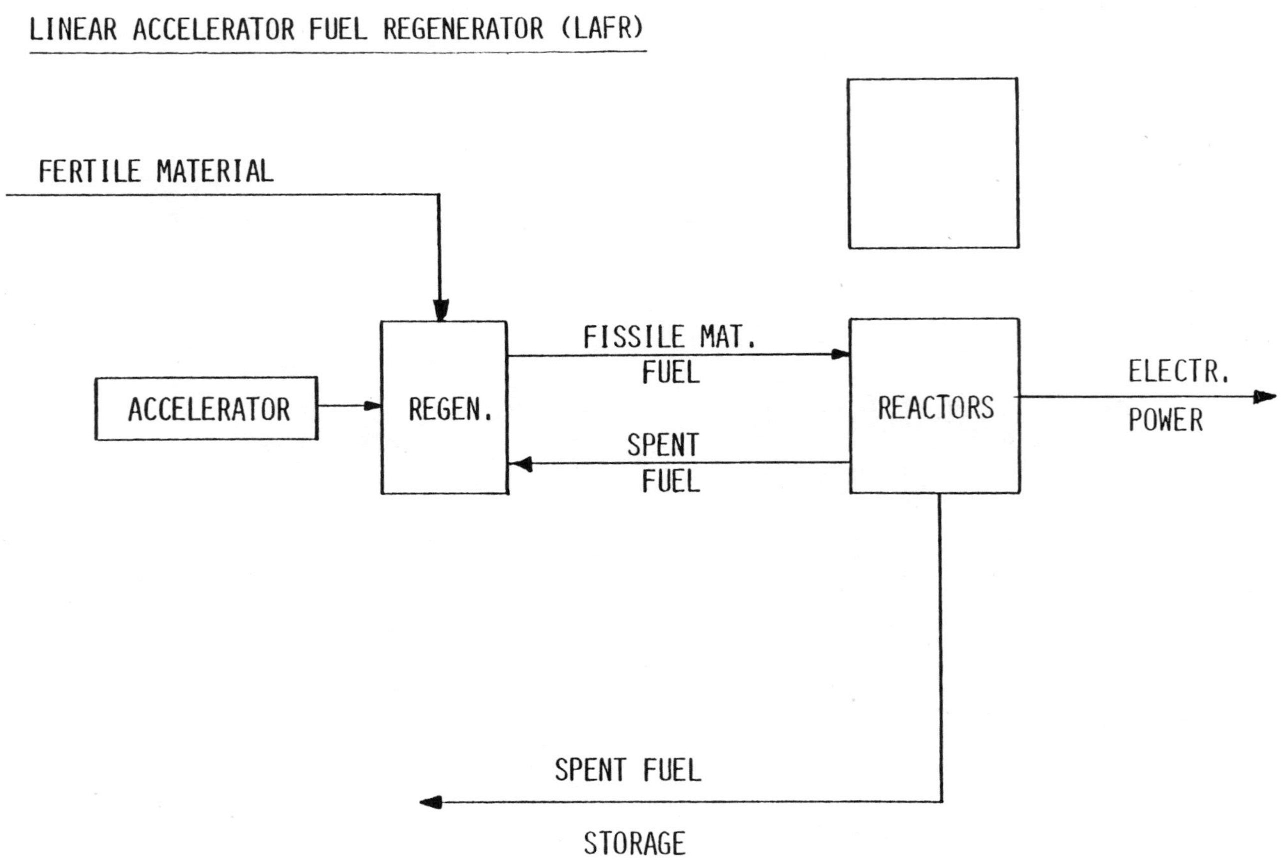

LINEAR ACCELERATOR FUEL REGENERATOR (LAFR)

FERTILE MATERIAL

ACCELERATOR

REGEN.

REACTORS

ELECTR. POWER

FISSILE MAT. FUEL

SPENT FUEL

SPENT FUEL STORAGE

Fig. 2 – Schematic Chart for a LAFR System

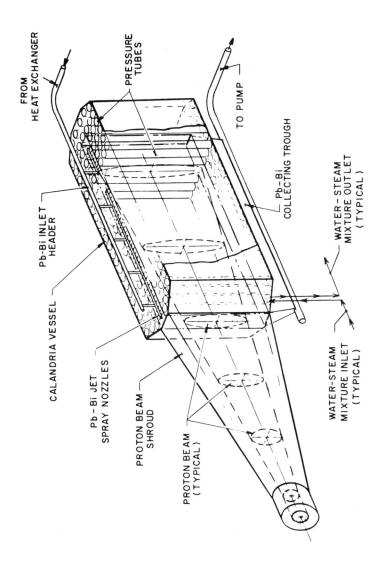

FROM HEAT EXCHANGER

PRESSURE TUBES

TO PUMP

Pb-Bi INLET HEADER

Pb-Bi COLLECTING TROUGH

CALANDRIA VESSEL

WATER-STEAM MIXTURE OUTLET (TYPICAL)

Pb-Bi JET SPRAY NOZZLES

PROTON BEAM SHROUD

WATER-STEAM MIXTURE INLET (TYPICAL)

PROTON BEAM (TYPICAL)

Fig. 3 - PWR Type Target Assembly

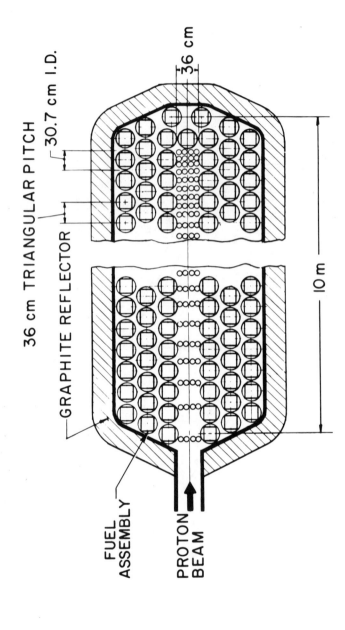

36 cm TRIANGULAR PITCH

30.7 cm I.D.

36 cm

GRAPHITE REFLECTOR

10 m

FUEL ASSEMBLY

PROTON BEAM

Fig. 4 – PWR Type Target Assembly Cross Section

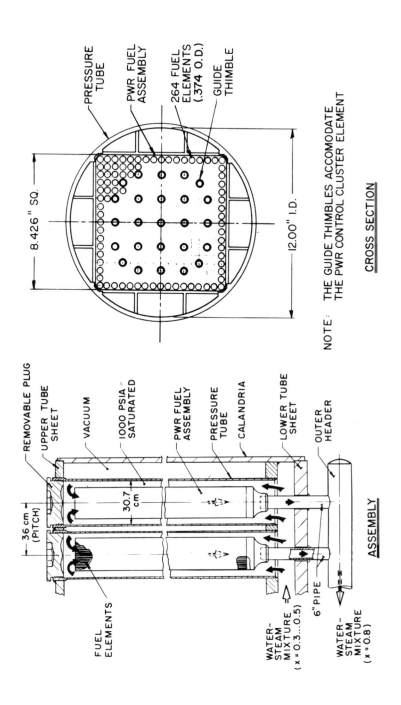

PRESSURE TUBE

PWR FUEL ASSEMBLY

264 FUEL ELEMENTS (.374 O.D.)

GUIDE THIMBLE

8.426" SQ.

12.00" I.D.

NOTE: THE GUIDE THIMBLES ACCOMODATE THE PWR CONTROL CLUSTER ELEMENT

CROSS SECTION

REMOVABLE PLUG

UPPER TUBE SHEET

VACUUM

1000 PSIA SATURATED

PWR FUEL ASSEMBLY

PRESSURE TUBE

CALANDRIA

LOWER TUBE SHEET

OUTER HEADER

36 cm (PITCH)

30.7 cm

FUEL ELEMENTS

WATER-STEAM MIXTURE (x = 0.3...0.5)

6" PIPE

WATER-STEAM MIXTURE (x = 0.8)

ASSEMBLY

Fig. 5 - PWR Type Pressure Tubes

1657

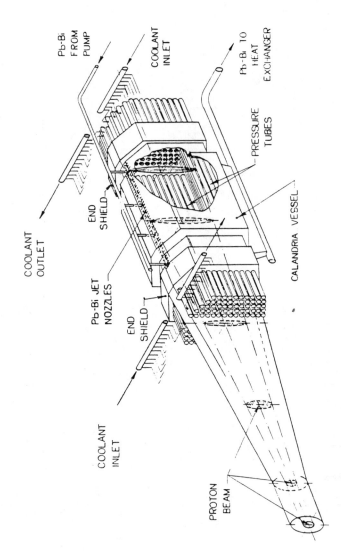

COOLANT OUTLET

Pb-Bi FROM PUMP

COOLANT INLET

Pb-Bi TO HEAT EXCHANGER

PRESSURE TUBES

END SHIELD

CALANDRIA VESSEL

Pb-Bi JET NOZZLES

END SHIELD

COOLANT INLET

PROTON BEAM

Fig. 6 – HWR Type Target Assembly

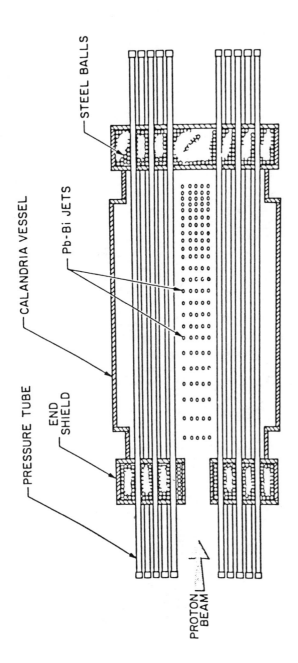

STEEL BALLS

CALANDRIA VESSEL

Pb-Bi JETS

PRESSURE TUBE

END
SHIELD

PROTON
BEAM

Fig. 7 – HWR Type Target Assembly, Cross Section

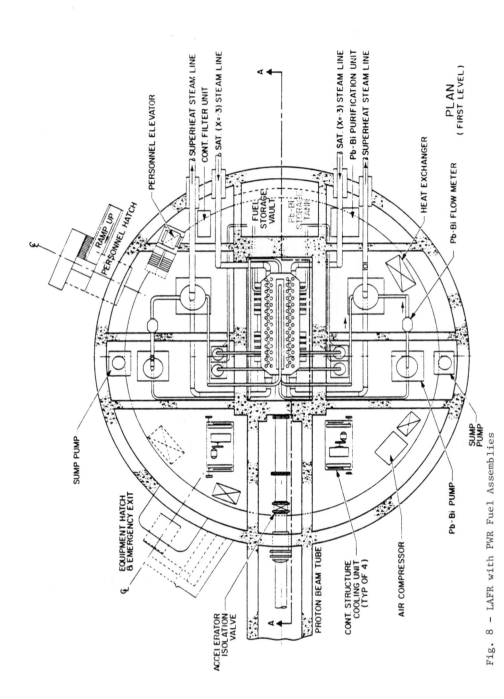

RAMP UP

PERSONNEL HATCH

PERSONNEL ELEVATOR

β SUPERHEAT STEAM LINE

CONT. FILTER UNIT

β SAT. (X = 3) STEAM LINE

A

FUEL STORAGE VAULT

Pb-Bi STORAGE TANK

β SAT. (X = 3) STEAM LINE

Pb-Bi PURIFICATION UNIT

β SUPERHEAT STEAM LINE

HEAT EXCHANGER

Pb-Bi FLOW METER

PLAN
(FIRST LEVEL)

SUMP PUMP

EQUIPMENT HATCH
& EMERGENCY EXIT

ACCELERATOR
ISOLATION
VALVE

PROTON BEAM TUBE

CONT. STRUCTURE
COOLING UNIT
(TYP OF 4)

AIR COMPRESSOR

Pb-Bi PUMP

SUMP
PUMP

A

Fig. 8 – LAFR with PWR Fuel Assemblies

1660

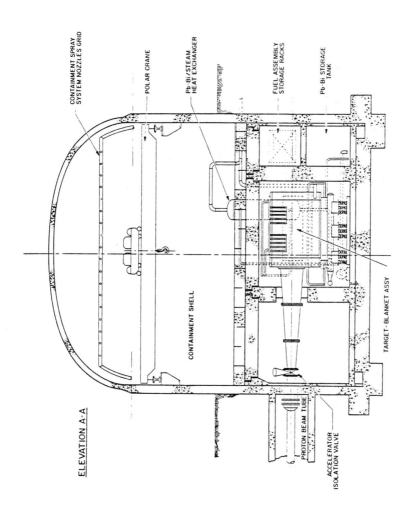

ELEVATION A-A

CONTAINMENT SPRAY SYSTEM NOZZLES GRID

POLAR CRANE

Pb-Bi/STEAM HEAT EXCHANGER

FUEL ASSEMBLY STORAGE RACKS

Pb-Bi STORAGE TANK

CONTAINMENT SHELL

TARGET-BLANKET ASSY

PROTON BEAM TUBE

ACCELERATOR ISOLATION VALVE

Fig. 9 – LAFR with PWR Fuel Assemblies

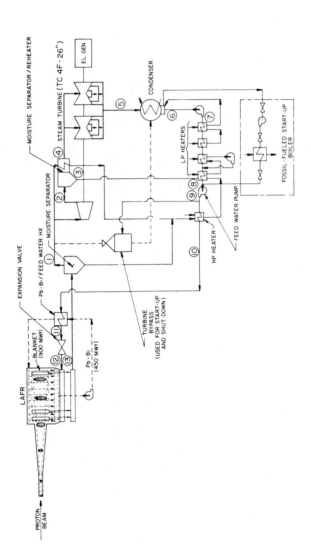

Fig. 10 – LAFR Facility Steam Cycle

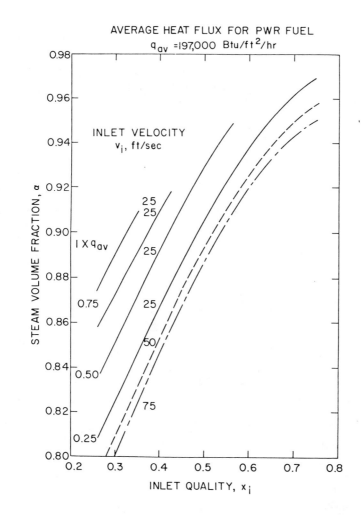

Fig. 11 – Steam Volume Fraction vs. Inlet Quality at Three Inlet
Velocities and Various Fuel Element Heat Fluxes for
PWR Fuel

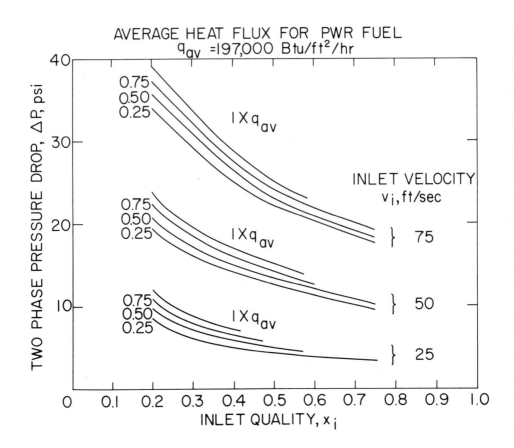

Fig. 12 — Two-Phase Pressure Drop vs. Inlet Quality at Three Inlet
Velocities and Various Fuel Element Heat Fluxes for PWR Fuel

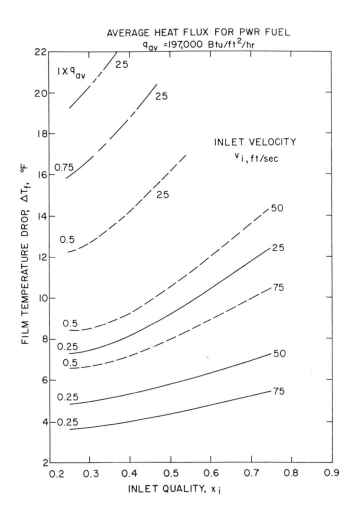

Fig. 13 – Two-Phase Film Temperature Drop vs. Inlet Quality at Three Inlet
Velocities and Various Fuel Element Heat Fluxes for PWR Fuel

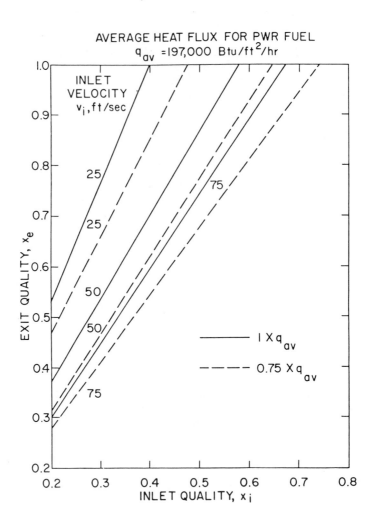

Fig. 14 - Two-Phase Exit Quality vs. Inlet Quality at Two Different Fuel
Element Heat Fluxes and Various Inlet Velocities for PWR Fuel

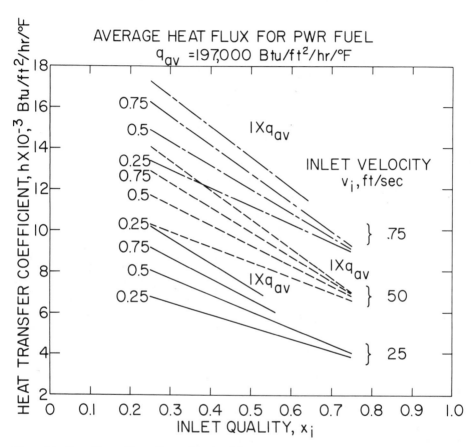

Fig. 15 Two-Phase Heat Transfer Coefficient vs. Inlet Quality of Three
Inlet Velocities and Various Fuel Element Heat Fluxes for PWR Fuel

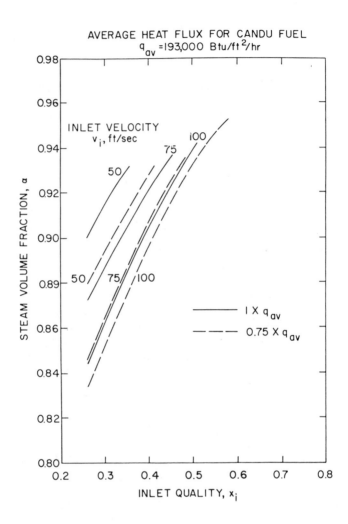

Fig. 16 – Steam Volume Fraction vs. Inlet Quality at Three Inlet
Velocities and Two Fuel Element Heat Fluxes for CANDU Fuel

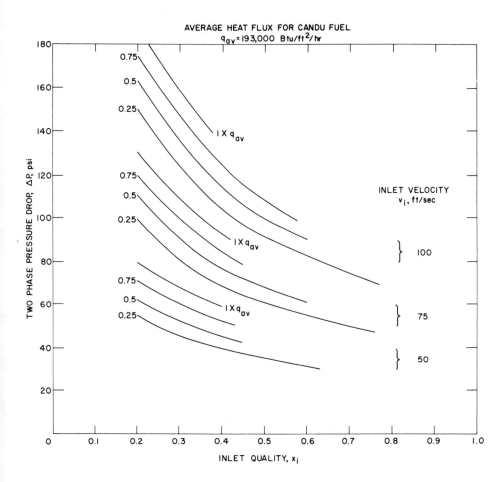

Fig. 17   Two-Phase Pressure Drop vs. Inlet Quality at Three Inlet
Velocities and Various Fuel Element Heat Fluxes for CANDU Fuel

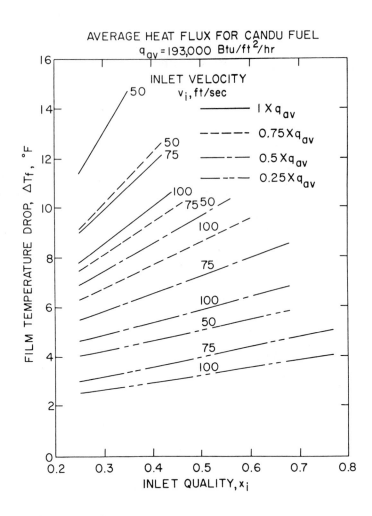

Fig. 18 - Two-Phase Pressure Drop vs. Inlet Quality at Three Inlet
Velocities and Various Fuel Element Heat Fluxes for CANDU Fuel

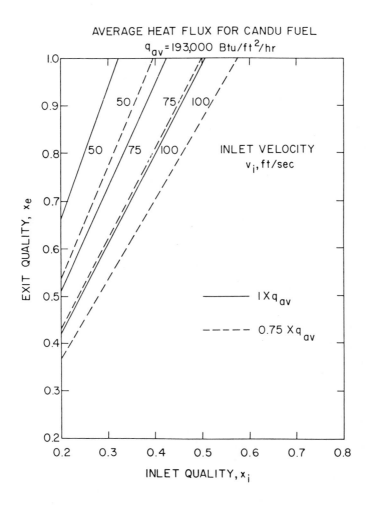

Fig. 19 – Two-Phase Exit Quality vs. Inlet Quality at Two Different Fuel
Element Heat Fluxes and Three Inlet Velocities for CANDU Fuel

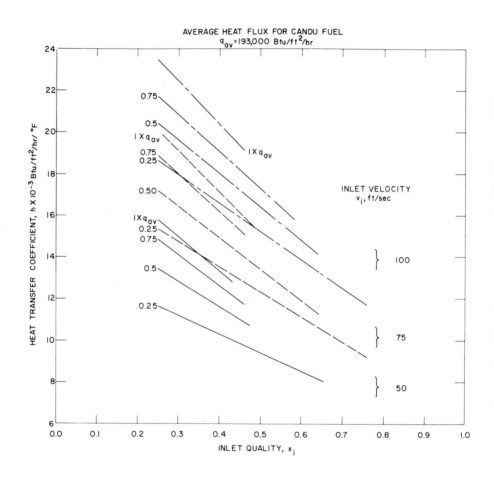

Fig. 20 Two-Phase Heat Transfer Coefficient vs. Inlet Quality at Three Inlet
Velocities and Various Fuel Element Heat Fluxes for CANDU FUEL

Shock Phenomena in Air-Water Two Phase Flow

K. AKAGAWA, T. SAKAGUCHI, T. FUJII, S. FUJIOKA,
and M. SUGIYAMA
Kobe University
Nada-ku, Kobe, Japan

ABSTRACT

Shock phenomena caused by a sudden valve closure for bubble flow region in air-water two phase flow were investigated. The experiment was conducted in a horizontal tube of 20.7 mm ID and 18.54 m length in the range of superficial water velocity $w_{\ell 0}$ from 1.6 to 3.2 m/s and of superficial air velocity w_{g0} from 0.045 to 0.97 m/s. The profiles of transient pressure, values of pressure rise at the instant of the valve closure, and propagation velocities of the pressure waves were investigated. The values of the pressure rise were analyzed with a homogeneous flow model and the predicted values agreed well with the experimental results.

INTRODUCTION

Shock phenomena in two phase flow caused by a sudden valve closure in a cooling system are an important problem for the safety assessment in nuclear reactors [1]. The shock phenomena caused by a sudden closure of a down-stream valve in a tube system in which water flows are called water hammer, and the value of the pressure rise and the transient behaviors of the pressure have been well investigated [2]. But there are few data available on the characteristics of shock phenomena in gas-liquid two phase flows. Padmanabhan and Martin [3] investigated the propagation velocity and the structure of the shock waves caused by a sudden valve closure in the range of void fraction from 0.005 to 0.08. This may be the only report concerning the shock phenomena in two-phase flows in the past. On the other hand, the propagation velocity of shock waves and pressure waves of moderate and large amplitudes in bubble-liquid mixture at rest, which are formed by a rupture of diaphragm in a shock tube, has been studied by Campbell & Pitcher [4], Van Wijnagaarden [5],[6], Miyazaki [7], Noordzij & Van Wijngaarden [8], Kuznetsov & Nakoryakov et al. [9], and Hijikata & Mori et al. [10].

The characteristics of shock phenomena are remarkably affected by the flow patterns such as bubble flow, slug flow, and mist flow, and by the rate of phase change between the gas and the

1673

liquid. The purpose of this study is to make clear the fundamental characteristics of the shock phenomena in a bubble flow
of air-water mixture. The values of pressure rise, the
profiles of transient pressure, and the propagation velocities
have been experimentally and theoretically investigated.
These characteristics are similar to those of water hammer because the bubble flow, in which the liquid is continuous and
the bubbles are distributed in the liquid as a discontinuous
phase, has a similar property to a homogeneous fluid, which
has much larger compressibility than that of water. Therefore,
the theoretical analysis has been done by a homogeneous flow
model and compared with the experimental results. The shock
phenomena in slug flow have been investigated in the same
apparatus and these will be presented in the report to follow
this one [11].

EXPERIMENTAL

A schematic diagram of the experimental apparatus is shown in
Fig. 1 . The horizontal test section was constructed from a
steel tube of 20.7 mm ID, 3.5 mm thickness, and 18.54 m length.
Water supplied from a gear pump flows through an orifice ①, a
three-ways solenoid valve ②, and a reservoir ③ having an air
space of 0.166 m³ volume, and then enters an air-water mixing
section ④ made of sintered steel tube of 20.7 mm ID and 298
mm length. Air supplied from a compressor enters the mixing
section through a critical nozzle ⑦ to measure the flow rate
and a solenoid valve ⑧ . The air-water mixture then flows
into the test section and flows out into atmosphere through a
quick-acting valve ⑤ and a pressure control valve ⑥ .
An acrylic pipe was also installed separately to observe the
flow pattern and to take photographs. The shock phenomena were
generated by operating a quick-acting valve. The valve closing
time was about 0.02 sec. The transient pressures were detected
by piezoelectric pressure transducers ⑨ at four locations each
6.16 m apart as shown in Fig. 1 and the signals were recorded
on a recorder through a D.C. amplifier. The pressures at the
initial and final steady states were measured using a Bourdon
tube type pressure gauge. The experiment was carried out for
a range of superficial water velocity from 1.6 to 3.2 m/s and
of superficial air velocity from 0.045 to 0.97 m/s. The velocities of the compression waves were determined from the time
delay of the wave front at the two pressure transducers ($z=0.02$,
6,16 or 12.34 m) and those of the rarefaction waves were obtained from the time delay of the tail edge of the compression
wave (which is at the same time the initial point of the de-
scending pressure profile).

The pictures of the flow are shown in Fig. 2 (a)∼(c). As seen
in the photograph of Fig. 2 (a), (b) the bubbles are distributed

in the top portion of the tube cross-section and also inter-
mittently along the tube axis, when the air flow rate is low
compared with the water flow rate and the void fraction $f_{g(o)}$ is
less than 7 %. For $f_{g(o)} > 7$ %, the distribution of the bubbles
is uniform along the tube axis as shown in Fig. 2 (c).
Therefore, in the former cases the profiles of the transient
pressure in each run at the same air and water flow rates were
a little different, but in the latter cases the reproducibility
of the profile was good.

EXPERIMENTAL RESULTS AND DISCUSSIONS

Profiles of Transient Pressure

An example of transient pressure caused by a sudden valve
closure is shown in Fig. 3 . These were measured at four locations along the test section. A compression wave with sudden
pressure rise at the wave front propagates upstream as shown by
line A, and the wave is reflected as a rarefaction wave at the
reservoir with an air space of compressible capacity and it
propagates downstream as shown by line B. The profile of the
second compression wave becomes smooth and the amplitude
decreases remarkably.

The profiles of the transient pressure at a location (z = 0.02
m) adjacent to the valve are shown in Figs. 4 and 5. The effects of air flow rate and water flow rate on the profiles of
the transient pressure, and the effect of void fraction as well
can be seen from these figures. When the air flow rate is low,
that is, the void fraction is low (Fig. 4 (a), (b)), the slope
of the initial pressure rise is large and the first compression
wave is accompanied by high-frequency pressure oscillations of
irregular amplitude and followed by a smooth rarefaction wave.
With increasing air flow rate at a constant water flow rate (
Fig. 4 (d) $\sim$ (g)), the slope of the pressure rise becomes
smaller and the values of the initial pressure rise, that is,
potential surge Δp_{ps} decreases, and the duration of the first
compression wave increases, and also the high-frequency oscillations disappear. When the air flow rate is constant, the
values of Δp_{ps} increases with increasing water flow rate. When
the void fraction is constant, the profiles of the transient
pressure are similar, as can be seen from Fig. 5 .

The profiles of the transient pressure are classified into
three types (1), (11), and (111) according to their characteristics as shown in Fig. 5 . Type (1) : the first compression
wave is accompanied by high-frequency pressure oscillations.
Type (11) : there is a slight slow pressure drop in the middle
of the compression wave plateau. Type (111) : there is a
gradual pressure rise in the plateau of the compression wave

and the pressure p_d at the tail of the first compression wave
is higher than p_{ps}, and there are no high-frequency oscillations. Noordzij et al. [8] has classified the profile of a
pressure wave passing along the tube, which contains a bubble-
liquid mixture at rest, into three types A, B, and C according
to the slope of the pressure rise and the presence of high-
frequency pressure oscillations. The profiles resemble Types
(1), (11), and (111) respectively presented in this report.
But it should be noted that the former classification is based
on the variation of a wave profile along the tube, while the
latter is based on the profile of a wave adjacent to the valve
at different flow rates. The high-frequency pressure oscillation at the back side of the shock has been investigated by
Van Wijngaarden [5], Hijikata and Mori [10] and it has been
proved that the oscillations were caused by the pressure oscillations of the bubbles.

The steep slope of the initial compression wave front in Type
(1) remains constant during the propagation of the wave and
also in some cases the wave front with a slow slope in the initial state becomes steeper during the propagation like a shock
wave in a gas. The slope of wave front in Type (11) decreases
as the wave propagates in the test section. The characteristics of the wave in Type (11) are those of the transitional
state between Type (1) and (111). The reason for p_d being
higher than p_{ps} is the presence of the static pressure gradient
by the friction loss in the tube and the addition of the static
pressure to the pressure rise of Δp_{ps}. Boundaries between Type
(1), (11), and (111) are shown in Fig. 6. These boundaries
correspond approximately to constant void fraction lines of
$f_{g(o)} = 0.07 \sim 0.08$ and 0.13 respectively.

Values of Potential Surge and Maximum Pressure Rise

The measured values of the potential surge are shown against
the void fraction $f_{g(o)}$ in Fig. 7. Here, the value of $f_{g(o)}$ was
calculated from Butterworth's Eq. (1) in the initial steady
state before the value closure.

$$f_g = (1 + 0.28X^{0.71})^{-1} \tag{1}$$

$$X = \{ (1-x)/x \}^{0.9} (\rho_g/\rho_\ell)^{0.5} (\mu_\ell/\mu_g)^{0.1}$$

The values of p_{ps} at $f_{g(o)} = 0$, that is, water single phase flow
in the figure are the calculated values of Joukowsky's equation,
Eq. (2), and these values coincide with the measured values.

$$\Delta p_{pso} = \rho_\ell w_{\ell o} a_\ell \tag{2}$$

Here, the measured value of the sound velocity in the water a_ℓ
was 1401 m/s and this value agrees well with the calculated
value of the well-known equation (3).

$$a_\ell = \{\frac{\rho_\ell}{K_\ell} + \frac{\rho_\ell D_p (1-\mu_p^2)}{E\ e}\}^{-1/2} \qquad (3)$$

It is seen from the figure that the values of the potential
surge in the bubble flow decrease remarkably with increasing
void fraction compared with the values of Δp_{pso}. The values of
Δp_{ps} are determined by only the initial and local conditions
adjacent to the valve, that is, by the water flow rate $w_{\ell o}$ and
the void fraction $f_{g(o)}$, and are independent of the tube length
and the pressure gradient in the tube. The experimental results can be expressed by the following empirical formula in
the range of $f_{g(o)}$ from 0.045 to 0.24.

$$\Delta p_{ps} = 0.019\ w_{\ell o}^{1.73}\ f_{g(0)}^{-1.3} \qquad [kgf/cm^2] \qquad (4)$$

The experiments were conducted under the condition that the
opening of the pressure control valve ⑥ in Fig. 1 was kept
constant : therefore, the static pressure in the test section
has been found to change with the water flow rate.
The pressure distributions are shown in Fig. 8. The value of
the potential surge depends not only on $w_{\ell o}$ and $f_{g(o)}$, but
also on the initial pressure $p_{(o)}$. But the effect of $p_{(o)}$ on
Δp_{ps} is not expressed in Eq. (4). Then, the value of exponent
of $w_{\ell o}$, 1.73, should be examined, because the effect of $p_{(o)}$
may be included in the value of 1.73. The potential surge will
be expressed by an analytical equation, Eq. (27), as a function
of $(\rho_\ell a_1 w_{\ell o}/p_1)$. This equation is approximated by Eq. (5) in
the range of ϕ from 0.5 to 4.

$$\frac{\Delta p_{ps}}{P_{(0)}} = 1.7\phi^{1.5} = 1.7(\frac{a_{(0)}\ \rho_\ell\ w_{\ell o}}{P_{(0)}})^{1.5} \qquad (5)$$

Also, the sound velocity $a_{(o)}$ is expressed by Eq. (6), which
will be discussed in connection with Eq. (19).

$$a_{(0)} = \sqrt{\frac{P_{(0)}}{f_{g(0)}\ (1-f_{g(0)})\rho_\ell}} \qquad (6)$$

Rearrangement of Eqs. (5) and (6) gives

$$\Delta p_{ps} = 1.75\{\frac{\rho_\ell}{f_{g(0)}\ (1-f_{g(0)})}\}^{0.75}P_{(0)}^{0.25}w_{\ell o}^{1.5} \qquad (7)$$

From the equation, it may be estimated that the potential surge is proportional to $p_{(0)}^{0.25}$ and $w_{\ell o}^{1.5}$. In this experiment $p_{(0)}$ was approximately proportional to $w_{\ell o}^{0.9}$; then the value of $p_{(0)}^{0.25}$ in Eq. (7) was proportional to $w_{\ell o}^{0.225}$. Consequently Eq. (7) can essentially expressed by

$$\Delta p_{ps} \backsim p_{(0)}^{0.25} \cdot w_{\ell o}^{1.5} \backsim w_{\ell o}^{1.725} \backsim w_{\ell o}^{1.73} \qquad (8)$$

This relation agrees well with the empirical Eq. (4). Therefore, it is concluded that the actual effect of the water flow rate is expressed by the exponent 1.5.

The measured values of the maximum pressure rise Δp_{max} are shown against $f_{g(0)}$ in Fig. 8. The maximum pressure rise in Type (1) occurs at an indefinite instant in the first compression wave and that in Type (111) at the tail of the compression wave, that is, the value of Δp_{max} coincides with that of Δp_d. The characteristics of Δp_{max} are different in the two regions divided by a dotted line as shown in Fig. 9. In the region where the void fraction is smaller than f_{gc}, the Δp_{max} decreases linearly on semilogarithmic co-ordinate with increasing void fraction, and in the region of larger void fraction than f_{gc}, the value of Δp_{max} is constant against the void fraction at a constant water flow rate. These are expressed by the empirical Eqs. (9) and (10).

$$f_{g(0)} < f_{gc} :$$

$$\frac{\Delta p_{max}}{a_{\ell} \rho_{\ell} w_{\ell o}} = \exp\{(7.1\, w_{\ell o} - 49.2)\, f_{g(0)}\} \qquad (9)$$

$$f_{g(0)} > f_{gc} :$$

$$\frac{\Delta p_{max}}{a_{\ell} \rho_{\ell} w_{\ell o}} = \exp\{(7.1\, w_{\ell o} - 49.2)\, f_{gc}\} \qquad (10)$$

Here,

$$f_{gc} = 0.073\, w_{\ell o}^{0.257} \qquad (11)$$

In Type (1), the values of Δp_{max} are considerably higher than that of Δp_{ps}, especially at a high water flow rate of $w_{\ell o} = 3.2$, as can be seen in Fig. 5. In Types (11) and (111), the values of Δp_{max} depend on the length of the tube and the static pressure gradient as described above. Therefore, Eq. (10) is valid only for the configuration of the apparatus used in this experiment.

Analysis of Potential Surge

The value of potential surge has been analyzed for an isothermal homogeneous two phase flow model with the following assumptions : (1) the flow is one-dimensional, (2) small bubbles
are distributed uniformly in the liquid, (3) there is no relative velocity between gas bubbles and the surrounding liquid
during the transient state and the steady state, (4) the liquid
is incompressible and the gas is compressed isothermally.
A model of compression wave with the propagation velocity c
caused by the quick valve closure is shown in Fig. 10 (a) on a
fixed co-ordinate.   The model is also shown on a co-ordinate
moving with the wave in Fig. 10 (b).

The continuity equation and the momentum equation for the
moving co-ordinate are given by Eqs. (12) and (13) respectively.

$$f_{g1}\rho_{g1}(c + w_{g1}) + (1 - f_{g1})\rho_{\ell}(c + w_{\ell 1})$$
$$= f_{g2}\rho_{g2}c + (1 - f_{g2})\rho_{\ell}c \qquad (12)$$

$$p_1 + f_{g1}\rho_{g1}(c + w_{g1})^2 + (1 - f_{g1})\rho_{\ell}(c + w_{\ell 1})^2$$
$$= p_2 + f_{g2}\rho_{g2}c^2 + (1 - f_{g2})\rho_{\ell}c^2 \qquad (13)$$

According to the assumption (4) above,

$$p_1 / p_2 = \rho_{g1} / \rho_{g2} \qquad (14)$$

The void fraction is expressed by

$$f_g = (1 + \frac{1-x}{x} \frac{\rho_g}{\rho_\ell} \frac{w_g}{w_\ell})^{-1} \qquad (15)$$

With the assumption (3), that is, $w_g = w_\ell$, Eq. (15) becomes

$$f_g = w_{go} / (w_{go} + w_{\ell o}) \qquad (16)$$

The potential surge and the propagation velocity were derived
from Eqs. (12),(13),(14), and (15).   From Eqs. (12) and (13)
the following equation is derived using the condition $\rho_\ell \gg \rho_g$

$$(c + w_{\ell 1})^2 = \{ \frac{p_1}{f_{g1}(1 - f_{g1})\rho_\ell} \}\{ \frac{(p_2/p_1) - 1}{1 - (\rho_{g1}/\rho_{g2})} \} \qquad (17)$$

Substitution of Eq. (14) into Eq. (17) gives

$$(c + w_{\ell_1})^2 = \left\{ \frac{p_1}{f_{g1}(1 - f_{g1})\rho_\ell} \right\} \frac{p_2}{p_1} \qquad (18)$$

The term $\{p_1/f_{g1}(1-f_{g1})\rho_\ell\}$ in Eq. (18) coincides with the square of the sound velocity in homogeneous flow with iso-thermal change, a_1 [12], [13]

$$a_1^2 = p_1 / \{ f_{g1}(1 - f_{g1})\rho_\ell \} \qquad (19)$$

Therefore, Eq. (18) can be expressed by

$$M^2 = \{(c + w_{\ell_1}) / a_1\}^2 = p_2 / p_1 \qquad (20)$$

This equation is equal to the shock wave relationship in bubble flow based on the isothermal homogeneous model derived by Campbell & Pitcher [4] and Noordzij & Wijngaarden et al. [8].

From Eq. (12), the wave velocity is expressed by

$$c = \{(1 - f_{g1}) / (f_{g1} - f_{g2})\} w_{\ell_1} \qquad (21)$$

The void fraction at the back side of the wave front f_{g2} is given from Eqs. (14) and (15).

$$f_{g2} = f_{g1}(p_1/p_2) / \{1 - f_{g1} + f_{g1}(p_1/p_2)\} \qquad (22)$$

Substitution of Eq. (22) into Eq. (21) gives

$$(p_2/p_1) = f_{g1}\left(\frac{c}{w_{\ell_1}} + 1 \right)/\left\{f_{g1}\left(\frac{c}{w_{\ell_1}} + 1 \right) - 1\right\} \qquad (23)$$

Rearranging Eqs. (20), (23), and $w_{\ell_0} = w_{\ell_1}/(1 - f_{g1})$, the propagation velocity of the compression wave front relative to upstream fluid ($c + w_{\ell_1}$) can be expressed by

$$(c + w_{\ell_1}) = a_1\left(\frac{\phi}{2} + \sqrt{1 + \frac{\phi^2}{4}} \right) \qquad (24)$$

$$\phi = \rho_\ell a_1 w_{\ell_0} / p_1 \qquad (25)$$

Thus, the propagation velocity ($c + w_{\ell_1}$) is a function of only a dimensionless characteristic number ϕ, and is greater than the sound velocity a_1. The pressure rise p_{ps} (which is equal to p_2) can be obtained by substitution of Eq. (24) into Eq. (20) as follows :

$$\frac{p_2}{p_1} = \frac{p_{ps}}{p_1} = \left[\frac{\phi}{2} + \sqrt{1 + \frac{1}{4}\phi^2} \right]^2 \qquad (26)$$

The potential surge Δp_{ps} is given by

$$\frac{\Delta p_{ps}}{p_1} = \phi \left[\frac{\phi}{2} + \sqrt{1 + \frac{1}{4}\phi^2} \right] \qquad (27)$$

Thus, the dimensionless potential surge $\Delta p_{ps}/p_1$ can be obtained as a function of ϕ.

When the values of ϕ are low ($\phi \ll 1$), the value of Δp_{ps} is approximately expressible by

$$\Delta p_{ps} \doteqdot p_1 \phi = \rho_\ell w_{\ell o} a_1 \qquad (28)$$

This first approximation is also derived as follows. The potential surge in two-phase homogeneous flow may be expressed by Eq. (29) analogously to Eq. (2) for a liquid flow, namely,

$$\Delta p_{ps} = \rho_{TP} w_{TP} a_1 \qquad (29)$$

Here, the density of a two-phase flow, ρ_{TP}, is given by Eq. (30) with the assumption (3), and the velocity w_{TP}, by Eq. (31).

$$\rho_{TP} = (w_{\ell o} \rho_\ell + w_{go} \rho_g) / (w_{\ell o} + w_{go}) \qquad (30)$$

$$w_{TP} = w_{\ell o} + w_{go} \qquad (31)$$

Substitution of Eqs. (30), (31), and the relation $\rho_\ell \gg \rho_g$ into Eq. (29) gives Eq. (32), and this coincides with Eq. (28).

$$\Delta p_{ps} = (w_{\ell o} \rho_\ell + w_{go} \rho_g) a_1 \doteqdot \rho_\ell w_{\ell o} a_1 \qquad (32)$$

Thus, Eq. (29) analogously derived is shown to be the first approximation of the potential surge for small values of ϕ.

The comparison of experimental results with calculated results given by Eq. (26) is shown in Figs. 11 and 12, in which the values of $p_{ps(ex)}/p_{ps(th)}$ are plotted against the void fraction f_{g_1} at $z = 0.02$ calculated by the assumption of no slip between the gas and the liquid, that is, $f_{g_1} = w_{go(o)} / (w_{go(o)} + w_{\ell o})$. As can be seen, the agreement is good in Type (11) and (111), and in Type (1) the experimental values are a little higher than the calculated values. The reason may be the nonuniformity of bubble distribution along the tube axis in the low void fraction condition; then in some cases the local void fraction adjacent to the valve is lower than the mean void fraction. The concentration of bubbles in the water is higher in the upper portion of the tube cross-section than in the lower portion, as can be seen in Fig. 2. The effect of the uniformity of the bubble distribution on the behavior of transient pressure has not been investigated in this study. When the mean value of the pressure rise in the first spike,

Δp_{psm}, is used as the magnitude of pressure surge as shown in
Fig. 3, the comparison is shown in Fig. 12. The agreement is
better than that in Fig. 11 for Type (1), and as the value of
p_{psm} is the same as p_{ps} in Type (11) and (111), the agreement
is good.

Shock Wave Relation or Finite Amplitude Wave Relation

Shock wave relation Eq. (33) in stationary liquid-bubble
mixtures was derived by Campbell & Pitcher [4]

$$p_2 / p_1 = (c / a_1)^2 \qquad\qquad (33)$$

Also the relation for pressure wave of finite amplitude by Mori
and Hijikata [11] was given in the same form. Then, Eq. (20)
for the pressure wave derived by a sudden valve closure corresponds to Eq. (33). Then, the experimental values of $p_{ps(ex)}$
and c_{ex} were examined by the correlation of Eq. (34).

$$(\frac{c_{ex} + w_{\ell 1}}{a_{(0)}})^2 = \frac{p_{ps(ex)}}{p_{(0)(ex)}} \qquad\qquad (34)$$

Here, $a_{(0)}$ is the value calculated from Eq. (6), using the
value of $f_{g(o)}$ which is calculated by Eq. (1), and c_{ex} is the
measured value of the propagation velocity of wave front which
is shown in Fig. 14. The correlation is shown in Fig. 13.
The experimental results for Types (1) and (11) agree well with
the correlation but those of low water flow rates for Type (111)
disagree with the correlation. Therefore, the compression
waves of Types (1) and (11) may be considered to be shock waves
or finite amplitude waves, and the compression waves with
slower pressure rise of Type (111) have a little different
characteristics from shock waves.

Propagation Velocities of Pressure Waves

Propagation velocities of sound (infinitesimal-amplitude
pressure wave) [12], [13], [14], finite amplitude pressure wave
[10], and shock wave [4], [5], [8], [9] in two-phase mixture at
rest have been investigated by many researchers. In these experiments for shock waves or pressure waves of finite amplitude
a pressure wave was produced by puncturing a diaphragm between
a high pressure vessel and the test section containing a liquid
-bubble mixture at rest, and the propagation velocity was
measured. On the other hand, in the present study the pressure
wave produced by the sudden valve closure propagates against
the flowing liquid-bubble mixture, and the propagation velocity
c_{ex} on the co-ordinate fixed to the apparatus was measured.
Therefore, the propagation velocity relative to the two-phase
mixture ($c + w_{\ell 1}$) should be used in order to compare the present experimental results with previous investigations de-

scribed   above.

The measured propagation velocities of the first compression
wave front c_{ex} are plotted against the mean void fraction $f_{g(m)}$
in the tube length between $z = 0.02$ and 6.18 m under the initial
condition in Fig. 14.   In the figure, the measured propagation
velocities of the tail of the first compression wave D_{ex}
(velocity of rarefaction wave) are plotted against the mean
void fraction which were calculated from Eq. (22) using the
value of p_d as the value of p_2.   In this figure it is seen that
the propagation velocity of the compression waves c_{ex} is from
about 150 m/s to 50 m/s in the range of void fraction $f_{g(m)}$ =
$0.045 \sim 0.24$ and that of the rarefaction waves, D_{ex}, which
corresponds to the compression wave is from 400 to 150 m/s,
and D_{ex} is about two or three times as large as c_{ex}.   One of
the reasons is that the rarefaction wave propagates in the
mixture at a higher pressure due to compression by the pressure
wave.   It is also seen that the value of c_{ex} increases with the
water flow rate in the figure, then it may be taken to mean
that the water flow rate has direct effects upon the propagation velocity, but actually the water flow rate does not affect the propagation velocity as shown below.   The mean pressure
in the test section under the stationary condition changes with
the water flow rate owing to the pressure loss along the tube
in this experiment, and the higher the water flow rate, the
higher the mean pressure as shown in Fig. 8.   Therefore, the
compression of the experimental results with the theoretical
analysis should be made at a reduced pressure.   Then, the
propagation velocity ($c_{ex} + w_{\ell 1}$) at the pressure p_1 is reduced
to the value at atmospheric pressure p_A.   Rearranging Eq. (18),

$$(c_{ex} + w_{\ell 1}) = \sqrt{\frac{p_A}{f_{g1} (1 - f_{g1})}} \left(\frac{p_{ps}}{p_A} \right) \qquad (35)$$

Then, the reduced velocity is defined as c_{ex}'

$$c_{ex}' = \frac{(c_{ex} + w_{\ell 1})}{\sqrt{p_{ps} / p_A}} = \sqrt{\frac{p_A}{f_{g1} (1 - f_{g1})}} \qquad (36)$$

The experimental results of c_{ex}' are plotted against $f_{g(m)}$ in
Fig. 15.   The experimental results agree well with the theoretical results given by Eq. (36) except in the region of higher void fraction $f_{g(m)} > 0.15$.   Therefore, it was verified that
the water flow rate did not affect the propagation velocity.

The propagation velocity of rarefaction wave D_{ex} is also re-

duced to that at atmospheric pressure, and is also modified by
the sound velocity equation [Eq.(19)].

$$
D_{ex}' = \frac{D_{ex}}{\sqrt{P_d / P_A}} = \sqrt{\frac{P_A}{f_{g_2}(1-f_{g_2})\rho_\ell}} \qquad (37)
$$

Here, it should be noted that the value of the void fraction
f_{g_2} in Eq. (37) is the value at the pressure p_d. The experimental values for D_{ex} are higher than those predicted by Eq.
(37), which is none other than the sound velocity.

CONCLUSIONS

Shock phenomena caused by a sudden valve closure in the bubble
flow region of air-water two phase flow were investigated and
results were summarized as follows.

  1 The profiles of the transient pressure were classified
into three types (1), (11), and (111) according to the slope of
the initial pressure rise and the presence of high-frequency
pressure oscillations at the back side of the compression wave.
The boundaries between Types (1) and (11), (11) and (111) were
approximately expressed by a void fraction of 0.07 and 0.13
respectively.

  2 The values of the potential surge were estimated by Eq.
(27), which was derived using a homogeneous two-phase flow
model.

  3 The propagation velocities of the compression wave front
for the three types were expressed by Eq. (18).

ACKNOWLEDGEMENTS

The authors wish to thank Mr. K. Tamekawa, Mr. T. Yamaguchi and
Mr. H. Muragawa for their assistance in carrying out this experiment.

NOMENCLATURE

$a_{(o)}$	sound velocity in mixture at pressure $p_{(o)}$, m/s
a_1	sound velocity in mixture at pressure p_1 , m/s
a_ℓ	sound velocity in water, m/s
c	propagation velocity of shock wave or moderate and large amplitude compression wave, m/s
D	propagation velocity of rarefaction wave, m/s
D_p	inside diameter of test tube, mm
E	Young's modulus, kgf/mm^2
e	test tube wall thickness, mm
$f_{g(o)}$	void fraction at pressure $p_{(o)}$
$f_{g(m)}$	mean void fraction in tube
f_{gc}	void fraction, see Fig. 9
K_ℓ	bulk modulus of water, kgf/mm^2
M	Mach number
p_A	atmospheric pressure, kgf/cm^2
p_d	pressure at tail of first compression wave, see Fig.4
p_{max}	maximum pressure rise, kgf/cm^2
p_{ps}	value of pressure rise just after sudden valve closure, see Fig. 4
p_{psm}	mean value of pressure rise in first spike, see Fig.4
p_r	pressure in reservoir, kgf/cm^2
w	velocity, m/s
w_{go}	superficial air velocity, m/s
$w_{\ell o}$	superficial water velocity, m/s
X	Lockhart-Martinelli parameter
x	quality
z	distance along axis of test section, see Fig. 1 , m
ρ	density, $kgf \cdot s^2/m^4$
μ	coefficient of viscosity, $kgf \cdot s/m^2$
μ_p	Poisson's ratio
ϕ	dimensionless characteristic parameter, defined in Eq. (25)

Subscripts

ex	experimental
g	gas
ℓ	liquid
th	theoretical
TP	two-phase mixture
1	condition in front of pressure wave
2	condition behind pressure wave

Superscript

	reduced value

REFERENCES

1. Hayashi, T., Murakami, Y. & Mochizuki, H.; Transient behavior of the primary cooling system for quick closure of
   check valves in proto type ATR " Fugen " (Safety Test and
   Analysis), Report of the Committee of Two-phase Flow Dynamics (in Japan) (1977), pp120-123.
2. Streeter, V. L. & Wylie, E. B.; Hydraulic transients,
   McGraw-Hill Book Co. (1967).
3. Padmanabhan, M. & Martin, C. S.; Shock-wave formation in
   flowing bubbly mixtures by steepening of compression waves,
   Int. J. Multiphase Flow, vol.4 (1958), pp81-88.
4. Campbell, I. J. & Pitcher, A. S.; Shock waves in a liquid
   containing gas bubbles, Proc. Roy. Soc., A., vol.243 (1958),
   pp534-545.
5. Van Wijngaarden, L.; Propagation of shock waves in bubble-
   liquid mixtures, Progress in Heat and Mass Transfer, (1972),
   pp637-649.
6. Van Wijngaarden, L.; On the equation of motion for mixtures
   of liquid and gas bubbles, J. Fluid Mech., 33, pt3 (1968),
   pp465-474.
7. Miyazaki, K.; Propagation of pressure waves in gas-liquid
   two phase system, Doctorial Dissertation, Osaka Univ.,
   (1973).
8. Noordzij, L. & Van Wijngaarden, L.; Relaxation effects,
   caused by relative motion, on shock waves in gas-bubble/
   liquid mixtures, J. Fluid Mech., vol.66, part1 (1974), pp
   115-143.
9. Kuznetsov, V. V. & Nakoryanov, V. E.; Propagation of purtur-
   bations in a gas-liquid mixtures, J. Fluid Mech., vol.85,
   part 1 (1978), pp85-96.
10. Hijikata, K., Mori, Y. & Nagasaki, T.; Behaviors of bubbles
    in two-phase shock wave, Conf. JSME, No.780-16 (1978),pp163
    -170.
11. Akagawa, K. et al.; Studies on shock phenomena in two-phase
    flow (3rd Report), will be presented JSME Conf.
12. Henry, R. E. & Grolmes, M. A.; Propagation velocity of
    pressure waves in gas-liquid mixtures, Cocurrent Gas-Liquid
    Flow, (1968), pp1-18.
13. Semenov, N. I. & Kosterin, S. I.; Results of studying the
    speed of sound in moving gas-liquid systems, Teploenergetika,
    11-6 (1964), pp46-51.
14. Crespo, A.; Sound and shock waves in liquids containing
    bubbles, The Physics of Fluids, vol.12, No.11 (1969), pp2274
    -2282.

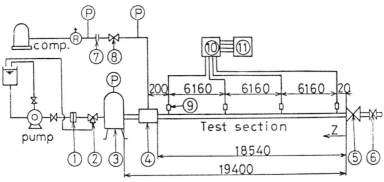

1 orifice
2 three-ways solenoid valve
3 reservoir
4 air-water mixing section
5 quick-acting valve
6 pressure control valve

7 critical nozzle
8 solenoid valve
9 piezoelectric pressure
   transducer
10 D.C. amplifier
11 recorder

Fig. 1   Experimental apparatus.

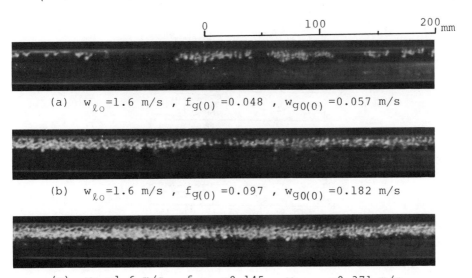

(a) $w_{\ell o}$=1.6 m/s , $f_{g(0)}$ =0.048 , $w_{g0(0)}$ =0.057 m/s

(b) $w_{\ell o}$=1.6 m/s , $f_{g(0)}$ =0.097 , $w_{g0(0)}$ =0.182 m/s

(c) $w_{\ell o}$=1.6 m/s , $f_{g(0)}$ =0.145 , $w_{g0(0)}$ =0.371 m/s

Fig. 2   Photographs of bubble flow.

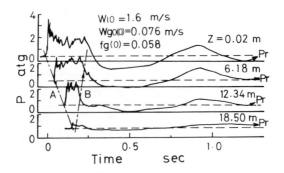

Fig. 3   Profile of the transient
pressure at four locations.

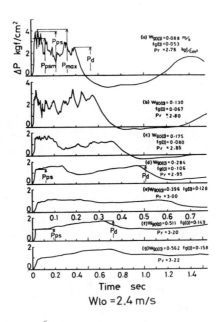

Fig. 4   Effect of the air flow
rate or the void fraction on the
profile of the transient pressure.

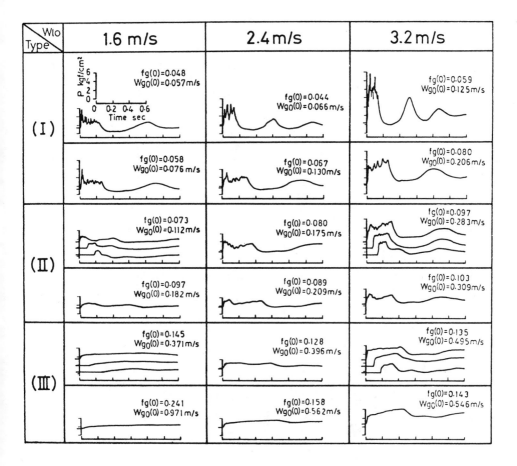

Fig. 5   Classification of the profiles of the transient
pressure.

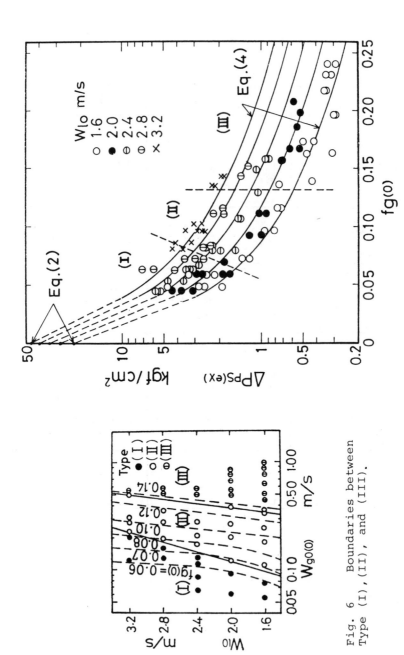

Fig. 7 The measured values of the potential surge and an empirical equation (4).

Fig. 6 Boundaries between Type (I), (II), and (III).

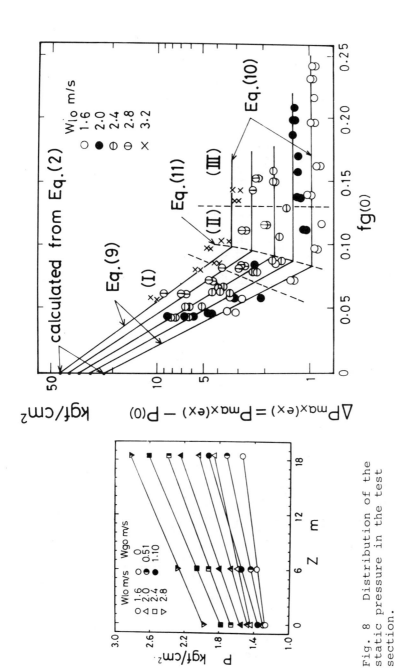

Fig. 8   Distribution of the static pressure in the test section.

Fig. 9   Measured values of the maximum pressure rise and the empirical equations.

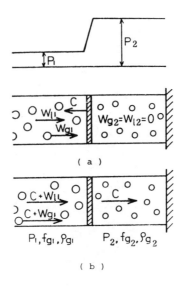

(a)

(b)

P_1, f_{g1}, ρ_{g1} P_2, f_{g2}, ρ_{g2}

Fig. 10   A model of
pressure wave.

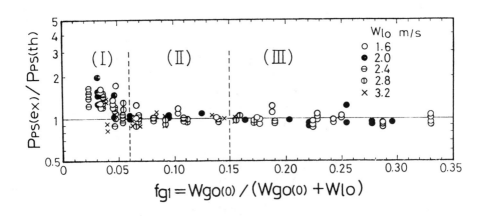

Fig. 11   Comparison of the experimental results with
calculated results for the potential surge.

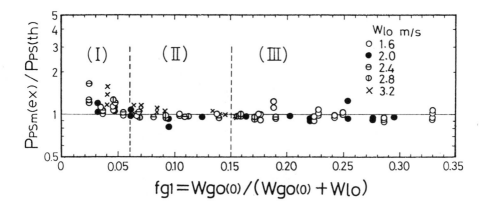

Fig. 12   Comparison of the experimental results with calculated results for the potential surge.

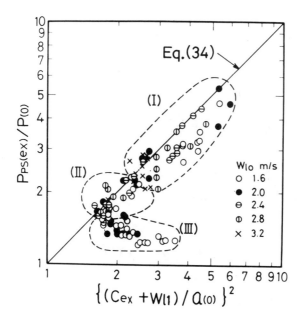

Fig. 13   Verification of the experimental results by equation (34).

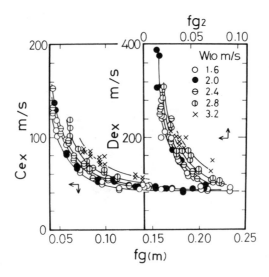

Fig. 14　Experimental results of velocities of compression wave and rarefaction wave.

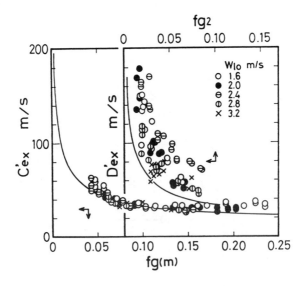

Fig. 15　Velocities of compression wave and rarefaction wave.

Heat Removal by Top Spray Emergency Core Cooling

M. NAITOH
Energy Research Laboratory
Hitachi Ltd.
316 Ibaraki, Japan

ABSTRACT

Water spraying experiments were conducted to find out a flow rate of falling water against ascending steam and a heat transfer coefficient during top spray emergency cooling with an 8 x 8 type simulated fuel rod bundle of real size. The bundle consisted of 62 heater rods and 2 water rods. The heater rods had an axially cosine-formed power distribution with a peaking factor of 1.4. As the results, (1) the experimental flow rate of falling water overcoming ascending steam could be well expressed by the analytical model based on the pressure balance of the fluids at the part of the upper tie plate and (2) the convective heat transfer coefficient was almost independent of the pressure within the range below 4.5 kg/cm^{2}a and slightly increased with a spray flow rate within the range from 66 to 400 cm^3/s.

INTRODUCTION

A core spray system is one of the emergency core cooling systems of a boiling water reactor, which functions to sprinkle water over a core to remove decay heat under the loss of coolant condition. The water partly evaporates in fuel bundles by taking heat away from superheated surfaces and the rest falls down to a lower plenum vessel, forming counter-current flow against the generated steam. At this stage, the flow rate of falling water may be reduced by restrictive force from ascending steam. This phenomenon is termed counter-current flow limiting (CCFL).

The problem is a heat removal rate from superheated rods, when water which can enter fuel bundles is reduced by CCFL. The heat is removed from the rods by radiation among gray surfaces and by other contributions. The latter is generically defined as convective heat transfer. However the radiant heat transfer has no direct relation with falling water, the convective heat transfer may depend on it. A convective heat transfer coefficient was calculated from BWR-FLECHT experiment where a full scale mockup of a fuel bundle was used, but effect of a flow rate on a coefficient was not mentioned, and moreover CCFL was

1695

not described[1]. We had performed CCFL experiments with an unheated bundle of real size and developed a CCFL correlation, but at this time heat transfer characteristics had not been investigated[2].

Thus a flow rate of falling water overcoming ascending steam was quantified, and effects of a flow rate and pressure on a convective heat transfer coefficient were clarified from water spraying experiments with an 8 x 8 type simulated fuel rod bundle of real size. This report sets forth this experimental study.

EXPERIMENTS

Figure 1 shows the schematic diagram of the experimental apparatus. The test bundle was a full scale mockup of a BWR fuel bundle of the 8 x 8 type. The bundle in the channel box was incased in the square shroud with upper and lower plenums. The gap between the channel box and the shroud was closed at the upper part thereby keeping out an inflow of spray. The upper plenum vessel was a square type with a side of 150 mm. The system pressure was adjusted by regulating the valve connected to the upper plenum vessel. The test section was covered with a heavy thermal insulation.

The bundle consisted of 62 heater rods with 12.3 mm diameter and 2 water rods with 15 mm diameter. These rods were arranged in the form of a square lattice with a pitch of 16.2 mm. Each rod was fixed in its place by a flange at its lower end, the seven spacers, and the upper tie plate. The spacers and the tie plate were the same as the real ones. The spacers were distributed at an interval of 496 mm to fix the arrangement of the rods. The tie plate also functioned as an electrode for heater rods, the tips of the rods being welded to it. The heater rods had the 3,759 mm heating length and the pseudo cosine power distribution with the peaking factor of 1.4, as shown in Fig. 2. Thermocouples were buried in sheaths of heater rods and in the channel box in order to measure surface temperatures. The axial locations of thermocouples are also shown in Fig. 2. Figure 3 shows the arrangement of the rods, power ratio among the rods, and the thermocouple locations. The water rods were arranged on the diagonal in the central region. The following two series of experiments were performed - (a) adiabatic CCFL experiment and (b) transient heat transfer experiment.

Adiabatic CCFL Experiment

In this experiment, the bundle was not electrically heated,

but steam was supplied to the lower plenum from an outside boiler simulating bundle-generated steam. The falling water in the bundle overcoming ascending steam was gathered in the measuring tank and its flow rate was calculated from a change of the water level. The scope of this experiment was as follows :

Flow rate of ascending steam	: 142 ~ 295 kg/h
Flow rate of spray water	: 45 ~ 1233 cm³/s
Temperature of spray water	: 92 ~ 98°C
Pressure in the upper plenum	: 1.03 ~ 1.73 kg/cm²a

Transient Heat Transfer Experiment

In this experiment, outside steam was not supplied. The experimental procedure was as follows:
(1) Air in the test section was displaced by steam which was generated by spraying in the heated bundle.
(2) The bundle was maintained at constant temperature - about 500°C, for 30 minutes.
(3) Then a bundle power was raised to a desired initial level.
(4) When the peak temperature of the rod surfaces reached to a desired initial level, spray was initiated at a desired flow rate and the power was then decreased on a time program. The power and surface temperatures were recored every 10 seconds by an online computer system. The scope of this experiment was as follows :

Initial bundle power	: 120 ~ 280 kW
Initial surface temperature	: 700 ~ 850°C
Pressure in the upper plenum	: 1.05 ~ 4.5 kg/cm²a
Flow rate of spray water	: 66 ~ 400 cm³/s
Temperature of spray water	: 88 ~ 97°C

RESULTS AND DISCUSSION

CCFL Characteristics

Figure 4 shows a relationship between a flow rate of injected spray water and a flow rate of falling water overcoming ascending steam. There appeared a region where a flow rate of falling water was almost the constant even when a flow rate of injected spray water was changed, because of constant restrictive force from the ascending steam. In this CCFL region, a flow rate of falling water depended on a height of a spray nozzle from the tie plate, as shown in Fig. 4. This dependence is thought to be caused by the following phenomenon.

CCFL would appear at the part of the upper tie plate, since its flow area was the smallest in the bundle. In general, the tie plate has a lot of flow passage holes, all of which do not

have the same shape, and furthermore velocity distribution of
ascending steam in the bundle is not uniform. Consequently,
it should be reasonable to consider that steam ascends through
some of the holes while water falls down through other holes,
rather than to consider that the flow pattern appearing in a
single hole would appear in every hole. The flow pattern at
the plate can, therefore, be modelled as follows : flow
passage holes of steam and water are entirely separated from
each other, and water near the plate is removed to a peripheral region from a central region where only the ascending
steam occupies. In this flow pattern, when the height of the
spray nozzle is low, dynamic pressure of spray water extends
more to the peripheral accumulated water than to the central
region, as shown in Fig. 5(a), resulting in increase of a flow
rate of falling water. On the contrary, when the height of
the spray nozzle is high, pressure on the tie plate becomes
uniform, as shown in Fig. 5(b). Usually the phenomenon shown
in Fig. 5(b) will appear in a real reactor pressure vessel,
since the distance between a spray nozzle and a channel is
long.

Thus, the effect of a flow rate of ascending steam on falling
water was investigated with the spray nozzle which height was
230 mm. This result is shown in Fig. 6. A flow rate of
falling water decreased with increasing pressure because of
increasing density of ascending steam under the condition of
the constant volumetric flow rate.

In conformity with above model of the flow pattern, the pressure difference between the two sides of the tie plate is
considered to be equal to the difference between the water
head and the pressure loss of water at the tie plate, and at
the same time, it is considered to be equal to the pressure
loss of steam at the tie plate, too. From this pressure
balance, a flow rate of falling water can be expressed by the
following equation, neglecting the frictional pressure loss[2].

$$Q_\ell = \sqrt{2gL - Q_g^2 \frac{Rf_1\{A_b-(1-\alpha)A_t\}^2-R\alpha^2}{\alpha^2\{A_b-(1-\alpha)A_t\}^2} \cdot \frac{(1-\alpha)(A_u-\frac{A_t}{A_c}\alpha P^2)}{\sqrt{f_2(A_u-\frac{A_t}{A_c}\alpha P^2)^2-(1-\alpha)^2}}} \quad , \qquad (1)$$

where

$$f_1 = (\frac{A_c}{A_tP^2})^2 + (\frac{1}{A_t})^2\{(\lambda c)_g + (\lambda e)_g\} \, ,$$

$$f_2 = (\frac{1}{A_t})^2\{1 + (\lambda c)_\ell\} \, ,$$

$$R = \rho_g^*/\rho_\ell \, .$$

Water entrainment in ascending steam, which is defined by the following equation, is taken into consideration to calculate the density - ρ_g^x.

$$E = a \, Q_\ell \, \frac{\rho_g}{z_g} \left(\frac{Q_g}{A_b} \right)^Z . \tag{2}$$

Thus, to solve the Eq.(1) the following values must be given - pressure loss coefficients, λ_c and λ_e, and ratio of flow area of steam to total, α.

The pressure loss coefficients were calculated based on the measured value of the pressure drop when steam alone flowed through the tie plate. For the ratio(α), it is calculated by the following equation, which expresses the most stable condition - where a flow rate of falling water is maximum[2].

$$\frac{dQ_\ell}{d\alpha} = 0 . \tag{3}$$

The coefficient a was calculated to be $a = 100$ by the least squares method for 7 x 7 and original 8 x 8 bundles.

The calculation with $a = 100$ was compared with the present results as shown in Fig. 6. The calculation agrees well with the experimental results, and the pressure effect on a flow rate of falling water can be well explained by the above correlation.

Heat Transfer Characteristics

Figure 7 shows an example of the changes of power and surface temperature at the midplane after spray initiation. However the corner rod had the power peak of 1.13, its temperature was lower than the other rods because of good heat transfer.

In the increasing period of surface temperature, a part of generated heat in a rod is generally accumulated in the rod and the rest is removed from the surface. This heat removal is due to radiant heat transfer among gray surfaces, and others. Since main contribution to the latter is convective heat transfer of generated steam with water droplets, it is generically defined as convective heat transfer, here. Then a convective heat transfer coefficient can be calculated by [3]

$$h^i = \frac{q_{conv}^i}{2 \pi \, r_z \, (T_c^i - T_w^i)} . \tag{4}$$

Considering accumulated heat and radiation, convective heat flux is written by

$$q_{conv}^{i} = \frac{k}{\Delta x}(T_m^i - T_c^i)2\pi r_i - \frac{T_c^{i-1} - T_c^i}{\Delta t}\rho_c C_c \pi (r_2^2 - r_1^2) - q_{rad}^{i} , \quad (5)$$

Average temperature of an insulator in a heater rod (T_m) is calculated by

$$T_m^{i} = T_m^{i-1} - \frac{q_0^{i} - (q_{conv}^{i} + q_{rad}^{i})}{\rho_m \rho_m C_m \pi r_i^2}\Delta t . \quad (6)$$

Radiant heat flux (q_{rad}) can be calculated with a computer code 'CIDER' where the following assumptions are involved [4].
(1)   Axial heat conduction in a rod is neglected. Consequently, all calculations become two-dimensional problems.
(2)   Radiant emissions and reflections are isotropic, and Lambert's cosine law is applicable.
(3)   A cylindrical rod surface is divided into narrow, equal, flat, lengthwise strips. Geometrical view factors within a plane perpendicular to the rod axes are determined between these strips. The channel box is also divided into strips.
(4)   A curved 'surface' consists of several strips. Temperature is assumed uniform over each curved 'surface'.

An emissivity of the rods and the channel box must be given in order to calculate radiant heat flux. Non-spray-experiments were, therefore, performed every 5 runs of water-spraying-experiments. In the experiments, the bundle was heated without spray and a steady state was maintained with electrical power input balancing heat loss. A measured distribution of surface temperature at this stage was compared with the calculation which was made with an estimate of the emissivity. Then the calculation was iterated until the difference of temperature distributions becomes smaller than a permitted limit in order to get the emissivity. The emissivity increased with progress of water spraying experiments - from 0.32 to 0.64 - so that an average emissivity for 5 runs of the water spraying experiments was used for the calculation of radiant heat flux. After the wetting front passed on the surface, the emissivity of 0.96 was used [5].

Thus the coefficient can be calculated if the initial values of q_{conv} and T_m are known ; They are given by the convergence calculation. Typical values of the calculated heat transfer coefficients are shown in Fig. 8 as a function of time. The coefficients along the diagonal shown in Fig. 8 had symmetry with respect to the other diagonal, and they were larger on outer rods near the channel box than on central rods. This trend of distribution of the coefficients would be caused by the flow pattern where water would fall down in the peripheral region and generated steam would ascend in the central region. The coefficient increased suddenly after the wetting front

passed the midpoint of the rod. On the contrary, however the
radiant heat flux to the channel wall increased after the
channel wetting front passed the midplane, the coefficient
did not notably change as shown in Fig. 8. The fluctuation of
the coefficients with time shown if Fig. 8 would be caused by
an error of the calculation of accumulated heat - the error of
temperature change at the time interval would become large
even if the error of the measured value of temperature for
each time was small. A time-smoothed coefficient is, however,
considered to be constant except the first increasing period,
as is evident from Fig. 8, so that this coefficient is used in
the following discussions.

The heater rods were divided into 4 groups as shown in Fig. 9
(6) and an averaged time-smoothed coefficient was calculated
for each group. Figure 10 shows the effect of a spray flow
rate on this average coefficient. This effect would be closely related to a steam generation rate and CCFL characteristics.

A steam generation rate was calculated by adding a condensing
rate by subcooling of spray water to a measured flow rate of
steam from the upper plenum after the separation of water
entrainment. The calculated steam generation rate changed
with time as shown in Fig. 11. However the power was maintained at the constant in the case shown in Fig. 11, the calculated steam generation rate reached the maximum after spray
initiation, then decreased and settled down at the constant.
When the bundle power decreased on the time program, the ratio
of the peak value to the constant value was large, but there
still appeared the constant region after reaching the maximum.
The calculated steam generation rate in the constant region
is shown in Fig. 12 as a function of a spray flow rate. CCFL
did not occur within the spray flow rate under 300 cm^3/s, but
the steam generation rate increased at the spray flow rate of
400 cm^3/s and CCFL occured. Since generated steam would
ascend in the central region of the bundle as was stated
previously, the effect of a spray flow rate on the average
coefficient of the group 4 was very similar to that on a steam
generation rate. On the contrary, the average coefficients
of the other groups did not increase when a spray flow rate
increased to 400 cm^3/s, since a flow rate of falling water did
not increase because of CCFL. From Fig. 10, even when the
spray flow rate was very small - 67 cm^3/s - the convective
heat transfer coefficient was larger than 11.6 W/m$^{2.}$℃ and effective cooling of the bundle should be maintained.

Figure 13 shows a pressure effect on an average coefficient.
The coefficient gradually increased with the pressure above
2 kg/cm^{2}a and the pressure effect was small within the experimental pressure range.

CONCLUSIONS

Two series of water spraying experiments were carried out with the 8 x 8 type simulated fuel rod bundle of real size - (a) adiabatic CCFL experiment and (b) transient heat transfer experiment. The main conclusions derived from these experiments are as follows:

(1) A measured flow rate of falling water overcoming ascending steam was well expressed by the CCFL correlation which was based on the pressure balance of the fluids at the part of the tie plate under the assumption that the flow passage holes of two fluids were entirely separated to each other.

(2) A convective heat transfer coefficient was calculated from the result of the transient heat transfer experiment. The average coefficient was larger than 11.6 $W/m^2.°C$ within the range of a spray flow rate over 67 cm^3/s. The average coefficient in the central region, especially in the group 4, increased with a spray flow rate, or with a steam generation rate, as contrasted with in the peripheral region. The pressure effect on the average coefficient was small within the experimental pressure range.

NOMENCLATURE

a : Proportional coefficient in Eq.(2) (1/m)
A_b : Flow area in bundle (m^2)
A_c : Cross-sectional area of flow passage hole (m^2)
A_t : Total cross-sectional area of flow passage holes (m^2)
A_u : Flow area in upper plenum vessel (m^2)
C : Specific heat ($W/kg·°C$)
E : Entrainment (kg/s)
g : Gravitational acceleration (m/s^2)
h : Heat transfer coefficient ($W/m^2·°C$)
k : Thermal conductivity of insulator ($W/m·°C$)
L : Thickness of tie plate (m)
P : Arrangement pitch of flow passage holes (m)
q_{conv} : Convective heat flux per unit length ($W/m·h$)
q_c : Heat flux transfered to insulator per unit length ($W/m·h$)
q_{rad} : Radiant heat flux per unit length ($W/m·h$)
Q : Volumetric flow rate (m^3/s)
r_1 : Radius of insulator (m)
r_2 : Radius of heater rod (m)
T_c : Rod surface temperature (°C)
T_m : Average temperature of insulator (°C)

T_w : Coolant temperature, assumed to be saturation temperature (°C)

α : Ratio of flow area of ascending steam to total at tie plate (-)

β : Packing density of insulator (-)

Δt : Time interval between time $i-1$ and i (s)

$\Delta \chi$: Equivalent thickness, $\Delta\chi = \tilde{h}/3$ (m)

λ_c: Pressure loss coefficient by contraction (-)

λ_e: Pressure loss coefficient by expansion (-)

γ : Density (kg/m³)

γ^*: Density with water entrainment (kg/m³)

Subscript

c : Cladding, or sheath
g : Steam
l : Falling water
m : Insulator

Superscript

i : Time

REFERENCES

1   J.D.Duncan and J.E.Leonard: GEAP-13197 (1971)
2   M.Naitoh, et al.: J. Nucl. Sci. Technol., 15[11], 806 (1978)
3   M.Naitoh, et al.: Nucl. Eng. Des., 44[2], 193 (1977)
4   M.Naitoh, et al.: Nucl. Eng. Des., 44[3], 315 (1977)
5   J.D.Duncan and J.E.Leonard: GEAP-13190 (1971)
6   B.C.Slifer and A.E.Rogers: NEDO-10329 (1971)

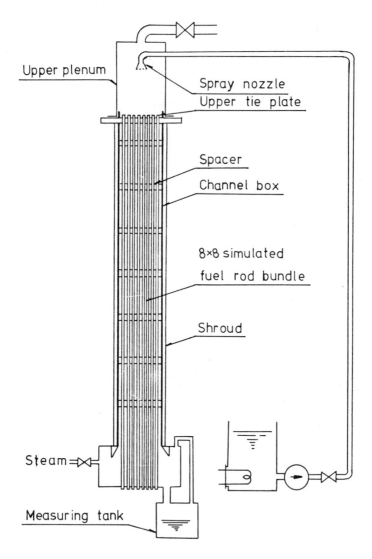

Fig. 1　Schematic diagram of experimental apparatus

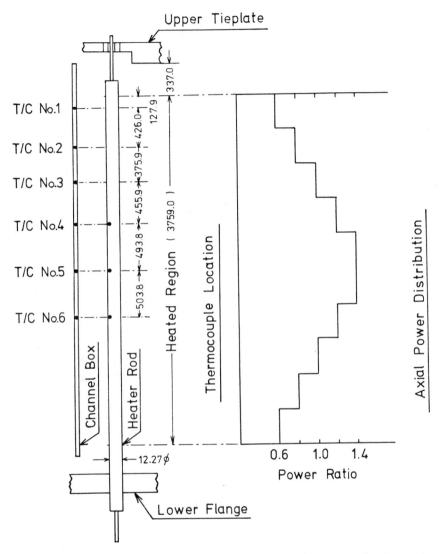

Fig. 2 - Axial Power Distribution & Therocouple Location

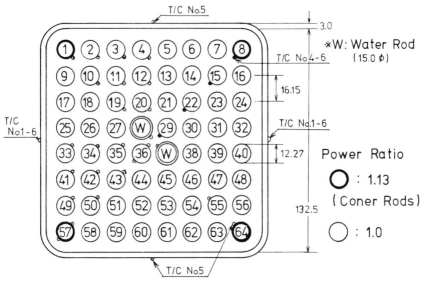

Fig. 3   Arrangement of rods

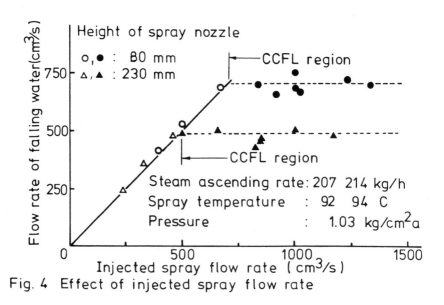

Fig. 4 Effect of injected spray flow rate

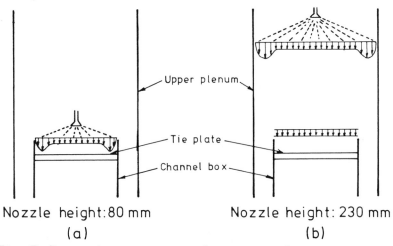

Nozzle height: 80 mm
(a)

Nozzle height: 230 mm
(b)

Fig. 5 Dynamic pressure of spray water

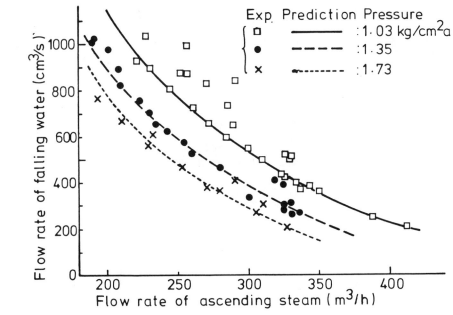

Fig. 6 CCFL characteristics

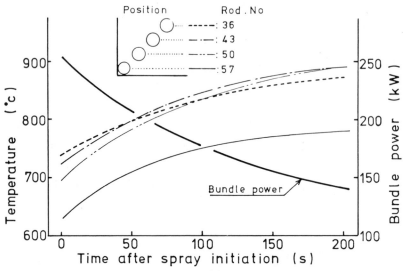

Fig. 7 Changes of power and surface
temperature at midplane

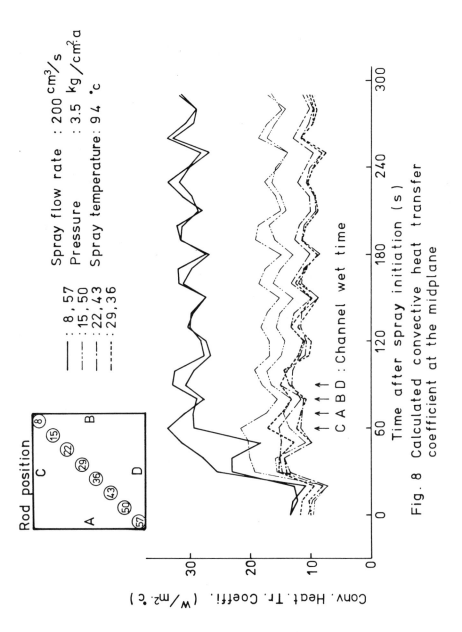

Fig. 8 Calculated convective heat transfer coefficient at the midplane

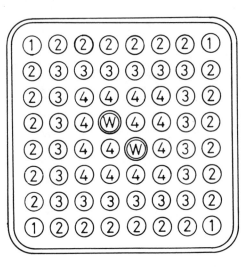

Fig. 9   Grouping of heater rods

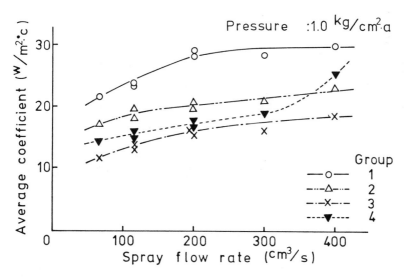

Fig.10 Effect of spray flow rate on average coefficient

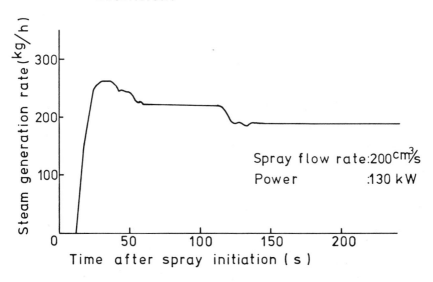

Fig.11 Time-transient of steam generation rate

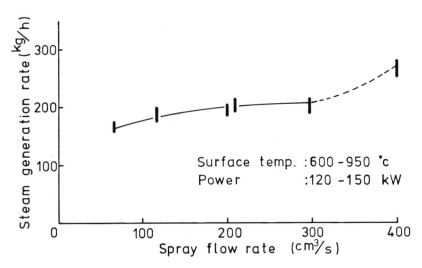

Fig. 12   Effect of spray flow rate on steam generation rate

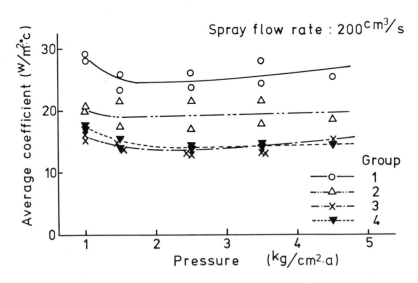

Fig. 13   Effect of pressure on average coefficient

Experimental Subchannel Investigation in a 16-Rod Test Section by Means of the Isokinetic Sampling Technique

H. HERKENRATH and W. HUFSCHMIDT
Commission of the European Communities
JRC, Ispra, Italy

F. LUCCHINI
Consorzio Nuclital
Genoa, Italy

ABSTRACT

Experiments based on the subchannel isokinetic technique have been carried out at the JRC of the European Community at Ispra, using a purposely designed 16-rod test section, simulating in a rather accurate way a typical BWR geometry. The adopted system allows the simultaneous determination of mass flow and enthalpy, at the end of the bundle active length, in four characteristic subchannels of the 16-rod lattice.

The results show some pronounced flow and enthalpy variations within the bundle, not accurately taken into account by current subchannel codes, such as COBRA-3C. In particular, low values both in mass flow and enthalpy have been found in corner subchannel, in disagreement with code predictions, but confirming previous General Electric experiments carried out in a 9-rod test section.

INTRODUCTION

In the Joint Research Center of the European Community at Ispra, Italy, a thermo-hydraulic experimental program is under way concerning flow and enthalpy interchange processes within boiling and pressurized water reactor fuel elements, both in steady-state and transient conditions. For this purpose two particular 16-rod test sections, simulating in a rather accurate way typical BWR and PWR geometries, have been designed and constructed by CISE of Milan, Italy. They are equipped with an "isokinetic probe" at the heated length top end, for the simultaneous sampling of up to five characteristic subchannels. Moreover, the high pressure water loop, BOWAL, of the JRC-Ispra has been appropriately modified, mainly by installing five condensors for calorimetric measurements.

Experiments with the BWR test section in steady-state conditions have been already performed and are presented and discussed in this paper. The analysis performed by Nuclital, Genoa, Italy, which contributes in the analytical part of the work, has

1713

evidenced some interesting features of this first series of
data, with particular reference to the prediction capability,
or incapability of classical subchannel codes, as COBRA-3C.

TEST SECTION

For this subchannel investigation in BWR conditions a particular
test section (named PELCO-S, Fig. 1) has been designed and constructed by CISE [1]. It consists of a square lattice 16-rod
bundle having an active length of 3.66m (12 feet), equal or
very close to length of the most recent BWR fuel elements.

The nominal geometry of the cross-section is defined by the
following parameters:

rod diameter	15	mm
rod pitch	19.5	mm
rod-to-wall gap	3.37	mm
corner radius (secant)	52.1	mm

Seven grid spacers are 500mm spaced along the heated length.
The upper spacer is located 360mm upstream of the heated length
end. The power distribution is uniform both axially and radially.

From the geometrical viewpoint the test section is thoroughly
similar to other test sections previously used for dryout experiments in the frame of Italian BWR programs [2,3]. It differs
from them only downstream of the heated portion, where the subchannel fluid extraction eqiupment (isokinetic probe) is installed.

Immediately downstream of the heated length (10mm) all the subchannels are split with very thin sheets (0.2mm). The flows of
five so separated subchannels (dark subchannels in Fig. 2) are
sampled by small removable pipes coming out from the test section top header. A similar but not sampled subchannel corresponds to each sampled subchannel, and in both, the static pressure is measured at the exact beginning of splitters by means
of small borings (Fig. 2). These ten pressure taps represent
the essential instrumentation for the isokinetic condition
achievement (see following sections). For constructive reasons
among the six different subchannel types present in the 16-rod
lattice (Fig. 3) only five subchannels were arranged for the
sampling. So the mass and energy balances on the overall flow
area cannot be strictly performed. However, flow and enthalpy
in the unsampled subchannel type 6 are not expected to be sensibly different from the values in subchannels 4 and/or 5 (Fig.
3). Therefore, indicative balances can be performed using these
values. (See on this subject the section devoted to the experimental procedure).

The grid spacer subchannel loss coefficients are very important
inputs for the code utilization, but unfortunately they are not
directly measurable. They were estimated with a "projected
area" method which gave (in terms of velocity head in the free
flow area) the following values:

subchannel 1	0.82
subchannel 2	1.70
subchannel 3 (not sampled)	0.86
subchannel 4	0.61
subchannel 5	0.62
subchannel 6 (not sampled)	0.62

BOWAL LOOP

In Fig. 4, the flow scheme of the modified BOiling WAter Loop
(BOWAL) is shown. The design data are listed in TABLE I.

From the vertical glandless circulation pump the water is sent
to the test section through measure orifices and two parallel
electrical preheaters (180 kw each) to vary the inlet conditions. At the test section outlet the five sampling pipes and
the main flow line are led to six X-ray voidmeters (at present
not yet in operation; they will have an important role in the
transient experiments planned in the near future). Then, the
sampled two-phase mixtures are led to five measure groups, each
mainly constituted by a condensor, a diaphragm for flow measurement in single-phase conditions, and a very sensitive regulation
valve. By means of heat balances at the condensors the outlet
enthalpy of the sampled subchannels can be determined.

In order to avoid possible instabilities due to evaporation effects in the cooling tubes, the condensors are cooled on the
secondary sides by water at high pressure, supplied by the
loop pump itself and brought to the desired low temperature
value by means of an auxiliary heat exchanger inserted in the
loop. The condensors are of the U-tube heat exchanger type,
and the co-current solution has been chosen for stability
reasons. The secondary water flows through ten parallel tubes,
and in the shell the steam-water mixture is condensed and subcooled. In order to accurately measure the mean inlet/outlet
temperatures, in each of the four connection nozzles of the
condensors silver crosses with embedded themocouples are mounted.
In the two outlet nozzles the crosses are preceded by small mixing chambers (Fig. 5). The flow regulation for the isokinetic
condition achievement is done by long-stroke calibrated valves.

The maximum cooling power of the five condensors is 200 kW each.
One MW is the cooling power of the auxiliary exchanger. Downstream of the condensors and regulation valves the sampled
flows are mixed with the main flow. The cycle is closed through

a separator, a condensor and a subcooler. A pressurizer is also
inserted in order to stabilize the operating pressure independently of the heat input to the test section. The rectifier
plant is able to supply the test section with 3.6 MW, with continuous regulation from 0 to 100% by regulating transformers.

For other details concerning BOWAL, see Refs. [4 and 5].

EXPERIMENTAL PROCEDURE

The method used for these experiments is the well known "isokinetic sampling technique", already adopted by many authors
in subchannel investigations, Refs. [6,7,8 and 9]. The pressure taps in the pairs of corresponding (sampled and reference)
subchannels are connected to five differential pressure transducers of the Barton-cell type, which have been calibrated and
brought to a sensitivity and reproducibility of about 1 mm water
column. The isokinetic regulation is based on the signals of
these transducers. It consists in setting to zero the differences in static pressure over the cross-section by means
of the sensitive regulation valves in the piping carrying the
single-phase flow beyond the condensors (a regulation valve is
also installed on the main flow line with the same purpose).
This procedure is necessary to compensate the influence of flow
splitting and to ensure the real free outlet conditions as in
the reactor channel "clean" geometry. More precisely, the pressure differences must be set to values close to but not necessarily equal to zero. In fact, before starting the experiments,
calibration tests were made without sampling pipes, in order to
establish the reference differences in static pressure in un-
disturbed conditions. They usually resulted slightly different
from zero (some millimeters of water column), probably owing to
small subchannel and pressure tap differences due to constructive tolerances.

For center subchannel 4, a side located pressure tap (4r) was
initially used as a reference measurement point, owing to the
absence of a strictly symmetrical subchannel, rather high
pressure differences were seen. The utilization of reference
pressure tap, 5r, located in a subchannel of equal cross-section,
was then preferred.

During the calibration tests without sampling pipes high differences in static pressure were also observed for subchannel
3 (pressure taps 3s and 3r) in spite of symmetry and cross-
section equality between sampled and reference subchannels.
Moreover, anomalous low values in the relevant sampled flow
were seen. After several proofs, changing also the reference
pressure tap, such differences could not be diminished. We
decided to eliminate the sampling of subchannel 3.

In conclusion, four subchannels have been tested among the six different types present in the bundle. Therefore, the data validity from the point of view of mass and energy conservation cannot be strictly checked by means of flow and heat balances. Indicative checks have been performed assuming conditions in subchannels 1 and 5. The comparisons with the overall inlet flow rates & electrical power input have shown a maximum deviation of ±8%. We consider this agreement rather acceptable taking into account the balance approximation, the measure and regulation complexity and the constructive tolerances, which can produce small differences in nominally equal subchannels.

Some non-isokinetic flow measurements have been also performed, in single-phase conditions and without power to the test section, in order to check the regulation sensitivity and to obtain data on the error related to a possible not exact achievement of isokinetic conditions. In Fig. 6, the sampled mass fluxes for two different flow rates are plotted vs the pressure difference between sampled and reference subchannels.

All measuring informations were sent, besides to the control panel where also the regulation device is installed, to a data acquisition system based on a 32K storage capacity mini-computer.

The measurements were performed after some hours of loop operation in the desired steady-state boundary conditions (flow rate, power, inlet quality, pressure) in order to avoid any possibility of errors in the calorimetric measurements due to a defective achievement of the regime conditions. As for measurement errors, a detailed analysis is reported in Ref. [5], where a maximum error of about ±3% has been estimated both for subchannel flow and enthalpy.

PRESENTATION OF RESULTS

The subchannel measurements have been carried out in the following range:

pressure	70 bar
mass flux	1000, 1500, 2000 kg/m^{2}s
inlet quality	-0.04
bundle power	320-2100 kW
average outlet quality	0.02-0.31

In this range about 200 experimental points [18] were carried out each characterized by simultaneous flow and enthalpy measurements in four monitored subchannels.

Mass Flow Distribution

In Figs. 7, 8 and 9, the ranges covered by the experimental results are plotted in terms of subchannel mass flux (normalized
with respect to the bundle average value) vs average outlet
quality. The normalization has been performed in order to make
easier the comparisons at different flow rates. The mass flux
average value has been derived from the flow balance performed
as described in the previous section.

The data appear rather scattered, as usual in this particular
kind of experiments, but the main experimental trends can be
clearly identified.

At all flow rates the corner subchannel (type 2 in Figs. 2-3)
is characterized by a mass flux much lower than the average value
$(G_i/G_{av} \simeq 0.6 - 0.75)$. This is qualitatively reasonable taking
into account the low equivalent diameter value and the high estimated spacer loss coefficient (1.7). The mass flux tends to
decrease increasing flow rate and outlet quality.

Also, for inner subchannel 5 the normalized mass flux is close
to one, with a slight tendency to increase with flow rate and
outlet quality.

As for central subchannel 4, the mass flux tendency to increase
with outlet quality is clearly more pronounced, and also dif-
ferneces of 20% are achieved with respect to the average value.

Quality Distribution

In Figs. 10, 11, 12 and 13, the ranges covered by the experimental results are plotted in terms of subchannel quality vs
outlet average quality.

The corner subchannel shows the most interesting results. In
fact, subchannel quality turns out to be lower than the average
value (especially at 1000 kg/m^2s), in spite of the low mass
flux found in this subchannel. On this point, in our opinion
the most interesting standing out from the experimental program, we shall return in the following sections.

As for the other channels, quality is in general rather close
to the average value. Some differences are present, as for
instance, at 1000 kg/m^2s for the side subchannel, but the only
difference truly noticeable appears to be that related to the
corner subchannel.

DISCUSSION OF RESULTS

Comparisons with Previous Data

A comparison of present data with other similar data available
in the open literature is not very easy, because several differences usually exist in test section geometry, spacer type
and position, heat flux distribution, tested subchannels. Attention has been paid to experiments reported in Refs. [6,7 and
8], but not sufficient points in common have been found with
present experiments. To our knowledge the only published data
obtained in realistic BWR conditions and geometry, and including
the sampling of the corner subchannel (characterized by the
above described peculiar behavior), are those performed at General Electric by Lahey et al. in a 9-rod bundle, [9]. These
experimentas are well known, because they clearly called in
question the capability of classical subchannel codes (as COBRA)
to predict in an adequate way subchannel flow and quality,
especially in multi-rod bundles. In fact in General Electric
experiments the corner subchannel was found to have not only
the lowest flow rate (this is reasonable owing to the high
loss coefficient), but also the lowest quality, in spite of
the high power/flow ratio. From a qualitative standpoint the
same behavior has been found in present experiments. A quantitative comparison is more difficult, owing to some differences
in experimental conditions, and taking into account some sensible
differences in test section geometry and spacer type ("pin"
spacers in General Electric's 9-rod bundle, "grid" spacers in
present 16-rod budnel). However, in Fig. 10 some General
Electric experimental points (selected with inlet conditions
rather close to the present ones) are plotted together with
present corner subchannel data. The comparison shows that in
present experiments corner subchannel quality has been found
similar or even lower than quality in General Electric experiments.

With reference to other subchannels, a qualitative comparison
showed a fairly good consistency between the two data sets.

Comparison with COBRA-3C Predictions

There are several subchannel codes available in the literature,
e.g. COBRA [10, 11], HAMBO [12], SASS [13], MATTEO [14], which
predict enthalpy and flow distributions in multi-rod bundles.
Other important subchannel codes are THINC and MIXER, respectively developed by Westinghouse and General Electric, but unfortunately they are not openly available. The general docu-
mentation on their features is rather scarce (THINC) or practically absent (MIXER).

For purposes of comparison with present data COBRA-3C [11], de-

veloped by D.S. Rowe at BNWL of Richland, has been chosen. It
is a well known code. Its features allow to consider it as a
reference code among those openly available.

Among the options to be specified using COBRA-3C, the selection
shown in TABLE II has been made (refer to [11] for details).
This selection takes the advice of the COBRA-3C author or is
related to some our reasonable assumptions. However, in order
to evaluate the impact on the results of the selection made by
the user, some additional runs were performed besides the
"standard" calculations, changing the listed variable values in
reasonable ranges. The calculations results so obtained will
be discussed later. The COBRA-3C "standard" calculations are
plotted in Figs. 7 through 13, together with the experimental
results.

As for mass flux, the predictions are on an average acceptable
with reference to corner subchannel 2 and central subchannel 4,
but the trends with outlet quality are quite different. As for
the other subchannels, mass flux is underpredicted in side subchannel 1, and overpredicted in inner subchannel 5. It must be
remarked that the predicted subchannel flow is somewhat affected
by the used subchannel spacer loss coefficients, not directly
measured but only estimated by means of a simple "projected
area" method. Small changes in loss coefficients can produce
acceptable predictions also for subchannel 1 and 5.

The COBRA-3C subchannel quality predictions are usually close
to the average value (Figs. 10 through 13) and are not sensibly
affected by possible small variations in subchannel spacer loss
coefficients. Therefore, the agreement with experimental results is rather acceptable, but with a remarkable exception for
the corner subchannel (Fig. 10). In fact, as already mentioned
in the previous sections, the corner subchannel presents a
quality much lower than the average value (even less than 50%).
On the contrary COBRA-3C, in agreement also with the behavior
at sight thinkable on the basis of the power/flow ratio, predicts a quality higher (5% approximately) than the average
value. A reasonable explanation can be advanced. The low
quality is probably due to the permanence on the unheated channel wall (whose extent is proportionally maximum in the corner
subchannel) of a rather thick liquid film. In typical BWR
conditions (annular dispersed flow) the liquid film presence is
well known and also experimentally supported [15], not only on
the heated rods, but also with greater reason on the unheated
channel wall. However, the models usually included in classical subchannel codes are not able to simulate such a situation.
For these codes the only parameter characterizing a peripheral
subchannel is the usually low equivalent diameter value with a
consequent tendency to predict low flow and then high enthalpy.

The same explanation was given by the researchers of General
Electric, on the basis of a similar experimental evidence in
the above mentioned 9-rod bundle measurements [9]. Moreover,
it is known, even if not publicly documented, that the General
Electric code MIXER has been modified in consequence of those
results in order to improve the accuracy on this particular
point. This has been obtained including in the code, besides
the two usual transport terms ("turbulent mixing" and "cross
flow"), a "void drift" term, forcing the steam to move from the
periphery to more open regions of the bundle. Even if the inclusion of this particular third transport term may be somewhat
questionable from a conceptual standpoint [16, 17], present data
seem to confirm the practical convenience of such code modification.

It must be recognized that the side subchannel 1 (a peripheral
subchannel too) does not show a behavior similar to the corner
subchannel. This is somewhat strange, but it must also be remarked that the wetted/heated perimeter ratio is 2.5 in the
corner subchannel and only 1.8 in the side subchannel.

As for the additional runs performed with options different
from those listed in TABLE II, no practical difference has been
found usually. The influence of subcooled voids was tested using Levy's model or ignoring subcooled void formation, but the
influence is negligible owing to the small inlet subcooling
used in present experiments consistently with BWR typical conditions. Homogeneous model was used both for two-phase friction
multipler and void fraction, instead of Armand's correlations
with very small quantitative effects. As for friction factor,
even values doubled or halved with respect to correlation to
TABLE II have shown negligible effects on subchannel flow distribution. Also the parameters related to the transverse momentum equation (present in COBRA-3C while often absent in other
subchannel codes), i.e. the "transverse momentum parameter -
s/1" and the "cross flow resistance - K_{ij}", were found to have
no practical influence even when changed in a very large range
(0.2 to 2.0). Some differences are evident only just upstream
of the spacers, owing to the local increase of the usually
small diversion cross flow, but the influence on flow and quality at the heated length top end is not appreciable.

A parameter able to produce some significant changes in the
predictions is the Rowe's turbulent mixing parameter [11], defined by the relationship $w' = \beta s \bar{G}$. Increasing β the quality
in all subchannels tends to the average bundle value. This effect is particularly evident for corner subchannel, since even
with the "standard" β value 0.02 the predicted quality in all
the other subchannels is rather close to the average value. So
by increasing β (values up to 0.1 have been tested) it is possible to move the corner subchannel quality predictions towards

the experimental results, practically without affecting other subchannels. However, it is not at all possible to match in this way the corner subchannel results, because the predicted quality cannot go under the average bundle value.

In conclusion also the only parameter, β, able to affect in some way the prediction results (and probably the most difficult parameter to be quantitatively defined in two-phase conditions [16]) cannot explain the observed corner subchannel behavior. The COBRA-3C prediction incapability on this particular point is confirmed, quite apart from the option selection of the user. Moreover, the large parametrization so performed allows to extend with sufficient confidence this conclusion ot other codes similar to COBRA-3C.

CONCLUSIONS

The analysis of these experimental data confirms that the sub-channel sampling technqiue can represent a very useful contri-bution to a better understanding of the complex thermo-hydraulic phenomena connected with two-phase flow in multi-rod bundles.

In particular the data here discussed have evidenced:

even with a radial uniform heat flux distribution some remark-able differences can exist in subchannel flow and quality,

low values of quality are present in the corner subchannel, in spite of the high power/flow ratio, this confirming previous data obtained by General Electric in a 9-rod bundle [9]; this fact is probably due to the permanence of a rather thick liquid film on the unheated channel wall,

the above mentioned phenomenon is not modelled, to our know-ledge, by any available open code. In particular COBRA-3C strongly overpredicts the corner subchannel quality, while the predictions are rather acceptable for the other subchannels.

NOMENCLATURE

f	single-phase friction factor
$\overline{G}$	average mass flux in two adjacent subchannels, kg/m^2s
G_{av}	bundle average mass flux, kg/m^2s
G_i	mass flux in subchannel i, kg/m^2s
K_{ij}	cross flow resistance between subchannels i and j
Re	Reynolds number

s	rod-to-rod gap spacing, m
w'	fluctuating mass flow rate due to turbulent inter-change, kg/m s
X_{av}	average quality at the bundle outlet
X_i	quality at subchannel i outlet
β	turbulent mixing parameter
ΔP_{sc}	pressure unbalance between corresponding subchannels, mm water column

ACKNOWLEDGEMENTS

The authors wish to acknowledge the contribution of all the people who participated to this work and in particular:

G.F. Fermani and the CISE staff for the construction of the test section, and

H. Hoffman, U. Jung, W. Schupp, F. Weckermann for the execution on the measurements.

REFERENCES

1. G.P. Gaspari et al., "PELCO-S: a BWR Test Section for Sub-channel Experimental Analysis", CISE Report PELCO No. 4 (1975).

2. F. Lucchini, V. Marinelli, "Experimental Data on Burn-out in a Simulated BWR Fuel Bundle", Nuclear Engineering and Design, Vol. 31, No. 3 (1975).

3. G.P. Gaspari et al., "Dryout Experiments in a 16-rod BWR Geometry with Six Different Radial Heat Flux Distributions", ASME paper 75-HT-24 (1975).

4. H. Herkenrath, P. Mork-Morkenstein, "The Pressurized and Boiling Water Loop of the Technology Division at Ispra", EUR-4683 e (1971).

5. H. Herkenrath, W. Hufschmidt, "The Pressurized and Boiling Water Loops BOWAL and PRIL for Boiling Mixing Studies of the Heat Transfer Division JRC Ispra/Italy", EUR 6045 EN (1978).

6. J.E. Casterline, F.S. Castellana, "Flow and Enthalpy Re-distributions between the Subchannels of a Heated Bundle", European Two Phase Flow Group Meeting, Harwell, England (1974).

7. M. Bayoumi et al., "Determination of Mass Flow Rate and Quality Distributions between the Subchannels of a Heated

Bundle", European Two Phase Flow Group Meeting, Harwell, England (1974).

8.   B. Gustafsson et al., "Flow and Enthalpy Distribution in a 9-rod Bundle", European Two Phase Flow Group Meeting, Harwell, England (1974).

9.   R.T. Lahey et al., "Out-of Pile Subchannel Measurements in a 9-rod Bundle for Water at 1000 psia", Paper 3-1, International Symposium on Two-Phase Systems, Haifa, Israel (1971).

10. D.S. Rowe, "COBRA-II: a Digital Computer Program for Thermal-Hydraulic Subchannel Analysis of Rod Bundle Nuclear Fuel Elements", BNWL-1229 (1970).

11. D.S. Rowe, "COBRA-3C: a Digital Computer Program for Steady-State and Transient Thermal-Hydraulic Analysis of Rod Bundle Nuclear Fuel Elements", BNWL-1695 (1973).

12. R.W. Bowring, "HAMBO, a Computer Program for the Subchannel Analysis of Hydraulic and Burnout Characteristics of Rod Clusters, Part 2, The Equations", AEEW-R-582 (1968).

13. C.C. St. Pierre, "SASS Code-I, Subchannel Analysis for the Steady-State", APPE-41 (1966).

14. G. Forti, "The Computer Program MATTEO for Subchannel Analysis of BWR Rod Bundles in Steady-State and Transient", EUR-5148 e (1974).

15. F.A. Schraub et al., "Two-Phase Flow and Heat Transfer in Multi-rod Geometries: Air-Water Flow Structure Data for a Round Tube, Concentric and Eccentric Annulus, and Nine-Rod Bundle", GEAP-5739 (1969).

16. J. Weisman, "Review of Two-Phase Mixing and Diversion Cross Flow in Subchannel Analysis", AEEW-R-928 (1973).

17. G. Ulrych, P. Suchy, "Flow in Rod Bundles and Subchannel Analysis", European Two Phase Flow Group Meeting, Erlangen, Germany (1976).

18. H. Herkenrath, W. Hufschmidt, "Experimental Investigation of the Enthalpy and Mass Flow Distribution between Subchannels in a BWR Cluster Geometry (PELCO-S)", EUR-Report (to be published).

TABLE I		
BOWAL LOOP DESIGN DATA		
Max. working pressure	bar	250
Max. loop temperature	°C	450
Max. pump flowrate	m³/h	50 30
Max. pump head	m	130 300
Max. test section power	MW	3.6
Max. preheating power	kW	360

TABLE II	
SPECIFIED OPTIONS FOR COBRA-3C "STANDARD" CALCULATIONS	
Friction factor	$f = 0.186\ Re^{-0.2}$
Two-phase friction multiplier	Armand
Void fraction	Armand
Subcooled voids	Levy
Transverse momentum parameter (s/l)	0.5
Crossflow resistance (K_{ij})	0.5
Turbulent mixing parameter (β)	0.02
See ref. 11 for details and explanations	

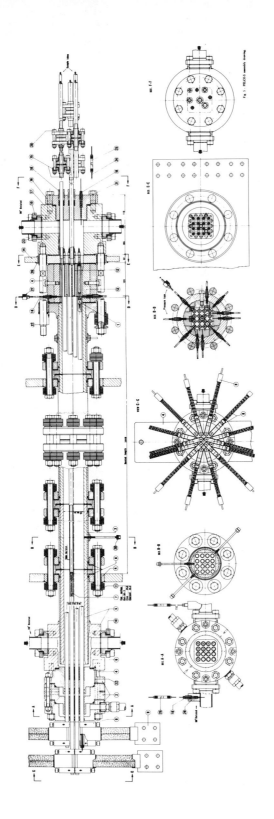

Fig. 1 - BWR Test Section PELCO-S [1]

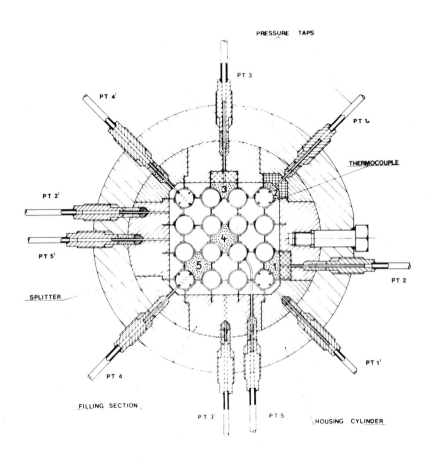

Fig. 2 - Probe Assembly Cross Section [1]

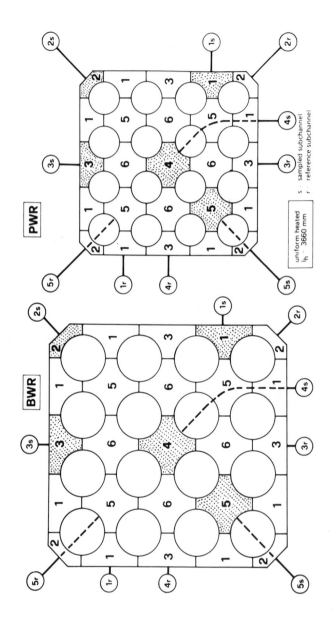

Fig. 3 - Cross-Section of Test Section Outlet with Splitters between the Subchannels and Appropriate Taps for Static Pressures (Isokinetic Measurements)

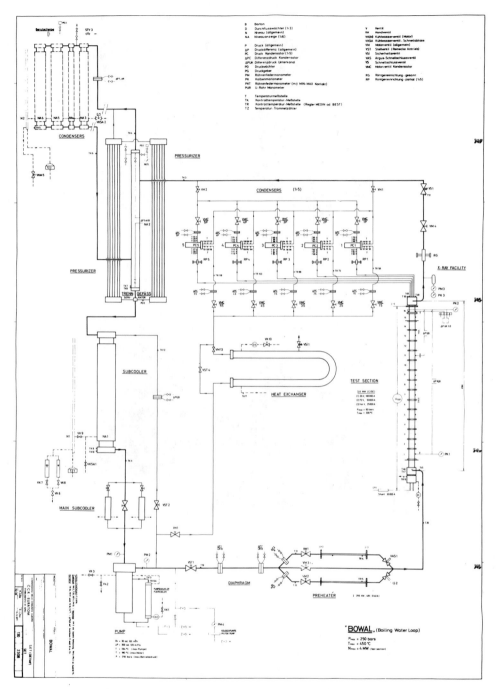

Fig. 4 - Schematic of BOWAL

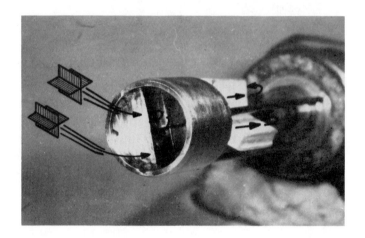

Fig. 5 - Flow Mixing Chamber and Silver Cross for the Mean
Outlet Temperatures of the Condensors for the Heat
Balance Measurements (Outer Diameter about 30mm,
4 Turnround Sheets)

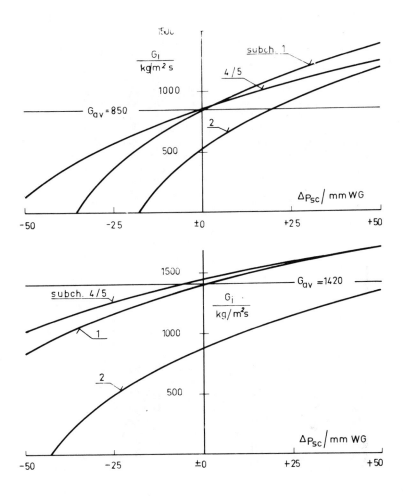

Fig. 6 - Influence of Non-Isokinetic Conditions on Mass Flow
Density in the Sampled Subchannels for an Entrance
Mass Flow Density of 850 kg/m^{2}s (above) and 1420 kg/m^{2}s
(below) (PELCO-S)

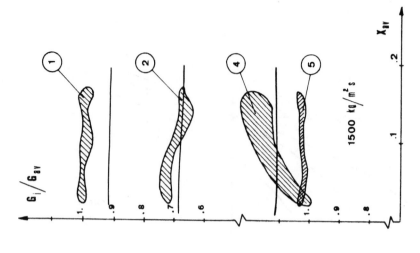

Fig. 8 - Mass Flux Distribution at
G_{av} = 1500 kg/m²·s

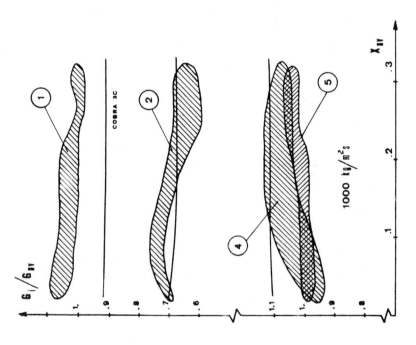

Fig. 7 - Mass Flux Distribution at
G_{av} = 1000 kg/m²·s

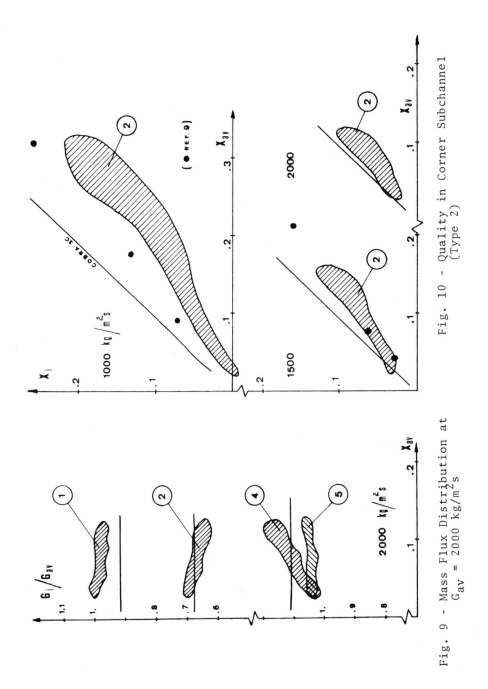

Fig. 10 - Quality in Corner Subchannel
(Type 2)

Fig. 9 - Mass Flux Distribution at
G_{av} = 2000 kg/m²s

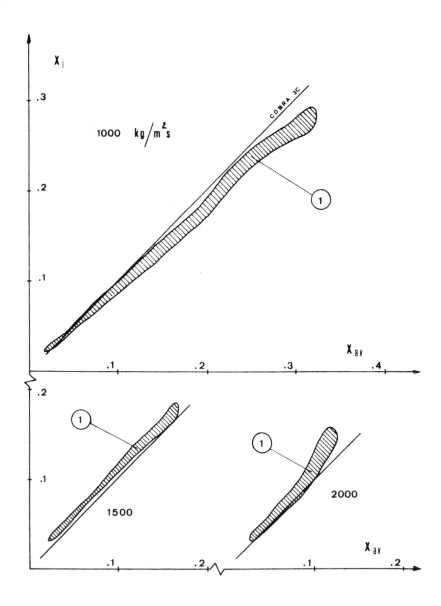

Fig. 11 - Quality in Side Subchannel (Type 1)

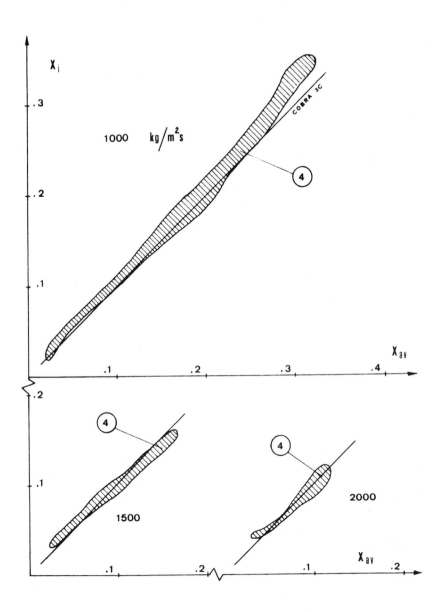

Fig. 12 - Quality in Central Subchannel (Type 4)

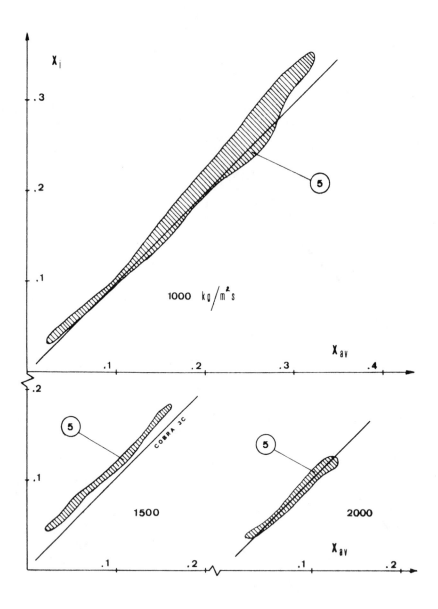

Fig. 13 - Quality in Inner Subchannel (Type 5)

Recent Progress in Study of Steam-Water Separators Used in Light-Water Power Stations

J.P. CERDAN
Electricite de France
78400 Chatou, France

ABSTRACT

The Research and Development Division of Electricite de France has at
Gennevilliers a test rig for steam-water separators. The types of mechanical separators corresponding to the most widely used models have been
tested under a joint program with the turbine manufacturers.

The characteristics and dimensions of the test installation have been
planned to reproduce the actual conditions under which the separators
operate.

Using the results obtained during the tests, it is possible to analyse
the behaviour of the separators and to evaluate the phenomena that occur
in them. The performances thus observed make it possible to determine
the use ranges for the principal models of mechanical separators and in
particular to establish a reasoned choice between the different equipment models available, and to calculate more accurately the size of the
dryer-superheater tanks.

As an extension to these tests, a new type of dryer with very high
through velocities has been perfected, with dimensions and efficiencies
that suggest that it will be developed industrially on an extensive
scale.

INTRODUCTION

The recent utilization of water-steam separators is, to a great extent,
linked to the choice of the "L.W.R. reactors" for the production of
electric energy. This type of reactors leads indeed to poor steam
characteristics at the turbine inlet. If the moisture rates in the turbine last stages are to remain within acceptable limits, and this as
well for the sake of the efficiency as for the one of the equipment
resistance, one or several steam "dryings" during the expansion have to
be considered. The separation of the liquid phase which already begins
within the turbine (drainage belts, suction slots) is essentially
carried out in the external separators which, incidentally, are often
associated with superheating devices.

A separator is a static apparatus which makes use to a variable extent according to its type of the inertial drop collection processes and of the turbulent diffusion processes. The separators are classified in two groups : the "mechanical" and the centrifugal separators. For the first ones, barriers placed in the flow collect the liquid phase (figures 1a and 1b) ; for the second ones, the flow is rotated and the drops are collected on the walls (figure 2).

The centrifugal separators have been less used these last years, the major reasons for this being the difficulties as regards their dimensioning (as a result of the uncertainty about the drop size at the turbine outlet) and the deficiencies of usual water-collecting devices after the centrifugation. The plants which are now in process of construction are for the greatest part equipped with mechanical dryers

Up to now, the actual or foreseeable performances of the different types of separators were not well known. The experience of their operation was generally insufficient and most of the tests conducted were not conclusive owing to the lack of representativeness of the experimental conditions and to the poor measurements means brought into use. At last, the mechanical separators are not well suited for estimations on account of their complicated geometry and of the variety of the phenomena which take place.

A proper dimensioning and an adequate prediction of the performance of this type of equipment were therefore difficult. However, such performance is decisive for the installation output or its disponibility (risks of erosion-corrosion of superheater bundles). On the other hand, to be looking for a reduction of the space occupied by the dryer elements is justified by the important profits which would be realized not only on the dryer elements and on the dryer-superheater vessel envelope but also on the machine-room.

The "Direction des Etudes et Recherches" of "Electricité de France" has therefore undertaken to construct a test rig enabling the reproduction of the actual conditions of separators' operation. Most of separators sold on the market have been tested in the form of complete modules such as those proposed by the manufacturers for actual installations and comprising their own discharge system for collected water.

1 - DESCRIPTION OF THE STEAM-WATER SEPARATORS TEST RIG

1.1 - <u>Installation characteristics (figure 3)</u>. The installation should widely cover the field of use of separators. In this respect, the steam-water mixture conditioning systems feeding the separators have been sufficiently dimensioned in order to enable the pressure, rate of flow, quality and drop size to be varied to a large extent.

The test chamber proper has a useful length of about 4 m and a 1 m^2 circular section. It can be operated in different positions so that separator elements operating with vertical or horizontal steam flows can be tested. Regularly disposed lateral plugs are provided for the connection of measurement and observation devices.

The test chamber is fed by 19 evenly-distributed discharge nozzles in which water and steam are mixed. As a matter of fact, the steam is humidified by water injection inside the nozzles (figure 4) and this in order to control the liquid phase granulometry. The means used for varying the drop size pertain to two different fields : in the field of mechanics the drop size depends on the relation between water and steam speed and in the thermodynamical field the temperature and pressure levels of the two fluids (steam condensation, drop "flashing") influence it. The nozzles are designed in such a way that, in operation, the flow areas (and therefore the speeds) of water and steam, the characteristics of which before injection are broadly variable, can be continuously modified.

The steam is supplied by a 45 MW boiler (flow-rate : 0 to 56 t/h, pressure : 18 bar) then throttled before de-superheating in an aerocooler with adjustable power. The water is injected at variable pressure (flow-rate : 0 to 25 t/h, pressure : 0 to 32 bar) and its temperature is regulated by an electric heater allowing 50 °C deviations from the test chamber temperature.

The on-site measurements carried out by us show that the drop dimensions obtained on the test rig cover the whole practical range.

·1.2 - Measurements carried out. The pressures, temperatures and rates of flow are measured on the test bench by "conventional" méthods, with, however, the usual precautions for the measurements in humid steam. The determination of the drier element pressure drop is forecast but this pressure drop is generally too low for being genuinely determined. On the other hand, the qualities and the drop sizes have been measured by special methods ; their interest goes widely beyond the test rig limits.

1.2.a - The method of quality measurement consists in doping the injection water with a non-volatile tracer, the trisodium phosphate being quite suitable for this process. The wetness of a humid steam sample is the ratio of concentrations of the sample condensate and of the injected water (after taking into account the thermodynamical exchanges during the injection). The samples which are taken should be representative and adequate probes had to be developed for this purpose. In some cases, it can be also useful to begin with the measurement of the flow pattern. The values of qualities obtained by this method on the test bench can be cross-checked either for the quality at the inlet of the dryer elements by a water flow balance or for the quality at the outlet of the dryer elements by a measurement of the condensate concentration for the whole flow leaving them. This method is easily carried into effect and very accurate since wetnesses lower than 0,01 % could be thus measured. It was furthermore successfully applied for H.P. exhausts of nuclear turbines.

1.2.b - The drop size measurement is grounded on the determination of a beam absorption through a steam flow, the quality of this latter being known. This method permits the access either to the granulometric spectrum for low-dimension drops (r < 1μ) or to a mean size in case of large drops. This mean size is defined by Sauter's radius :

$$r_m = \frac{\Sigma_{ni} \times r_i^3}{\Sigma_{ni} \times r_i^2}$$

The practical application of such a method for high or mean pressure flows is difficult : the alignment and stability of the emission and reception optical systems are not easy to control, a condensation occurs on the ports... The device developed on the steam-water separators test rig has been used at Fessenheim power station (PWR - 900 MWe).

2 - OPERATION OF MECHANICAL SEPARATORS

It will not be dealt here with questions of dimensioning for water recovery systems operating together with the separators. We shall limit ourselves to an analysis of the operation of the plate-type separators. The wire-mesh technique (figure 1b) seems indeed to be less and less used by the manufacturers. On the other hand, it requires comparatively low steam velocities and leads to very bulky plants. The great sensitiveness of this type of dryer to possible overspeeds also requires the use of sophisticated steam supply systems, difficult to implement.

The test results on the whole have shown that the plate separator working is conditioned by two types of processes : on the one hand the drop collection proper and on the other hand the interactions between collected water, steam flow and drainage system (recarry-over, choking).

2.1 - Droplet collection. Very small droplets are difficult to be collected : their inertia is not sufficient and, when the steam direction changes, they go following the streamlines.

The separation of drops with a given size is improved when the steam velocity increases.

Other parameters have to be taken into account, such as the steam quality (which promotes the drop increase in size when passing through the dryer elements), the streaming film configuration (inducing collections by turbulent diffusion) but they have only a minor effect and moreover this effect would be difficult to make clear.

The collecting power of a separator will be measured by its separation efficiency (defined as the ratio of the separated water flow-rate to the water flow-rate to be separated) for a given drop size or granulometric spectrum.

2.2 - <u>Recarry-over of collected water</u>. There are many causes for this recarry-over which generally progressively appears :

- at low steam velocities a rather low wetness is observed at the outlet of the dryer elements owing to the drop stripping from the collected water streaming films. The drops which are stripped in the last portion of the dryer elements are not completely collected and give rise to the moisture which is observed downstream. This moisture therefore depends not much on the quality at the inlet (of course within the limits of the dryer element drainage system capacity). It is essentially determined by the steam dynamic pressure.

- at high steam velocities, the drop stripping becomes higher and is accompanied by a drag effect on the streaming films which can cause their spreading out up to the dryer element edge. Moreover, the steam flow conditions the capacity of the collected water drainage elements. High steam velocities can lead, with the effect of local turbulences, on the one hand to bad conditions of streaming films suction (insufficient depression inside water collecting elements), on the other hand to the film rupture and to considerable recarry-over processes. In this case, the wetnesses downstream depend on the wetnesses upstream, in particular owing to the drainage components decrease of capacity, and are liable to grow up very much. Only such type of process will be called "recarry-over".

2.3 - <u>Drainage system choking</u>. When a recarry-over takes place, a faulty laying-out of the collected water catching elements can lead to a reduction of their capacity on account of the effect of aerodynamical processes in relation to the steam flow. For their part, the choking processes are only a result of an insufficient dimensioning of the collecting elements or even of the whole drain recovery system. The separator choking only takes place beyond a certain water flow-rate at the inlet, independently of the steam velocity.

3 - <u>ANALYSIS OF THE TEST RESULTS</u>

The tests are not easy to interpret owing to the multiple parameters involved and their simultaneous effect on processes of different nature. In order to facilitate the analysis, we shall eliminate the factors which seem not to be essential : viscosity of both phases, water surface tension... As main variables, we have chosen the drop mean size (r_{drops}), the quality above the dryers ($x_{upstream}$), the steam dynamical pressure

$(1/2\rho V^2)$. This last term enables to satisfactorily correlate tests which have been performed at pressures near to each other (6 to 12 bar). The separator working will be studied through 3 criteria corresponding to the processes that we have just described : droplet separation power, conditions for the appearance of recarry-over processes, choking hazards. Other criteria could be considered but, in our opinion, they would not be determining. For instance the pressure drop of the dryer elements will not be considered ; it is generally very low and often not sufficient for ensuring a good flow distribution at he separator inlet.

3.1 - The study of the droplet collection can be made from the curves represented figure 5 which shows the results obtained for one of the separators tested. Let us remind that the drop radii which are mentioned are mean sizes in Sauter's meaning. The analysis of the curve trend is rather complicated owing to the very strong drop size dependence on the qualities realized in the test chamber, as the experience has shown that fine droplets could be obtained only for low moistures. The curves, figure 5, are therefore plotted for different $x_{upstream}$ values. So, it has to be determined for each case if the $\frac{x_{downstream}}{x_{upstream}}$ variations must be ascribed to the drop size or to the upstream quality variations. On the contrary, the drop size field of influence on the dryer working can be easily determined by the study of the curve position. In this field, an improvement of the collection for increasing values of ρV^2 shall be noted. Such values should, however, remain low enough in order that the recarry-over processes do not become the major ones (case of the curve corresponding to $(\rho V^2)3$).

For the separator studied and for dynamical pressures between $(\rho V^2)_1$ and $(\rho V^2)_2$, the drop size effect appears under 200 µ and becomes very important under 50 µ.

3.2 - The recarry-over processes are characterized by a strong dependence of the downstream quality on the upstream quality ; they can therefore be studied from curves such as the curve figure 6. For low values of the dynamical pressure, a downstream wetness which is about constant or even decreasing (owing to the upstream quality secondary effects on the drop size, the collection by streaming films...) is well observed. For high values of the dynamical pressure, the increase of $x_{downstream}$ with $x_{upstream}$ indicates the presence of recarry-over processes.

Thus, for one of the tested separators, the results show a threshold of recarry-over corresponding to a value of ρV^2 comprised between $(\rho V^2)_2$ and $(\rho V^2)_3$.

3.3 - The choking of a dryer could be detected from curves giving the non-collected water flow-rate a function of the water flow-rate at the inlet. This type of process could not be very clearly observed during the tests that we have conducted.

3.4 – Conclusions. The behaviour and the performance levels of several
industrial separators which have been tested are quite different. As a
guidance, the qualities obtained at the outlet of different separators
with identical feed conditions are shown figure 7. Good separation efficiencies can be obtained at low velocity with some separators but such
efficiencies quickly lower ; on the contrary, the behaviour of other
separators is rather poor at low velocities but their reliability is
rather good in case of considerable overspeeds. The choice of a separator will therefore closely related to the steam distribution at the
inlet of the actual separators. The separators will be dimensioned
taking into account the uncertainties as regards the liquid phase distribution. Low wetnesses at the outlet, even for high wetnesses at the
inlet, will be unquestionably maintained with the provision of steam
through velocities lower than the carry over thresholds of the selected
separators.

4 – PROSPECTS FOR THE FUTURE : HIGH VELOCITY SEPARATORS

The analysis of the results obtained with mechanical separators makes it
possible for Electricité de France to consider the possibility of
building small size dryers operating with through velocities 10 times
higher than the usual figures. This new type of units, the "High Velocity
separators" offer very promising performances.

4.1 – Description and operating principle. High Velocity Separators
(H.V.S.) are a special type of centrifugal separators. However, the
design of conventional separators often leads to serious water recarry-
over and, on another hand, their size and their geometry does not make
it possible for the small drops to be always caught by the walls. To
eliminate the former drawback and favour the evacuation of the water,
it appeared interesting to draw it up by steam bleeding, making use,
for instance, of the bleeding point usually found at the H.P. turbines
exhausts. On the other hand, an improvement in water drop centrifugation
can be obtained through a reduction in separator diameter. The H.V.S.
are, therefore, made of separating cells fitted in parallel within the
connecting pipes. A cell operating principle is shown on figure 8.

At the inlet of the dryer, a cascade (A) gives the water/steam mixture
a swirling movement ; the water is thrown on the walls and discharged
into an annular space (F) from which steam is also drawn off. To reduce head
losses, which are often one of the drawbacks of centrifugal separators,
a cascade is also fitted at the unit outlet (B) to straighten the flow
and to recover the kinetic rotation power. The pressure drop inside the
cell itself and inside the downstream pipes is thus considerably reduced
(uniform velocity distribution).

Selection of a separation cell dimensions is the result of a compromise.
Indeed, if one wishes to increase the diameter, one must, in order to

maintain a correct centrifugation, either increase the flow-rate, hence, pressure drop, or the length of the unit, hence, its bulk and pressure drop owing to the comparatively large amount of loss in the space between the two cascades. It seems that the best solution consists in using cells with a reduced diameter and short length and assembling them inside the pipes. The present arrangement is shown on figure 9, where some of the separation cells laid in honeycomb shape can be seen inside one of the connecting pipes at turbine HP body output.

The geometry of the rotating and straightening blades was determined by computation in order to obtain the best water drop centrifugation with the lowest possible head loss. Reckonings were validated by model tests during which proper operation of the 2 blade assemblies was checked, and also the overall pressure drop of the unit.

4.2 - Performances. H.V.S. should make it possible to reach a very high drying efficiency with a very acceptable head loss.

Tests were run in Gennevilliers with a first generation of H.V.S. The problem was essentially concerned with the choice of a geometry for the drawn water removal annular space. The moisture level at the outlet of the roughly built cells (without flow straighteners) was lower than 0,1 % for steam bleedings representing about 10 % of the main flow-rate. Those results were obtained with drop sizes very close to those measured at Fessenheim turbine HP exhaust. It should be noted that, if tests with units of the second generation should confirm this separation efficiency, the recovery of kinetic rotation energy by the straightening grid should make it possible to obtain a slightly superheated steam at H.V.S. outlet.

H.V.S. pressure drop depends on the flow-rate resulting from the selected size. With an inlet velocity close to that which is usually found inside the connecting pipes (45 m/s) pressure drop within the separating cells would be lower than 100 mbar.

Nevertheless, moisture within the connecting pipes is, at the present time, the source of a comparatively high head loss. This can be suppressed if the steam is dried immediately below the HP body outlet. Moreover, a reduction in size of the superheating vessels should allow a simplification in piping layout. It is, therefore, probable that the balance of head losses between the HP and LP turbines will be in favour of the H.V.S.

4.3 - Development prospects. A reduction in separator size should first reduce the cost of superheaters-dryers, of their shells and, more generally, of the machine hall. On the other hand, the possibility of drying the steam immediately at the outlet of the HP turbine will eli-minate the problem of erosion/corrosion within connecting pipes, which may then be made of carbone steel (for a 900 MW unit, the piping length is about 500 m with a diameter of approximatively 1 m). Moreover, a reduction in size of the superheating vessels allows a simplification in piping layout.

On a longer term, H.V.S. make it possible to consider a modification of the expansion cycle proper, and, in particular, to look to multi-drying cycles with no intermediate superheating. Such cycles offer many advantages, but they were seldom used owing to the size of the separators offered in the trade. A comparison between a 2-drying cycle combined with a P.W.R. nuclear boiler and a conventional cycle (one drying and superheating) shows large power gains and an appreciable reduction in investment charges.

5 - CONCLUSION

The tests run by Electricité de France in Gennevilliers made it possible to analyse the operation of the main types of mechanical separators and to compare their performances. Their operating range can now be defined and a justified selection can be made from the various types of equipment.

On the other hand, the separator test rig allowed the development of a new type of dryer, the High Velocity Separator, with a small size and very promising performances. Industrial development of these units is provided by a close cooperation between Electricité de France, Alsthom-Atlantique and Stein-Industrie. Two prototypes will soon be fitted in Bugey II plant (P.W.R. 900 MW) for industrial tests at the beginning of 1980. If these tests are conclusive, H.V.S. may be very quickly included in the projected plants.

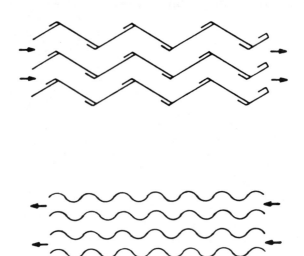

Fig. 1 a – MECHANICAL PLATE DRIERS

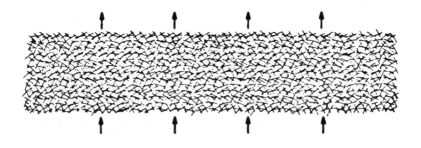

Fig. 1 b – WIRE –MESH TYPE DRIER

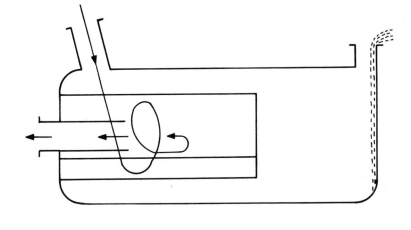

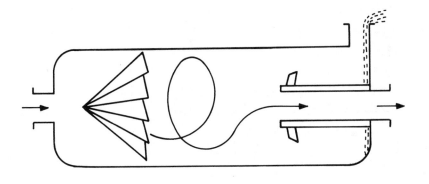

FIGURE 2 - CONVENTIONAL CENTRIFUGAL DRIERS

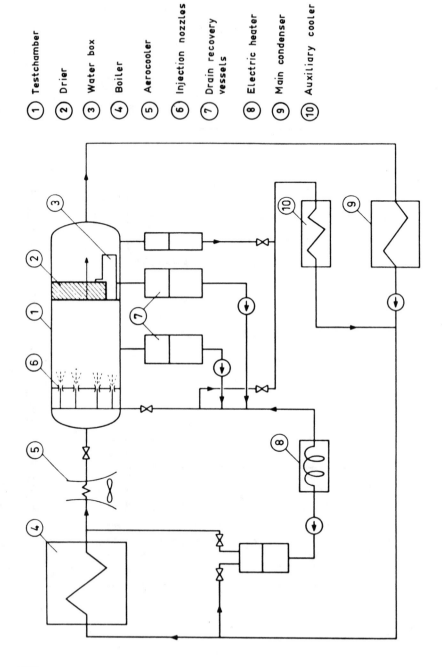

1. Testchamber
2. Drier
3. Water box
4. Boiler
5. Aerocooler
6. Injection nozzles
7. Drain recovery vessels
8. Electric heater
9. Main condenser
10. Auxiliary cooler

Fig. 3 – SEPARATOR TEST RIG

1748

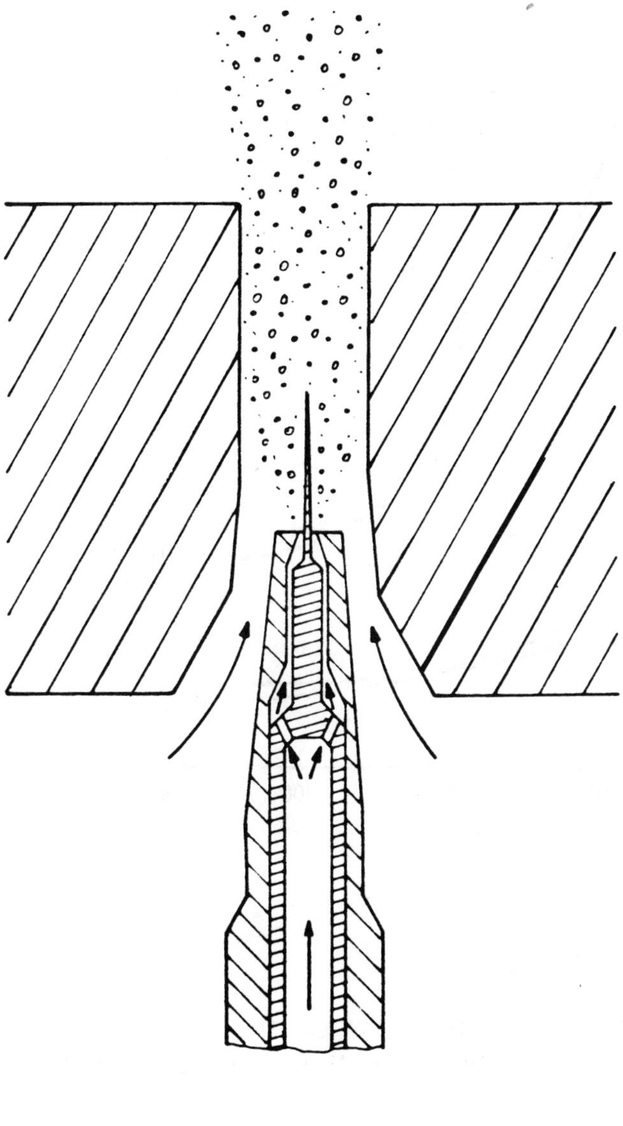

Fig. 4 – CROSS-SECTION OF AN INJECTION NOZZLE

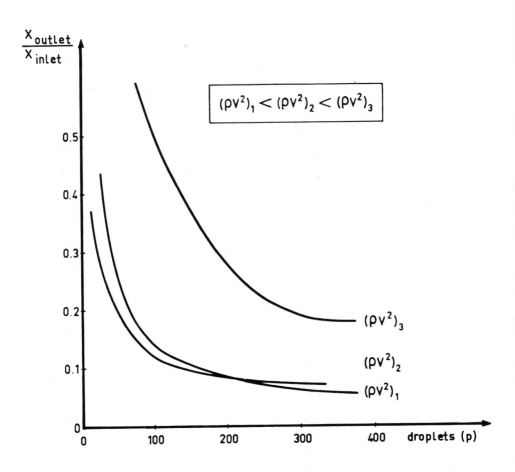

Fig. 5 - RELATION BETWEEN THE DROP SIZE
AND THE EFFICIENCY OF A SEPARATOR

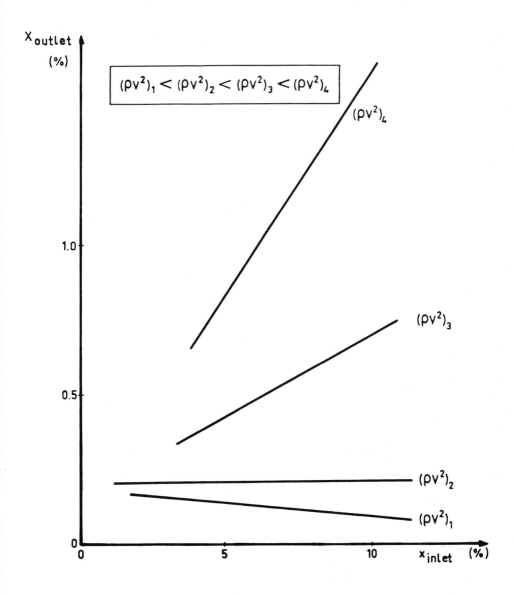

Fig. 6 — EFFECT OF THE DYNAMICAL PRESSURE

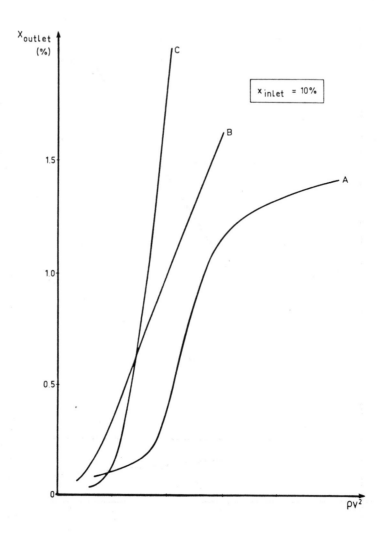

Fig. 7 : COMPARISON OF PERFORMANCE OF SEVERAL SEPARATORS

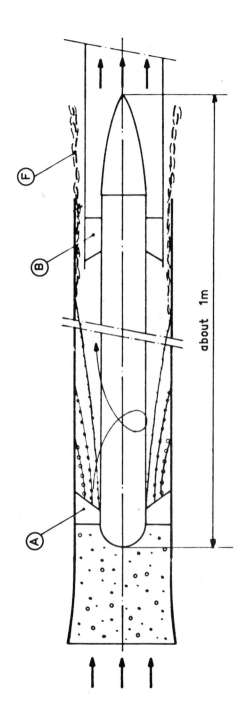

about 1m

Fig. 8 – SCHEME OF A HIGH VELOCITY SEPARATOR CELL

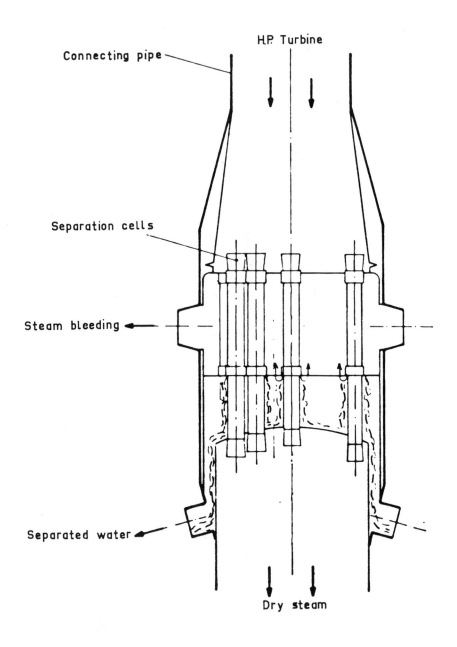

Fig. 9 – HIGH VELOCITY SEPARATOR (Stein industrie arrangement)

DATE DUE